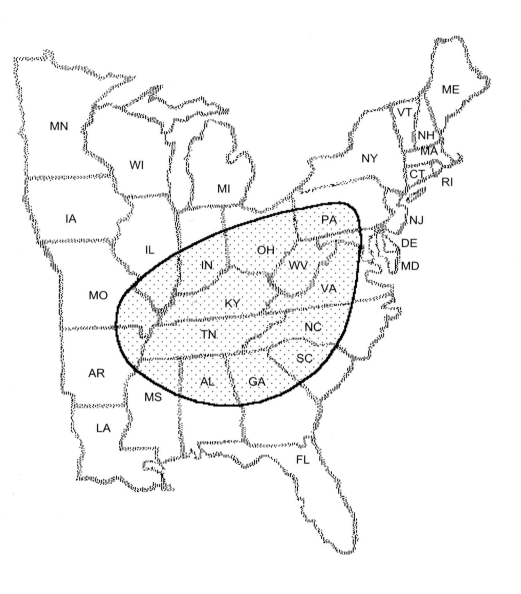

Enjoy the wildflowers and the "Wildflowers of Tennessee."

Jack B. Carman

WILDFLOWERS
of TENNESSEE

JACK B. CARMAN

Highland Rim Press
Tullahoma

Library of Congress Control Number: 2001087172
ISBN: 0-9708418-0-9

Published by
Highland Rim Press
Tullahoma, TN

Printed in China

Cover Photographs
The Tennessee State Wildflower
Passionflower
Passiflora incarnata
Photo by
George Hornal

Tennessee Coneflower
Echinacea tennesseensis
Photo by
Jack Carman

CONTENTS

DEDICATION

To my wife Dorothy, who has given me encouragement and
unwavering support throughout the compilation of this work,
and to
the people of Tennessee.

SPECIAL THANKS
To my good friend George Hornal, who collaborated in the
writing of the Introduction and whose outstanding photographs
appear throughout this book,
and
To my good friends Doug and Crystal Malone who provided
inputs on the consistency and clarity of the text.

Contributing Photographers

Bob Hale	Dan Pittillo
Alan S. Heilman	Wally Roberts
John MacGregor	Glenn Taylor
Doug Malone	Clay Thurston

INTRODUCTION

INTRODUCTION

Purpose

Tennessee is blessed with an abundance of flowering plants that reside within its borders. A heightened appreciation of our flora and an increased interest in all branches of natural history have arisen during the last three decades. Awareness and interest promote a desire for knowledge. Acquisition of knowledge leads to the realization that humanity occupies a small but intricate niche among the great diversity of life, and hopefully promotes a desire for protection. Without a strong conservation and preservation ethic, we may lose many of the wildflowers that grace our lives. We, as concerned citizens, should support the preservation of natural habitats, the eradication of air and water pollution, the prevention of erosion, and the removal of invasive, alien vegetation. By being vigilant today, Tennesseans can ensure tomorrow's generations the opportunity to experience the beauties of nature that have existed throughout our history. If, in some small measure, this book fosters an increased appreciation and interest in our native flora, and instills a desire for its conservation and preservation, then the purpose and goals of the book will have been accomplished.

Scope

The state of Tennessee, lying between the temperate 35th and 37th parallels, and reaching from the Mississippi River on the western side to the peaks of the Appalachians on the eastern side, is home to an exceptionally diverse flora. The latitude, moderate climate and ample rainfall along with variations in topography, elevation, geology and soil type all contribute to an abundance of flowering plants. For many Deep South species, Tennessee is the northernmost limit of their range. Likewise, some wildflowers more common in the northern United States extend south into Tennessee as the southernmost limit of their range. Some far northern species have found the high elevation of the Blue Ridge Mountains to their liking. The flora of Tennessee is as unique and varied as the state itself, and truly representative of the flora of the eastern United States, particularly the Southern and Central Appalachian regions, and the Tennessee, Ohio and mid-Mississippi river valleys.

This is the first statewide photographic volume for Tennessee wildflowers. It emphasizes field photography and field descriptions which provide an optimum comprehensive overview of the state's flowering plants. More than 780 beautiful color photographs are presented alongside the easy-to-read descriptions. More than 1100 of Tennessee's 2800 vascular plants are described. Since this guide is principally of wildflowers, the rushes, sedges and grasses have been omitted except for a few representative examples. Ferns and trees have been excluded, but many showy shrubs and common vines are included. Thorough coverage of rare and endangered species from all areas of Tennessee is provided. Novice, student and professional botanists should find this work an indispensable addition to their library or field pack.

Grand Divisions of Tennessee

As signified by the three stars in the state flag, Tennessee from the advent of statehood has consisted of three grand divisions: West, Middle and East Tennessee. The eastern border of West Tennessee and the western border of Middle Tennessee is the Tennessee River where it flows north through the state, from the northeastern corner of Mississippi through Hardin County and along the eastern borders of Decatur, Benton and Henry counties, prior to its confluence with the Ohio River in northwestern Kentucky. The eastern border of Middle Tennessee and the western border of East Tennessee is the central and eastern time zone boundary which extends along the western borders of Hamilton, Rhea, Roane, Morgan and Scott counties.

Physiographic Regions of Tennessee

Tennessee is a trapezoidal-shaped state with a long narrow profile, measuring no more than 115 miles from north to south, but about 510 miles from southwest to northeast. As shown in the generalized map on page 7, portions of five of the six major physiographic provinces of the southeastern United States are contained within the borders of the state: Coastal Plain, Interior Low Plateau, Appalachian Plateau, Ridge and Valley, and Blue Ridge Mountains. Only the Piedmont that extends from east central Alabama northeast through Georgia, the Carolinas, Virginia and Maryland is outside of Tennessee's borders.

West Tennessee
West Tennessee is about 110 miles wide and lies within two subdivisions of the Coastal Plain Province: the Mississippi River Valley and the Plateau Slope. The Western Valley of the Tennessee River (a narrow corridor not shown in the map on page 7), is considered a distinct subdivision by some authorities, and forms a physical boundary between the Coastal Plain of West Tennessee and the Interior Low Plateau of Middle Tennessee.

The Mississippi River Valley, the alluvial flood plain along the river, is usually less than 10 miles wide in Tennessee. The terrain is predominately flat and elevations generally range from 200 to 300 ft. In the north, Reelfoot Lake level is 282 ft.

The Plateau Slope is relatively flat in the western portion, but transitions to rolling hills in the eastern portion. A gradual increase in elevation occurs from west to east, and elevations on the eastern side of the Plateau Slope typically range from 350 to 500 ft (Kentucky Lake level is 358 ft).

Major streams of West Tennessee include the Tennessee, Mississippi, Wolf, Loosahatchie, Hatchie, Forked Deer and Obion rivers. Much of the area has been converted to farmland, but undisturbed areas include upland forests, scattered upland grassy barrens, and swamp and bottomland hardwood forests along creeks and rivers. West Tennessee is host to many aquatic plants, and to wildflowers whose normal range is the midwestern prairies and the Coastal Plain of Arkansas, Louisiana and Mississippi.

Middle Tennessee
Middle Tennessee is about 180 miles wide, with the western three-fourths a part of the Interior Low Plateau Province and the eastern one-fourth lying within the Cumberland Plateau subdivision of the Appalachian Plateau Province. In Middle Tennessee, the Interior Low Plateau consists of the Western Highland Rim, Central Basin and Eastern Highland Rim subdivisions. Actually, the Western Highland Rim and the Eastern Highland Rim are connected to the north in Kentucky and to the south in Alabama, and completely encircle the Central Basin. The generalized physiographic map on page 7 does not show the narrow corridors of the Central Basin that extend northward through the Macon and Clay county area, and southward through the Lincoln and Giles county area. The trend of general elevation increase from west to east noted in West Tennessee is continued in Middle Tennessee.

The rolling landscape of the Western Highland Rim is dissected by the Tennessee, Buffalo, Duck and Cumberland rivers, and their many tributaries. Rich and unusual floral populations are found on seepage slopes and many aquatic plants occur in the lower Duck River and Kentucky Lake embayments. The Western Highland Rim area north of the Cumberland River, often called the Northern Rim, contains portions of the Pennyroyal Plain and Big Barren subsections that extend southward from Kentucky into northern Middle Tennessee. Both areas contain midwestern prairie species normally found in Illinois and Missouri.

The Central Basin terrain generally ranges from 200 to 600 ft lower elevation than the surrounding Highland Rim. The level of J. Percy Priest Lake in Davidson County is 489 ft. Major watercourses include the Cumberland, Stones, Duck and Elk rivers. At many sites in the Central Basin, the limestone bedrock that underlies Middle Tennessee is at or near the surface. In areas where the soil is too shallow to support the larger hardwood trees, open areas called cedar glades are found. Cedar glades support many interesting and endemic species that have adapted to the harsh glade environment relatively free of competition. As the Central Basin is almost exclusively a Tennessee region, comprehensive coverage of its floral populations is given.

The Eastern Highland Rim is about 25 miles wide and is sandwiched between the Central Basin to the west and the Cumberland Plateau to the east. The level of Tims Ford Lake in Franklin County is 889 ft and that of Dale Hollow Lake in Clay County about 650 ft. Major streams include the Duck, Elk, Collins, Caney Fork, Obey and Cumberland rivers. The Eastern Highland Rim has remnant grassy barrens that contain many midwestern prairie flora and many disjunct populations of Alabama, Georgia and mid-Atlantic seaboard Coastal Plain species.

The Cumberland Plateau, about 25 to 50 miles wide in Middle Tennessee, abruptly rises about 800 ft above the Eastern Highland Rim and has a somewhat flat to rolling landscape. Major watercourses include the Obey, Obed, Sequatchie and Tennessee rivers. The Sequatchie Valley is a part of the Cumberland Plateau, but is not considered a separate physiographic subdivision of the Appalachian Plateau. The Cumberland Plateau is capped with sandstone and shale, and provides habitat for a variety of plants, including additional Coastal Plain species.

East Tennessee
East Tennessee is about 45 miles wide to the south and 175 miles wide to the north. It contains portions of three physiographic provinces: Appalachian Plateau, Ridge and Valley, and Blue Ridge Mountains. Major watercourses include the Cumberland, Big South Fork, Tennessee, Ocoee, Hiwasse, Little Tennessee, French Broad, Pigeon, Holston, Clinch and Powell rivers.

The Cumberland Plateau barely extends into East Tennessee in the southern half of the state, but the Cumberland Plateau and Cumberland Mountain subdivisions of the Appalachian Plateau Province include all or portions of Anderson, Campbell, Claiborne, Morgan and Scott counties in the north. The Cumberland Mountain subdivision is distinct because of mountains that rise above the Cumberland Plateau.

The Ridge and Valley Province lies east of the Appalachian Plateau. This region is composed of a series of low ridges and valleys that run diagonally across the state, generally parallel to a line between Chattanooga and Bristol. The level of Norris Lake in the Union County area is 1020 ft and that of Douglas Lake in the Jefferson County area is 1000 ft.

To the east of the Ridge and Valley along the North Carolina border, the Unaka Mountains of Tennessee define the western edge of the Blue Ridge Province. Maximum elevation in the state is reached at Clingman's Dome in the Great Smoky Mountains at just over 6600 ft.

Essentially all of the East Tennessee area provides prime habitat for wildflowers. The high mountains, including the Great Smoky Mountains and Roan Mountain, with their spruce-fir forests, cove hardwoods, and heath and grassy balds, are virtually a natural living botanic greenhouse. The Ridge and Valley and Appalachian Plateau have numerous streams, rich wooded slopes and coves, seepage slopes, barrens and lake shores that provide for significant plant diversity including aquatic, Coastal Plain and midwestern prairie species.

Book Layout

Plant families are presented phylogenetically (the order botanists consider to be the more primitive to the more advanced). The order followed is that of Gleason and Cronquist, *Manual of Vascular Plants of the Northeastern United States and Adjacent Canada*, NYBG 1991. The genera within families and species with each genus are arranged alphabetically, except for the trillium (considered to be a separate family by some) which is presented at the end of the Lily Family. Plants within the same family or of closely-related families sometimes have similar flower characteristics that may aid in identification. The photographs are intended to be the primary means for plant identification when using this book, but each image is accompanied by a brief description which includes:

Family Names
The scientific (Latin) and common (English) family names are shown at the top of each page, or at the beginning of each description for pages with two families.

Common Name
Some plants have well-known common names used throughout their range, but others may have names that vary by region. Sometimes, more than one plant is known by the same common name, and many plants do not have well-known common names. The names given herein are those that seemed most familiar and most appropriate.

Scientific Name
Scientific plant names consist of two Latin words: the genus name followed by the species name. This Latin binomial is followed by the name of the person(s) who published a valid name for the plant. In this book, an asterisk (*) following the author's name denotes that the plant is considered to be non-native or alien. Each plant will always have a unique scientific name. However, scientific names are occasionally changed, as earlier published names are discovered or the plant is reclassified. A previous scientific name may be included at the end of the description for those plants that have recently had scientific name changes. Scientific names used in this book generally follow the *Checklist of the Vascular Plants of Tennessee* by Wofford and Kral.

Plant Description
Distinguishing features of the plant are included, such as: type (e.g., annual, biennial or perennial, herb, shrub or vine); size and habit; leaf type, shape and arrangement on the stem; inflorescence type; flower size and shape; fruit; and other features that may help distinguish the plant from "look-alikes." Other information relating to edibility or poisonous aspects, medicinal uses, or unusual characteristics may also be included. Not all of the characteristics previously mentioned are provided for every description, but only those necessary for its identification.

An attempt has been made to keep the descriptions non-technical, but some botanical terms could not be avoided. These were essential because of space limitations or the need to convey a precise meaning. A complete glossary is provided for the technical terms used in the text (see pages 17 through 23). Also, to assist with the understanding of terms used, a set of illustrations is included that show: leaf parts and arrangements; leaf shapes; leaf margin, tip, base and attachment characteristics; flower parts and types; and inflorescence types (see pages 8 through 12).

Frequency of occurrence, habitat, distribution or range, and approximate flowering time are also provided. Frequency of occurrence categories were defined according to the number of documented occurrences from the 95 Tennessee counties as follows:

Category	Number of Counties
Common	48 or more
Frequent	32 to 47
Occasional	11 to 31
Infrequent	6 to 10
Rare	5 or less

Documented occurrences were defined by the *Atlas of Tennessee Vascular Plants, Vols. 1 and 2*, and the *Tennessee Natural Heritage Program Rare Vascular Plant List*. As the atlas volumes were compiled from herbarium specimens, the noted frequency of occurrence is likely conservative except for the common and rare categories, and is applicable only to the state of Tennessee.

INTRODUCTION

Habitat refers to location(s) where the plant is more likely to be found. Generally, this information applies to the overall range of the plant, not just to Tennessee.

The plant's distribution within Tennessee is noted (as defined by Tennessee rare plant list and atlas volumes) and in most cases, the general range outside the state. Abbreviations of state names used in the general distributions follow the 2-letter designation of the U.S. Postal Service. Other abbreviations used are defined as follows:

Abbreviations

c	central	nw	northwest
CAN	Canada	s	south
e	east	sc	south central
ec	east central	se	southeast
n	north	sw	southwest
nc	north central	U.S.	United States
ne	northeast	wc	west central

The approximate flowering period is applicable for the general range of each plant, in most cases, rather than for Tennessee only. Flowering times vary considerably from year to year, especially in early spring, and with latitude and elevation. In the Smoky Mountains, plants growing at low elevation may flower 3 or more weeks before plants of the same species growing at high elevation.

Additional Species

Descriptions of closely-related (or other) plants may be appended. As such, many more plant species are introduced. Characteristics are included that allow these additional species to be distinguished from the one in the photograph.

Plant Identification Tips

The phylogenetic order of presentation used in this book assembles plants in groups having similar flower types. This is, in itself, an aid to plant identification. However, for those who are unable to associate flower shapes with families, line drawings of 64 typical flower shapes denoting likely associated plant families are included on pages 13 through 16. For an unknown wildflower, review the line drawings for a similar shape. If one is found, then check the photographs and descriptions for the family(s) noted. Hopefully, this will shorten the search time required for identification. Remember that all flower families or all flower shapes for each family are not represented in the line drawings, only the more common ones. Also, note that the line drawings are intended solely to present typical shapes and characteristics, and are not drawn to scale relative to each other.

For amateur wildflower enthusiasts, two references are recommended: The Peterson Field Guide 17, *A Field Guide to Wildflowers*, by Roger Tory Peterson and Margaret McKenny, and *Newcomb's Wildflower Guide* by Lawrence Newcomb. Both contain excellent illustrations (no photographs) and each has a unique system to aid in the identification of plants.

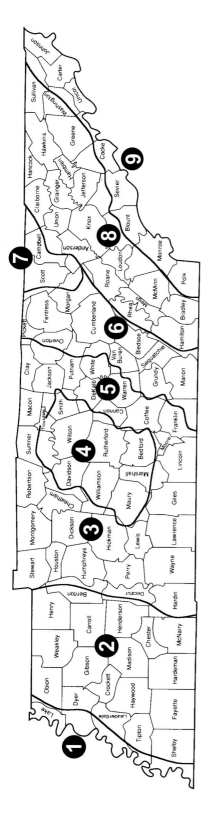

Generalized Physiographic Map of Tennessee

Coastal Plain
1. Mississippi River Valley
2. Plateau Slope

Interior Low Plateau
3. Western Highland Rim
4. Central Basin
5. Eastern Highland Rim

Appalachian Plateau
6. Cumberland Plateau
7. Cumberland Mountains

8. Ridge and Valley

9. Blue Ridge Mountains

LEAF PARTS AND ARRANGEMENTS

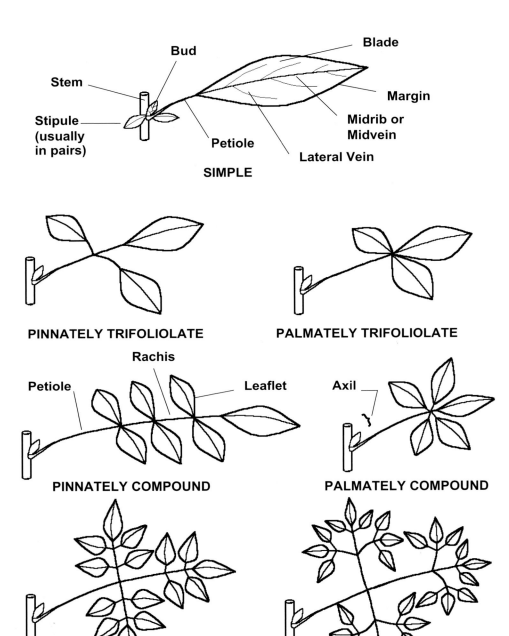

SIMPLE

PINNATELY TRIFOLIOLATE

PALMATELY TRIFOLIOLATE

PINNATELY COMPOUND

PALMATELY COMPOUND

BIPINNATELY COMPOUND

TERNATELY DECOMPOUND

LEAF SHAPES

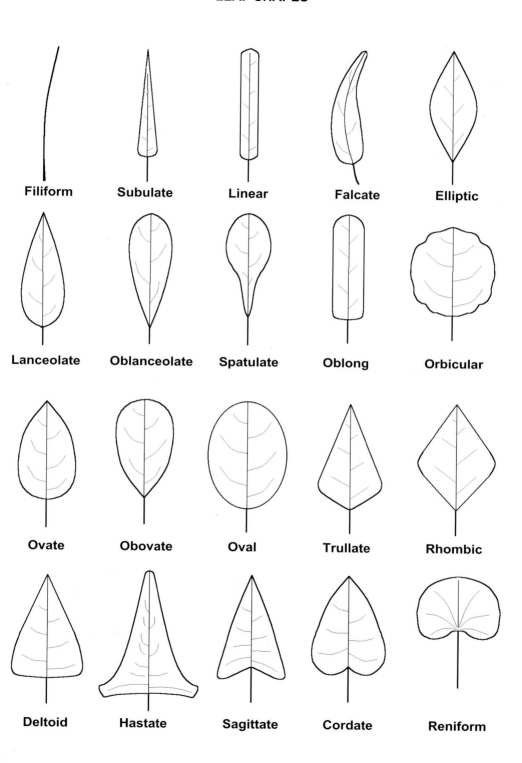

Filiform   Subulate   Linear   Falcate   Elliptic

Lanceolate   Oblanceolate   Spatulate   Oblong   Orbicular

Ovate   Obovate   Oval   Trullate   Rhombic

Deltoid   Hastate   Sagittate   Cordate   Reniform

LEAF MARGINS, TIPS, BASES AND ATTACHMENTS

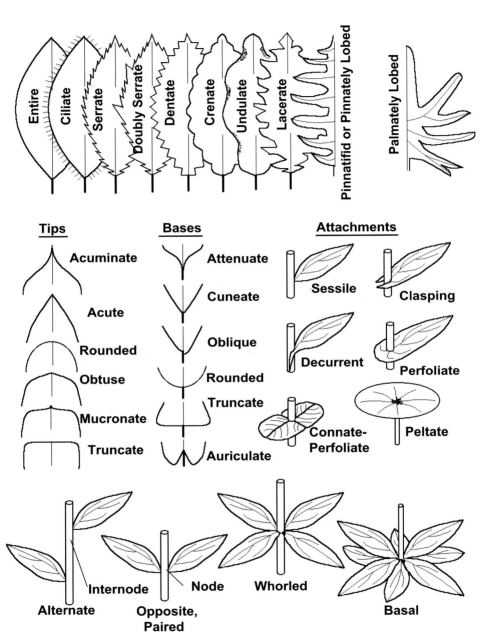

FLOWER PARTS

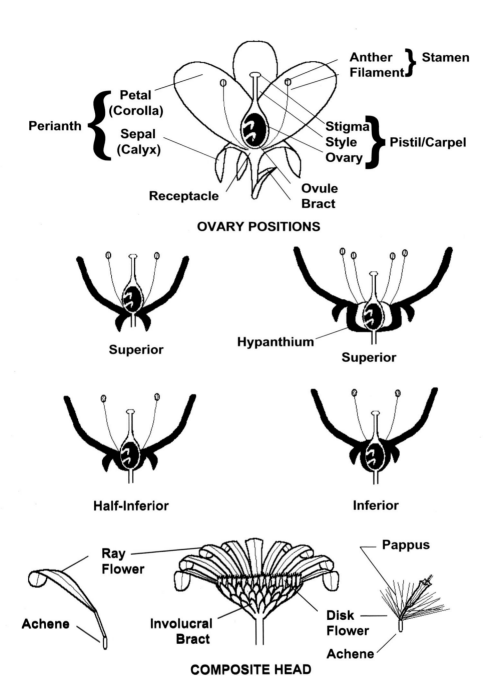

OVARY POSITIONS

Anther } Stamen
Filament

Petal
(Corolla)

Sepal
(Calyx)

Perianth

Stigma
Style } Pistil/Carpel
Ovary

Receptacle

Ovule
Bract

Superior

Hypanthium

Superior

Half-Inferior

Inferior

Ray
Flower

Pappus

Achene

Involucral
Bract

Disk
Flower

Achene

COMPOSITE HEAD

INFLORESCENCE TYPES

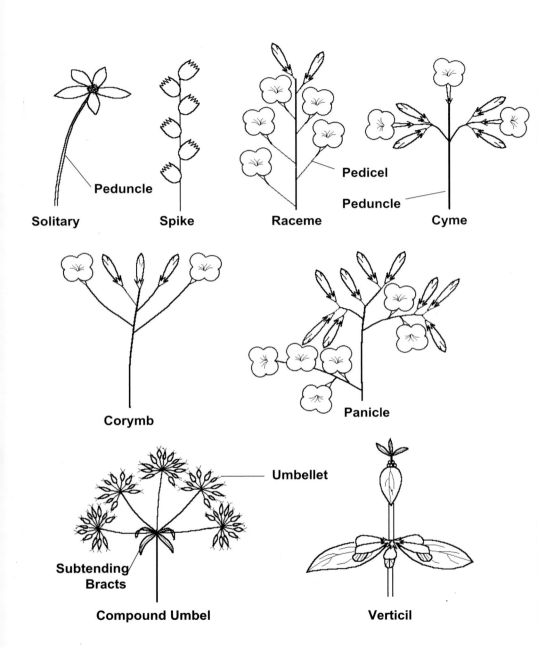

Peduncle

Solitary

Spike

Pedicel

Peduncle

Raceme

Cyme

Corymb

Panicle

Umbellet

Subtending Bracts

Compound Umbel

Verticil

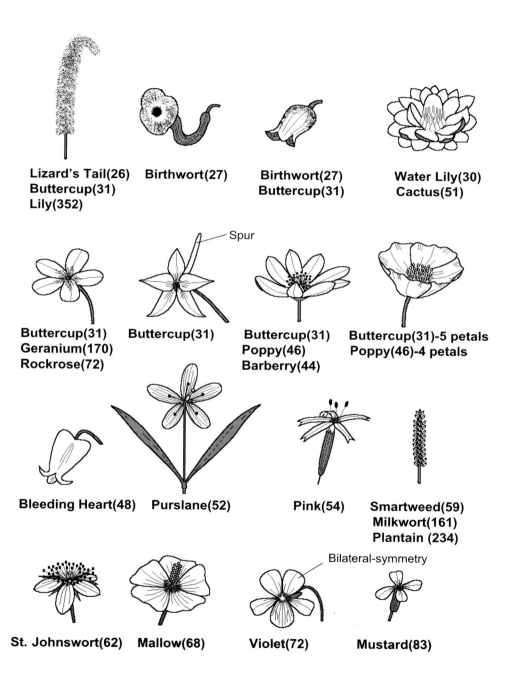

Lizard's Tail(26)
Buttercup(31)
Lily(352)

Birthwort(27)

Birthwort(27)
Buttercup(31)

Water Lily(30)
Cactus(51)

Spur

Buttercup(31)
Geranium(170)
Rockrose(72)

Buttercup(31)

Buttercup(31)
Poppy(46)
Barberry(44)

Buttercup(31)-5 petals
Poppy(46)-4 petals

Bleeding Heart(48)

Purslane(52)

Pink(54)

Smartweed(59)
Milkwort(161)
Plantain (234)

Bilateral-symmetry

St. Johnswort(62)

Mallow(68)

Violet(72)

Mustard(83)

FLOWER SHAPES

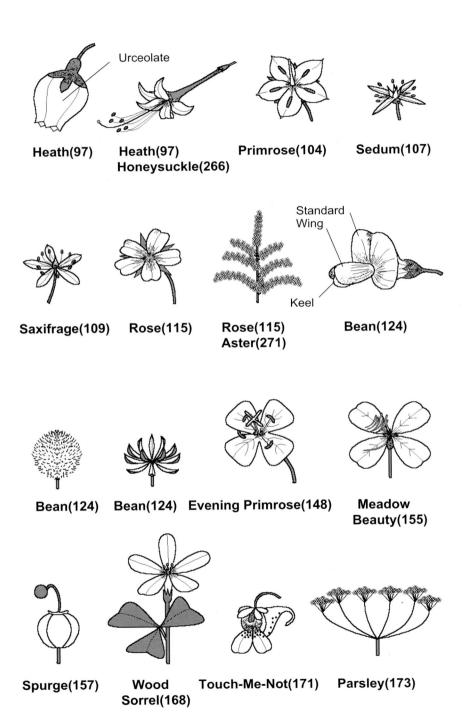

Urceolate

Heath(97) **Heath(97)** **Primrose(104)** **Sedum(107)**
Honeysuckle(266)

Standard
Wing
Keel

Saxifrage(109) **Rose(115)** **Rose(115)** **Bean(124)**
Aster(271)

Bean(124) **Bean(124)** **Evening Primrose(148)** **Meadow**
Beauty(155)

Spurge(157) **Wood** **Touch-Me-Not(171)** **Parsley(173)**
Sorrel(168)

FLOWER SHAPES

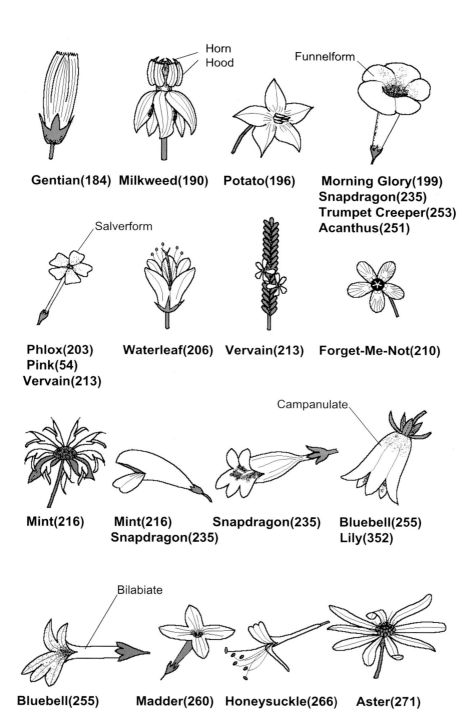

Gentian(184) Milkweed(190) Potato(196) Morning Glory(199)
Snapdragon(235)
Trumpet Creeper(253)
Acanthus(251)

Horn
Hood

Funnelform

Salverform

Phlox(203) Waterleaf(206) Vervain(213) Forget-Me-Not(210)
Pink(54)
Vervain(213)

Campanulate

Mint(216) Mint(216) Snapdragon(235) Bluebell(255)
Snapdragon(235) Lily(352)

Bilabiate

Bluebell(255) Madder(260) Honeysuckle(266) Aster(271)

FLOWER SHAPES

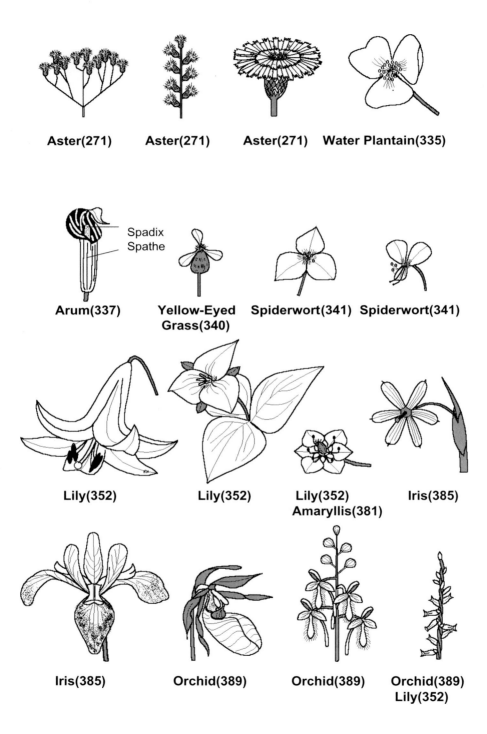

Aster(271)   Aster(271)   Aster(271)   Water Plantain(335)

Spadix
Spathe

Arum(337)   Yellow-Eyed   Spiderwort(341)   Spiderwort(341)
             Grass(340)

Lily(352)   Lily(352)   Lily(352)   Iris(385)
                          Amaryllis(381)

Iris(385)   Orchid(389)   Orchid(389)   Orchid(389)
                                           Lily(352)

GLOSSARY

Acaulescent. Having below-ground stems in the form of rhizomes, opposite of caulescent.

Achene. A small, dry, one-seeded fruit that is indehiscent (see sketch on p. 11).

Acuminate. Tapering to a slender point (see sketch on p. 10).

Acute. Forming an angle less than 90 degrees at the base or apex of a blade (see sketch on p. 10).

Alien. Exotic plant which has been introduced.

Alternate. Situated singly at each node, as leaves on a stem (see sketch on p. 10).

Angled. With a projecting or sharp corner.

Annual. Plant growing from seed to fruit in one year, then dying.

Anther. The pollen-bearing part of the flower stamen (see sketch on p. 11).

Anthesis. Period during which a flower is fully expanded and functional (in bloom).

Apex. The tip, point, or summit of a structure.

Appressed. Lying flat against.

Aquatic. Growing in water.

Ascending. Growing obliquely or curved upward.

Attenuate. Gradually tapering to a very slender point (see sketch on p. 10).

Auricle. A small projecting lobe at the base of a blade.

Auriculate. Having an auricle (see sketch on p. 10).

Awn. A slender terminal bristle, usually stiff.

Axil. The space between two organs, such as a stem and leaf (see sketch on p. 8).

Axillary. In an axil.

Barbellate. Laterally or marginally barbed.

Basal. Located at the base of a plant (see sketch on p. 10).

Beak. Short and stout terminal appendage on a seed or fruit.

Bearded. Bearing a tuft or ring of rather long hairs.

Berry. Fleshy or pulpy fruit developed from a single ovary, usually many-seeded.

Biennial. A plant growing for two years, blooming the second year, and then dying.

Bilabiate. Distinctly divided into two "lips" (see sketch on p. 15).

Bilateral-symmetry. When divided down the middle, having similar shapes on the left and right sides (see sketch on p. 13).

Bilobed. Having two lobes.

Bipinnate. Twice pinnate (see sketch on p. 8).

Bisexual. Having both male and female reproductive organs.

Blade. The expanded terminal part of a flat organ (e.g., leaf, petal, see sketch on p. 8).

Bract. Reduced leaf, particularly at the bases of flower stalks, and surrounding the bases of head inflorescences in the Aster Family (see sketches on p. 11).

Bracteate. Having bracts.

Bristle. Short, stiff hair or hair-like growth.

Bud. A new, undeveloped, vegetative shoot or flower (see sketch on p. 8).

Bulb. A swollen structure composed of circular layers (technically leaf layers) as in an onion, usually underground.

Bulblet. A new small bulb arising around the parent bulb; a bulb-like structure produced by some plants in place of flowers.

Bulbous. Pertaining to a bulb.

Calcareous. Pertaining to soils that are predominately lime-based.

Calyx. The outer set of flower parts, usually green and beneath the petals (see sketch on p. 11).

Campanulate. Bell-shaped, usually descriptive of a corolla or calyx (see sketch on p. 15).

Canescent. Pale or gray from a fine, close pubescence.

Capillary. Hair-like in shape.

Capsule. A dry fruit with two or more rows of seeds and splitting open at maturity.

Carpel. A separate simple pistil, or section of a compound pistil.

Caudex. A short, often woody, persistent stem at or just beneath the ground surface, serving as the organ from which new aerial stems arise each year.

GLOSSARY

Caulescent. Producing above-ground stems, opposite of acaulescent.

Cauline. Pertaining to the stem.

Ciliate. Marginally fringed with spreading hairs (see sketch on p. 10).

Circumneutral. Denoting neither acidic or basic.

Circumscissile. Dehiscent by an encircling transverse line, so that the top comes off as a lid or cap.

Clasping. Usually, partially surrounding the stem (see sketch on p. 10).

Claw. The narrow spoke-like base of some petals or sepals.

Cleft. Deeply cut.

Colonial. Tending to form colonies.

Coma. A tuft of soft hairs, usually terminal on a seed.

Composite. Small individual flowers (disk and ray) borne in a close head having a close involucre of bracts (see sketch on p. 11).

Compound. Composed of two or more separate parts united into one whole (see sketches on p. 8).

Conic. Pertaining to the shape of a cone.

Connate. Two like organs that are grown together or attached (see sketch on p. 10).

Cordate. Heart-shaped, with the point at the terminal end (see sketch on p. 9).

Corm. A swollen underground base of a vertical stem, bulb-like but solid.

Corolla. All petals of a flower, either separate or united, i.e., the inner series of the perianth (see sketch on p. 11).

Corona. A structure exhibited in some flowers between the corolla and the stamens, often simulating an additional part of the perianth.

Corymb. A flat-topped or rounded inflorescence, with the outer flowers on the longest pedicels and opening first (see sketch on p. 12).

Creeping. Growing along the ground surface, usually emitting roots from the nodes.

Crenate. An edge with rounded teeth (see sketch on p. 10).

Crenulate. Diminutive of crenate.

Cuneate. Wedge-shaped (see sketch on p. 10).

Cylindric. Pertaining to the shape of a cylinder.

Cyme. An inflorescence consisting, in its simplest form, of a flower that terminates a stalk and two flowers on branches that arise below it. These two lateral flowers also may each be accompanied by two lateral flowers, etc., such that the inflorescence may be broad and flat with hundreds of flowers. The central flower opens first (see sketch on p. 12).

Cymose. Like a cyme or pertaining to a cyme.

Deciduous. Falling after completion of the normal function, e.g., the dropping of leaves in autumn.

Decompound. More than once compound (see sketch on p. 8).

Decumbent. Prostrate at the base, but with an erect or ascending tip.

Decurrent. Extending downward, e.g., the extension of a leaf down the stem (see sketch on p. 10).

Decurved. Bent downward.

Deflexed. Abruptly bent downward.

Dehiscent. Opening at maturity by natural splitting, as a fruit releasing its seeds.

Deltoid. Triangular in shape (see sketch on p. 9).

Dentate. Margin with teeth spreading and pointed (see sketch on p. 10).

Denticulate. Diminutive of dentate.

Dioecious. Bearing male and female flowers on separate plants.

Discoid. Resembling a disk. In the Aster Family, flowers of a head that are tubular and perfect.

Disk Flower. A rayless flower of the Aster Family (see sketch on p. 11).

Dissected. Divided into lobes or divisions.

Downy. Woolly, covered with short, soft hairs.

Eared. A leaf having one or two small lobes near the base.

Elliptic. A margin with the shape of a geometric ellipse (see sketch on p. 9).

Elongate. Being lengthened or extended.

GLOSSARY

Emergent. Emerging, rising from a liquid or other surrounding medium.
Endemic. A plant native to a restricted geographic region.
Entire. A margin without teeth (see sketch on p. 10).
Exserted. Projecting out or beyond.
Extirpated. Eradicated from an area through loss of habitat, digging, etc.
Falcate. Shaped like a sickle (see sketch on p. 9).
Female Flower. A flower having pistils but no pollen-bearing stamens.
Filament. The slender stalk of a flower stamen below the anther (see sketch on p. 11).
Filiform. Thread-like, long and very slender (see sketch on p. 9).
Flaggy. A hard stone that has been split into many flat, horizontally-disposed pieces.
Follicle. A dry fruit dehiscent usually along one side only.
Fringed. A margin with a divided and projecting edge (often consisting of fine hairs).
Fruit. The structure which contains the seeds and is produced by a flower.
Funnelform. Corolla shaped like a funnel, e.g., Morning Glory (see sketch on p. 15).
Glabrous. Smooth and lacking pubescence (hairs).
Gland. A secreting organ usually producing nectar or oil, may be internal or external.
Glandular. Containing or bearing glands.
Glaucous. Appearing covered with a whitish powder.
Globose. Spherical in shape.
Halberd. Having two divergent basal lobes (same as hastate).
Hastate. Having two divergent basal lobes (see sketch on p. 9).
Head. An inflorescence of small flowers crowded closely together at the end of a stalk (see sketch on p. 11).
Herb. A plant (annual, biennial, or perennial) with stems dying back to the ground at the end of the growing season.
Hood. A strongly-arching flower part, usually concave (see sketch on p. 15).
Horn. An accessory flower structure, curved or straight, beak-like as found in the Milkweed Family (see sketch on p. 15).
Hyaline. Translucent or transparent.
Hypanthium. A saucer-shaped, cup-shaped, or tubular organ below, around, or adhering to the sides of the pistil. The sepals, petals, and stamens are attached at or near its outer or upper margin (see sketch on p. 11).
Imbricate. Overlapping, having the appearance of shingles.
Indehiscent. Not opening naturally at maturity.
Inferior. Descriptive of a pistil surrounded by and sides fused to the hypanthium, the pistil appearing to be located below the sepals and petals (see sketch on p. 11).
Inflorescence. A complete flower cluster, including flowers, pedicels, peduncle and bracts.
Internode. The portion of the stem between nodes (see sketch on p. 10).
Involucral. Pertaining to an involucre.
Involucre. A series of bracts at the base of a flower or inflorescence (see sketch on p. 11).
Irregular. A flower with different-shaped parts, but having bilateral-symmetry.
Keel. The two lower united petals of the Bean Family flowers (see sketch on p. 14).
Labellum. The lip, or median member of the inner perianth or corolla of an orchid.
Lacerate. A margin that is irregularly jagged or torn (see sketch on p. 10).
Lanceolate. Shaped like a lance-head, much longer than wide and widest below the middle (see sketch on p. 9).
Lateral. Situated on or arising from the side of an organ.
Leaf. An ordinary green expanded organ growing from a stem (see sketch on p. 8).
Leaflet. A single segment of a compound leaf (see sketch on p. 8).
Linear. Narrow and elongate, with essentially parallel sides (see sketch on p. 9).
Lip. Either the upper or lower projecting parts of the corolla of mints, snapdragons, etc.; the odd petal (usually lower) of an orchid.
Lobe. A part of a flower or leaf that extends beyond the main body.

GLOSSARY

Male Flower. A flower having stamens and no functional pistil.

Margin. The border or edge of an organ, e.g., a leaf (see sketch on p. 8).

Membrane. A thin, soft, pliable sheet or layer of a plant.

Mesic. Moderately moist.

Midrib. The central vein of a leaf (see sketch on p. 8).

Minute. Very small.

Morphology. The features collectively, of the form, shape and structure of a plant or plant part.

Mucronate. Tipped with a sharp, slender point (see sketch on p. 10).

Native. A plant that is natural to an area or region.

Nerve. The vein of a leaf or similar organ.

Node. A point on a stem from which leaves, branches or flowers arise (see sketch on p. 10).

Oblanceolate. With the outline of an inverted lance-head (like lanceolate but with the terminal half broader, see sketch on p. 9).

Oblique. Slanted or with unequal sides (see sketch on p. 10).

Oblong. Elongate and with nearly parallel sides (see sketch on p. 9).

Obovate. Having the outline of an egg, widest above the middle (see sketch on p. 9).

Obovoid. Egg-shaped, being widest above the middle.

Obtuse. Blunt or rounded at the end, the angle at the end greater than 90 degrees (see sketch on p. 10).

Ocrea. A tubular stipule (sheath) surrounding the stem above the node, as in the Smartweed Family.

Ocreola. Sheath surrounding a cluster of flowers, as in the Smartweed Family.

Opposite. Located directly across from each other, as in paired leaves (see sketch on p. 10).

Orbicular. Essentially circular in outline (see sketch on p. 9).

Oval. Broadly elliptic (see sketch on p. 9).

Ovary. The basal enlarged area of the pistil in which the seeds develop (see sketch on p. 11).

Ovate. Having the outline of an egg, widest below the middle (see sketch on p. 9).

Ovoid. Egg-shaped, being widest below the middle.

Ovule. The young or undeveloped seed (see sketch on p. 11).

Paired. Leaves located directly across from each other (see sketch on p. 10).

Palmate. Radiately lobed or arranged (see sketches on pp. 8 and 10).

Panicle. A rebranching flower cluster of the raceme type (see sketch on p. 12).

Paniculate. Arranged in a panicle.

Pappus. The modified calyx of hairs, scales, or bristles from the summit of the achenes of many species of the Aster Family (see sketch on p. 11).

Pedicel. The stalk of each single flower (see sketch on p. 12).

Peduncle. The main flower stalk, supporting either one flower or a cluster of flowers (see sketches on p. 12).

Peltate. Shield-shaped, centrally attached instead of at the base or margin (see sketch on p. 10).

Pendant. Hanging.

Perennial. Living several years.

Perfect. Descriptive of a flower with both stamens and pistils.

Perfoliate. A leaf blade completely surrounding the stem. The stem appears to pass through the leaf (see sketch on p. 10).

Perianth. The calyx and corolla collectively, or the calyx alone if the corolla is absent (see sketch on p. 11).

Petal. One of the parts of the corolla, usually brightly colored (see sketch on p. 11).

Petaloid. Having the appearance of a petal.

Petiolate. Having a petiole.

Petiole. The basal, stalk-like portion of an ordinary leaf (see sketch on p. 8).

Phyllaries. The involucral bracts of the Aster Family.

Pilose. Sparsely beset with short, straight hairs.

GLOSSARY

Pinnate. Pertaining to leaflets arranged along both sides of a common axis (rachis) (see sketch on p. 8).

Pinnatifid. With deep lobes, clefts, or divisions pinnately arranged (see sketch on p. 10).

Pistil. The central organ(s) of a flower consisting of the ovary containing the seeds, the style, and the stigma (see sketch on p. 11).

Pistillate. Having pistils and no pollen-bearing stamens, a female flower.

Plumose. Structured like a feather with lateral divisions of fine fibers.

Pod. A dry dehiscent fruit.

Pollen. The spores within the anther containing the male plant cells.

Pome. A fleshy fruit with a core (ovary portion), e.g., an apple.

Prostrate. Flat on the ground.

Pubescent. Having hairs on the surface.

Raceme. An elongate inflorescence with single-flowered stalks attached along the side of a common axis (see sketch on p. 12).

Rachilla. A small rachis.

Rachis. The main axis of a pinnately-compound leaf, excluding the petiole (see sketch on p. 8).

Radiate. Spreading radially from a common source.

Ray Flower. The outer flowers in the flower head of many members of the Aster Family, generally showy (see sketch on p. 11).

Receptacle. Enlarged end of the pedicel to which the other flower parts are attached (see sketch on p. 11).

Recurved. Curved away from other structures.

Reflexed. Abruptly turned or bent toward the base.

Regular. Flowers having the members of each set of parts the same size and shape.

Reniform. Kidney-shaped (see sketch on p. 9).

Resinous. Possessing a natural organic resin.

Revolute. Rolled outward or backward.

Rhizome. An underground fleshy stem, usually horizontal, from which scales, leaves, roots, or stems arise from the nodes, e.g., the iris.

Rhombic. Having the form of a rhombus (see sketch on p. 9).

Rib. One of the principal longitudinal veins of a leaf (see sketch on p. 8).

Ribbed. Having ridges.

Rootstock. Enlarged, underground plant part from which the roots and stem(s) grow.

Rosette. Leaves arranged in a circle at the base of a plant.

Rounded. Having the shape of a semicircle (see sketch on p. 10).

Sac. A pouch or cavity, especially in a flower part.

Sagittate. Arrow-shaped with two basal lobes (see sketch on p. 9).

Salverform. With a slender tube and abruptly spreading corolla (see sketch on p. 15).

Saprophytic. Living on dead organic matter, neither parasitic or making its own food.

Scabrous. Rough to the touch.

Scale. A very small, thin, flat structure, e.g., an appressed leaf or bract.

Scape. A leafless stem bearing flowers and rising from the ground or near it.

Secund. Arranged on one side of an axis.

Seed. The propagative part of a plant developed from an ovule in the fruit.

Sepal. One of the parts of the calyx or outer set of flower parts (see sketch on p. 11).

Separate. Separated, not joined.

Serrate. Having sharp teeth pointed terminally (see sketch on p. 10).

Serrate, Doubly. Having sharp teeth of different sizes pointed terminally (see sketch on p. 10).

Sessile. Without any kind of stalk (see sketch on p. 10).

Sheath. A tubular structure which surrounds another structure such as a grass stem.

Simple. A leaf with a single blade (see sketch on p. 8).

Solitary. Having a single flower on a peduncle (see sketch on p. 12).

Spadix. A fleshy stalk on which numerous small flowers grow (see sketch on p. 16).

GLOSSARY

Spathe. A large bract around the spadix (see sketch on p. 16).

Spatulate. Broadest toward a rounded end (see sketch on p. 9).

Spike. An unbranched inflorescence of sessile flowers (see sketch on p. 12).

Spikelet. A small spike.

Spine. A thorn.

Spur. A sac-like or tubular extension of some part of a flower (see sketch on p. 13).

Squarrose. Abruptly spreading or recurved at some point above the base.

Stalk. The main support on which an organ grows.

Stamen. The pollen-producing organ of a flower, consisting of anther and filament (see sketch on p. 11).

Staminate. Having stamens and no functioning pistil, a male flower.

Staminode. A modified stamen that does not produce pollen.

Standard. The uppermost petal in a typical flower of the Bean Family (see sketch on p. 14).

Stellate. Star-shaped.

Stem. Usually refers to the main stalk or branches of a plant (see sketch on p. 8).

Sterile. Does not produce viable fruiting bodies or pollen.

Stigma. The top of the pistil that receives the pollen (see sketch on p. 11).

Stipule. A structure (or pair) at the base of the petiole, usually attached to the stem. May be small and leaf-like or modified into tendrils, spines, etc. (see sketch on p. 8).

Stoloniferous. Producing long, creeping stems on the surface of the ground.

Striate. Marked with fine and usually parallel lines.

Style. The slender stalk that typically connects the stigma(s) to the ovary (see sketch on p. 11).

Subcordate. More or less cordate.

Subtended. Enclosed or embraced in its axil (see sketch on p. 12).

Subulate. Awl-shaped; tapered from the base to a pointed tip (see sketch on p. 9).

Succulent. Fleshy and juicy.

Superior. Descriptive of an ovary free of other flower organs, i.e., attached above the receptacle (see sketch on p. 11).

Taproot. A large, elongated root, usually vertical.

Tendril. A usually slender, coiled, elongated organ of a climbing plant that attaches to other objects.

Tepal. Used to denote sepals and petals, when of similar form and color.

Terminal. At the end of.

Ternate. Borne in threes (see sketch on p. 8).

Terrestrial. Growing on land, not aquatic.

Tomentose. With matted, soft, wool-like hairs.

Toothed. Descriptive of a margin with small, sharp lobes.

Trifoliate, Trifoliolate. With three leaves or three leaflets (see sketch on p. 8).

Trilobed. Divided into three lobes.

Trullate. Having the widest portion below the middle and with straight margins; trowel-shaped (see sketch on p. 9).

Truncate. An apex or base which is nearly straight across, appearing as if cut off (see sketches on p. 10).

Tuber. A compact, usually horizontal, underground stem that stores food (e.g., potato).

Tubercule. A small swelling or projection, usually distinct in color or texture from the organ on which it is borne.

Tubular. Having the shape of a tube.

Tuft. A small cluster of hairs, blades of grass, etc., close together or attached at the base.

Umbel. A flower cluster in which the flower stalks arise from the same point. In a compound umbel, the arrangement is repeated (see sketch on p. 12).

Umbellet. One of the clusters of a compound umbel (see sketch on p. 12).

Undulate. With a wavy surface or margin (see sketch on p. 10).

GLOSSARY

Urceolate. Urn-shaped, wide at the bottom and constricted at the tip (see sketch on p. 14).

Uvula. Hanging fleshy lobe.

Vein. Any of the vascular bundles externally visible, as in a leaf (see sketch on p. 8).

Verticil. A whorl; usually referring to a whorl of flowers or leaves at a node (see sketch on p. 12).

Villous. Covered with fine long hairs, but not matted.

Viscidia. Sticky bodies of an orchid flower that aid in the transfer of pollen.

Whorled. A circle of three or more leaves or branches arising from a single node (see sketch on p. 10).

Wing. A flat structure emerging from the side or summit of an organ; also the lateral petals in the Bean and Milkwort families (see sketch on p. 14).

Winged. Having a wing.

Tennessee State Flowers

In 1919, the General Assembly passed a joint resolution asking the school children of Tennessee to choose the state flower. In the ensuing vote, the Passionflower was chosen. However in 1933, the Legislature adopted a resolution designating the Iris as the state flower, but failed to formally rescind the resolution which designated the Passionflower as the state flower. The confusion was eliminated in 1973 when the General Assembly designated the Passionflower as the state wildflower and the Iris as the state cultivated flower.

The Passionflower (*Passiflora incarnata*, see p. 82) is a perennial found in the southern U.S. and also in South America. Other common names include Maypops, Apricot Vine and the Indian name Ocoee. The Indians believed the Ocoee to be the most abundant and beautiful of all their flowers. The name Passionflower has been attributed to early Christian missionaries of South America who saw symbols of the Crucifixion in parts of the unusual flower – the three crosses, the crown of thorns, nails and cords.

Irises (see pp. 385 to 388) are perennials of the genus *Iris*. In the numerous species and varieties are found essentially all of the colors of the rainbow. The act naming the Iris as the state flower did not name a particular color, but by common acceptance, the purple Iris is considered to be the Tennessee state flower.

PHOTOGRAPHS
and
DESCRIPTIONS

George Hornal

CALYCANTHACEAE : SWEET SHRUB FAMILY
Tennessee has only one species.

Sweet Shrub
Calycanthus floridus L.
A highly-variable, aromatic shrub from 3 to 10 ft tall. Leaves are opposite, ovate to elliptic, entire, from 2 to 6 in. long. Flowers, from 1 to 3 in. wide, are somewhat urn-shaped and solitary on short leafy branches along the stems. The tepals are maroon or brown-purple, linear-oblong, spreading or erect. The flowers have a strong strawberry-like fragrance when crushed. Occasional. Stream banks, rich moist woods. In TN, found from the Eastern Highland Rim east, also in Sumner, Montgomery, Hickman and Hardin counties, and in the e U.S., found from s NY and OH south to the Gulf Coastal Plain. Apr-May. Bubby Bush and Carolina Allspice are other common names. The genus name is from the Greek *calyx* (calyx or cup) and *anthos* (flower).

Author Carl Linnaeus is designated by the letter "L." throughout. Born Carl von Linne, he supposedly changed his name to make it more Latin-sounding.

Jack Carman

SAURURACEAE : LIZARD'S TAIL FAMILY
Tennessee has only one species.

Lizard's Tail   *Saururus cernuus* L.
Erect, usually colonial perennial from 2 to 4 ft tall with branched and jointed stems. The leaves are numerous and alternate with long, basally-sheathing stalks and a broad heart-shaped blade from 2.5 to 6 in. long. The flowers are borne in a dense terminal spike, from 2.5 to 6 in. long, that is drooping at the tip. The flowers have no sepals or petals, but the 6 to 8 stamens are white and showy. The fruit is nearly round, strongly wrinkled, about 0.06-in. wide. Frequent. Low damp woods, margins of swamps, lakes, stream banks. Found throughout TN (more common in West TN), and most of the e U.S. May-Aug. American Indians used a root poultice for wounds and inflammations. Tea made from the whole plant was used as a wash for general illness and rheumatism. The common name and genus name, from the Greek *sauros* (lizard) and *oura* (tail), define the shape of the nodding flower spike.

In Tennessee, the Birthwort Family is represented by 3 genera and 9 species with one additional variety.

Genus *Aristolochia*
Three species are found in Tennessee. The genus name is from the Greek *aristos* (best) and *lochia* (delivery). By the Doctrine of Signatures, the flowers were once used to aid in childbirth since they were thought to resemble an unborn baby.

Dutchman's Pipe
Aristolochia macrophylla Lamarck
Nearly smooth, perennial, climbing, twining, woody vine to 65 ft long. The leaves are alternate, heart-shaped, from 4 to 16 in. long and wide. The flowers, about 1.6 in. long, are borne on long stalks from the leaf axils, strongly bent (pipe-shaped) and purplish-green colored. The pipe face is about 1 in. wide with 3 equal lobes and a purple-brown mouth. Occasional. Rich mountain woods. In TN, found from the Eastern Highland Rim east, also in Giles County, and in the Appalachians, found from s PA to n GA. Apr-Jun.

George Hornal

Jack Carman

Pipe Vine
Aristolochia tomentosa Sims
Perennial climbing, twining, downy, woody vine to 80 ft long. Leaves are alternate, heart-shaped to nearly round, from 4 to 8 in. long and wide, and softly pubescent beneath. The flowers, about 1.6 in. long, are borne on long stalks from the leaf axils, strongly bent (pipe-shaped), tan colored and covered with matted woolly hairs. The pipe face is about 1 in. wide with 3 equal lobes and a purple-brown mouth. Occasional. Wet woods and stream banks. Found in West and Middle TN, also Claiborne and Hamilton counties, and in the U.S., from s IN to KS south. Apr-May.

Virginia Snakeroot (*A. serpentaria* L.) is erect, to 24 in. tall with arrow-shaped leaves and small pipe-shaped flowers on stalks from the lowest leaf nodes. The pipe face has 3 unequal lobes. Frequent. Rich upland woods. Found throughout TN and the e U.S. May-Jun.

Wild Ginger   *Asarum canadense* L.
Small perennial with a pair of hairy heart-shaped leaves from 3 to 5 in. wide on long stalks arising from the rootstock. A single flower, on a 1 to 2 in. peduncle from the leaf axil, consists of a reddish-brown calyx from 0.8 to 1.6 in. long with 3 long, spreading to reflexed, pointed lobes. The flower usually lies on the ground. The root has been used as a ginger substitute. Common. Rich woods. Found throughout TN. Extended range from New Brunswick to Ontario and MN south to n GA and n AL. Apr-May. The genus name is from the ancient Greek name *asaron* of obscure derivation.

George Hornal

Southern Heartleaf (*Hexastylis contracta* Blomquist) is similar to Shuttleworth's Ginger shown on page 29, but has a 1-in. brown calyx with a 2nd constricted band around the calyx. Infrequent. Rich woods. Found in the Cumberland Plateau in TN (Pickett, Scott, Fentress, Overton, Cumberland, Morgan, Putnam, White, Van Buren and Bledsoe counties). May-Jul. Five *Hexastylis* species are found in Tennessee.

George Hornal

Little Brown Jug
Hexastylis arifolia (Michaux) Small
        var. *ruthii* (Ashe) Blomquist
Small perennial with several smooth, arrow-like, mottled, evergreen leaves on long stalks arising from the rootstock. One to several flowers, on about 1 in. stalks arising from the rootstock, consist of a brown urn-shaped calyx about 1 in. long with 3 small erect lobes. The flowers lie on the ground. Frequent. Rich woods. Eastern Highland Rim east in TN, and most of the se U.S. Mar-May.

Variable-Leaf Heartleaf (*H. heterophylla* (Ashe) Small) has roundish evergreen leaves with cordate bases. The brownish calyx, about 0.5-in. long, is constricted at the top and has 3 small spreading lobes greater than 0.2-in. long. Infrequent. Rich woods. Found in Roane, Claiborne, Hawkins, Sullivan, Carter, Unicoi, Washington, Greene and Cocke counties in TN. Apr-Jun.

Virginia Heartleaf (*H. virginica* (L.) Small) is similar to *H. heterophylla*, but the 3 small spreading calyx lobes are less than 0.16-in. long. Rare. Moist or dry woods. Johnson, Scott and Unicoi counties. Apr-May.

Jack Carman

ARISTOLOCHIACEAE : BIRTHWORT FAMILY

Shuttleworth's Ginger *Hexastylis shuttleworthii* (Britten & Baker) Small
Small perennial with several smooth, heart-shaped to round, evergreen leaves on long stalks arising from the rootstock. One to several flowers, on about 1 in. stalks arising from the rootstock, consist of a brown jug-shaped calyx to 1.6 in. long, constricted at the top and with 3 large, spreading lobes mottled with purple. The flowers lie on the ground. Infrequent. Rich woods. Found in the se U.S. highlands and in Franklin, Hamilton, Polk, McMinn, Monroe, Blount, Morgan and Greene counties in TN. Apr-Jun.

NELUMBONACEAE : LOTUS FAMILY

American Lotus, Water Chinquapin *Nelumbo lutea* (Willdenow) Persoon
Aquatic perennial rising to 3 ft above the water surface. Leaves from 12 to 28 in. wide have long stalks and a round blade that is centrally peltate. Some leaves may float while others are raised to 3 ft above the water.   Solitary flowers, from 6 to 10 in. wide, have numerous yellow tepals, are quite showy, and are elevated above the water surface. Mature seedpods are about 4 in. wide and flat on top with acorn-like fruits. Pods are at first erect, but droop as drying occurs. Occasional. Quiet water of ponds, lakes and sloughs. Thinly scattered in TN and irregularly across the e U.S. Jul-Sep. Two Lotus Family species are found in TN.

Sacred Lotus (*Nelumbo nucifera* Gaertner*) has pink flowers about 10 in. across and has been reported from Montgomery County. Introduced from the Orient and likely escaped.

Jack Carman

Jack Carman

Yellow Pond Lily, Spatterdock   *Nuphar luteum* (L.) Sibthorp & Smith
                                                      ssp. *macrophyllum* (Small) Beal

Aquatic perennial arising from a large rhizome. Leaves usually extend above the water surface and are 8 to 16 in. long, nearly round with a broad triangular cleft at the base. Flowers, from 1.25 to 2 in. wide, are bowl-shaped and yellow, and occur at or just slightly above water level. Occasional. Lakes, ponds, sluggish streams. More prevalent in West TN, scattered in Middle and East TN. Extended range from s ME to WI south to FL and TX. May-Sep. *Nuphar advena* (Aiton) Aiton f. The blades and stem-like stalks of the water lily and pond lily leaves die back each year, and contribute to the organic buildup in lakes and marshes. American Indians used root tea for blood diseases, chills with fever, and heart ailments. However, large doses can be potentially **toxic**.

The Water Lily Family has 2 genera with one species each found in Tennessee.

Fragrant Water Lily   *Nymphaea odorata* Aiton

Aquatic perennial from a rhizome with or without knotty tubers. Leaf blades, from 4 to 12 in. wide, are floating, peltate, rotund and cleft, often red or purple beneath. White flowers, from 3 to 8 in. wide, are borne at the surface of the water, and have 40 to 100 stamens and numerous ascending petals. Infrequent. Quiet waters of ponds and lakes. Found in Lake, Obion, Stewart, Lewis, Davidson, Putnam and Sevier counties in TN. More common on the Coastal Plain but found throughout the e U.S. and se CAN. Jul-Aug. Root juice mixed with lemon juice has been used as a folk remedy to remove freckles and pimples.

Jack Carman

CABOMBACEAE : WATER SHIELD FAMILY

Two genera with one aquatic species each are found in TN and both have long-petioled leaves that are peltate.

Water Shield
Brasenia schreberi J.F. Gmelin

Perennial with submerged stems to 6 ft long. The leaves are numerous, alternate, long-stalked and have floating oval blades from 2 to 4 in. long, half as wide. Underwater parts and the lower surfaces of leaves are coated with mucilage. Flowers are solitary on stout stalks and found just above the water level. Sepals and petals are similar, dull reddish, about 0.5-in. long. Occasional. Not often found, but often locally abundant. Ponds of Middle and West TN, and the e U.S. Jun-Jul.

Fanwort (*Cabomba caroliniana* Gray) has small floating peltate leaves (to 0.8-in. long) without mucilage. Petals are white with a yellow base. Rare. Similar habitat. Lake, Obion, and Weakley counties in TN. U.S. range from NJ to OH and MO south to FL and TX. May-Jun.

Jack Carman

Jack Carman

RANUNCULACEAE : BUTTERCUP FAMILY

Southern Monkshood
Aconitum uncinatum L.

Weak perennial with smooth stems to 5 ft long that arise from a turnip-like root and often lean on other plants. Leaves, to 6 in. long, are numerous, alternate, stalked, deeply 3 to 5 cleft into toothed lobes. The inflorescence is usually small with a few flowers in loose clusters, terminal on the stem and arising from the leaf axils. The flowers, from 0.6 to 0.9-in. high, are irregular and blue, and have an upper sepal shaped like a helmet. Occasional. Rich woods. In TN, found from the Eastern Highland Rim east, also in Davidson, Hickman and Lewis counties. The extended range is from s PA to n GA west to IN and AL. Aug-Oct. **Plants are very poisonous.**

Wolfsbane (*A. reclinatum* A.Gray) is similar, but arises from slender roots and has whitish or yellowish flowers. Rare. Rich woods in the mountains and Piedmont from sw PA south to n GA. Found in Carter County in TN. Jun-Sep.

Jack Carman   George Hornal

White Baneberry, Doll's Eyes   *Actaea pachypoda* Elliott

Perennial from 16 to 32 in. tall with smooth stems and large, 2 or 3 times ternately-compound leaves on long stalks. The leaflets, to 6 in. long, are ovate or ovate-oblong, sharply-toothed. The small white flowers are borne in a compact raceme on a long stalk that extends well above the leaves. The fruits are round and white, and each fruit is on a thick red stalk from 0.4 to 1.2 in. long. Common. Rich woods. Found throughout TN, and the eastern U.S. and CAN. Apr-May, Aug-Oct (fruit). The fruit resembles the porcelain eyes once used in dolls, hence the common name Doll's Eyes. **The berries are poisonous.** *Actaea alba* (L.) Miller. *Actaea* is the ancient name for elder, and was transferred by Linnaeus to this genus.

Jack Carman

The Buttercup Family is represented by 19 genera and 63 species in Tennessee.

Genus *Anemone*

The flowers have no petals, but sepals are whitish and petal-like. Pistils and stamens are numerous. Plants have deeply-divided basal leaves and a whorl of leaves on the stem beneath the flower stalks. The genus and common names are from the Greek *anemos* (wind), of somewhat questionable application. Four species are found in TN.

Wood Anemone
Anemone quinquefolia L.

Delicate perennial from 4 to 8 in. tall that arises from a slender rhizome. The solitary basal leaf is long-stalked and palmately divided with 3 to 5 leaflets that are coarsely toothed. Stem leaves are similarly shaped but smaller. A single flower terminates the stem and usually has 5 white sepals, from 0.4 to 0.9-in. long, that are often reddish beneath. The fruiting head is almost round, about 0.4-in. wide. Frequent. Rich woods. Found in most of the se U.S., and from the Eastern Highland Rim east in TN, also in Lawrence and Wayne counties. Mar-May.

Jack Carman

Thimbleweed   *Anemone virginiana* L.

Loosely-hairy, colonial perennial to 3 ft tall. Basal and stem leaves are similar, to 3 in. long, stalked and 3-lobed with the lateral lobes deeply incised. Lower stem leaves are usually whorled, upper stem leaves opposite. Several flowers, solitary on long stalks extending well above the leaves, have 5 whitish sepals about 0.5-in. long that are very downy beneath. The cylindric fruiting head, to 1.2 in. tall, is believed to resemble a "thimble." Common. Rich woods. Found throughout TN and the e U.S. May-Jul.

Carolina Anemone (*Anemone caroliniana* Walter), to 16 in. tall, usually has 3 long-stalked basal leaves and 2 to 3 sessile leaves located halfway up the stem. All leaves are 3-lobed, but the lobes are deeply incised into narrow segments. A solitary flower terminates the stem and has 5 to 15 bluish to white sepals from 0.4 to 0.9-in. long. The fruiting head is almost cylindric, from 0.5 to 0.8-in. tall. Rare. Cedar glades. Found in Bedford, Davidson, Rutherford and Wilson counties in TN. U.S. range from SD to IN and NC south to GA and TX. Apr-May.

Wild Columbine
Aquilegia canadensis L.

Branched perennial from 1 to 4 ft tall that arises from a stout rhizome. Stem and basal leaves are stalked and 2 or 3 times ternately compound. The leaflets, to 2 in. long and wide, are mostly 3-lobed, the lobes incised and with rounded tips. Nodding flowers, to 1.6 in. long, terminate the branches. The 5 sepals are red, and the 5 petals have yellow blades and hollow red spurs that contain the nectar. Numerous yellow stamens form a column that projects well beyond the petals. Frequent. Dry woods, limestone bluffs and limestone glades, occasionally moist areas. Found from the Western Highland Rim east in TN, and from Saskatchewan to Nova Scotia south to TX and FL. Apr-Jun. A favorite of hummingbirds. The genus name is thought by some to originate from *aquila* (the eagle), from the supposed resemblance of the spurs to claws; by others from *aqua* (water) and *legere* (to collect), from the fluid at the base of the hollow spurs.

Jack Carman

Jack Carman

Marsh Marigold   *Caltha palustris* L.

Poisonous perennial from 8 to 24 in. tall with hollow stems that are branched above. The basal leaves have long stalks and glossy, rounded blades from 2 to 6 in. wide. Stem leaves are similar, but much smaller with short stalks. Flowers, from 0.6 to 1.6 in. wide, are without petals but have 5 to 9 shiny, bright yellow sepals and numerous stamens. Rare. Marshes, wet woods and meadows. A northeastern species extending south to TN and NC in the mountains. Known from Carter, Greene and Johnson counties in TN. Apr-Jun. *Caltha* is the Latin name of a strong-smelling yellow flower, probably the common marigold and derived from *calathos* (a cup).

Genus *Cimicifuga*

Basally-disposed compound leaves have deeply-lobed, broad, sharp-pointed leaflets. Flowers are without petals, but have numerous showy white stamens. The genus name is from the Latin *cimex* (a bug) and *fugere* (to drive away). Three species are found in TN and all are **poisonous**.

Black Cohosh
Cimicifuga racemosa (L.) Nuttall

Perennial with flower stems to 8 ft tall and principal leaves with 20 or more leaflets. White flowers are about 0.5-in. wide, in a crowded raceme to 1 ft (or more) long on a narrow branched vertical stalk. Flowers have staminodes and one (rarely 2 or 3) ovary that is sessile. Frequent. Rich woods. A mostly northeastern species extending south into the eastern 2/3 of TN. May-Jul.

American Bugbane (*Cimicifuga americana* Michaux) is similar, but shorter (to 5 ft tall), and each flower has 3 to 8 stalked ovaries. Infrequent. Found in rich woods from s PA to NC and TN in the mountains. Found in Fentress, Polk, Union, Sevier, Cocke and Carter counties in TN. Jul-Sep.

Appalachian Bugbane (*Cimicifuga rubifolia* Kearney) has 1 to 3 sessile ovaries per flower but no staminodes, and principal leaves usually have 9 or less leaflets. Occasional. Rich woods. Ridge and Valley, Western Highland Rim in TN. U.S. range from sw VA to NC and TN, with disjunct populations in w KY and s IL. Sep.

Jack Carman

Genus *Clematis*

Perennial, usually climbing, herbaceous or somewhat woody vines with opposite leaves. Flowers are without petals but sepals are showy, and stamens and ovaries are numerous. Seeds have a long, persistent, often feathery style. Eight species are found in TN. *Clematis* is an old name of a climbing plant with long and lithe branches, and is derived from *clema* (a shoot).

Blue Jasmine   ***Clematis crispa*** L.

Climbing herbaceous vine with pinnately compound leaves having 2 to 4 leaflet pairs that are smooth, lance-shaped, usually entire, from 0.4 to 4 in. long. Flowers are solitary and terminal on each branch. Thick sepals, from 1 to 2 in. long, are blue to purple, the tips normally reflexed and wavy or crisped. The mature styles are from 0.8 to 1.2 in. long, densely pubescent. Infrequent. Marshes and wet woods. A Coastal Plain species found in West TN (Obion, Weakley, Dyer, Lauderdale, Shelby, Hardeman and Hardin counties), and most of the se U.S. Apr-Aug.

Jack Carman

Leather Vase Vine   ***Clematis viorna*** L.

Climbing perennial. Leaves have 2 to 4 leaflet pairs that are green beneath. Sepals, from 0.6 to 1 in. long, are leathery, red to pink to purple, thinly hairy on the back, densely hairy on the margins. Mature styles are densely feathery throughout. Frequent. Wet woods and thickets. Found in the eastern 2/3 of TN and from PA to MO south to GA and MS. May-Jul.
Bluebill (*Clematis pitcheri* T. & G.) is similar, but leaves have 3 to 5 pairs of leaflets. Sepals to 1 in. long are dull purplish. Mature style hairy near the seed but smooth toward the tip. Rare. Montgomery County. U.S. range from IN to NB south to TN and NM. Jun-Aug.
Pale Leatherflower (*Clematis versicolor* Small *ex* Rydberg) usually has 4 leaflet pairs that are glaucous beneath. Sepals purplish, 0.6 to 1 in. long. Mature styles are feathery throughout. Frequent. Mostly Middle and East TN, and from KY to OK south to TN and AR. Jun-Jul.

Jack Carman

Jack Carman

Virgin's Bower   *Clematis virginiana* L.
Smooth climbing perennial to 17 ft long with angled stems. Leaves normally have 3 leaflets that are ovate, toothed, from 1 to 4 in. long. Numerous showy flowers about 1 in. wide have petal-like sepals that are white or whitish, widely spreading. Mature styles are feathery throughout. Frequent. Wet woods, stream banks, fence rows, woods borders. Found throughout TN, it ranges from Nova Scotia to Manitoba south to GA and LA. Jul-Sep.

Yam-Leaf Clematis (*Clematis terniflora* DC.*) is similar, but the leaves usually have 5 leaflets that are not toothed. Occasional. Cultivated and often escaped, it might be found in open areas almost anywhere in Middle and East TN. Jul-Sep. Introduced from Japan.

George Hornal

Rocket Larkspur
Consolida ambigua (L.) Ball & Heywood*
Branching annual from 1 to 3 ft tall. The leaves are sharply dissected into numerous lobes that appear almost filiform. The inflorescence is a long raceme with irregular flowers, from 0.8 to 1.6 in. wide, that have united petals and a single, long, narrow spur projecting backwards. The flower color is highly variable, from blue to violet to pink or white. Seeds are densely hairy. Occasional. Introduced from Europe, and commonly cultivated and escaped. Fields, roadsides, barrens. Officially recorded in Middle TN, also McMinn, Blount and Knox counties. The extended range is from Nova Scotia to MN south. May-Sep. Sometimes placed in the genus *Delphinium*, it differs mainly by being annual and having a single ovary. *Delphinium ambiguum* L.*, *Delphinium ajacis* L.*

Jack Carman

Genus *Delphinium*

Irregular flowers have a single long spur that projects backward, numerous stamens, and usually 3 (but occasionally 5) pistils. **All plant parts are poisonous.** Larkspurs have caused the death of many cattle, especially in the western states. The genus name is from the Greek *delphinus* (a dolphin), alluding the shape of the flower. Three species are found in TN.

Tall Larkspur
Delphinium exaltatum Aiton

Perennial to 7 ft tall. Leaves are alternate, pale beneath, and divided into lance-shaped segments from 0.4 to 1.0 in. wide, the segments with 1 to 4 coarse sharp lobes above the middle. The inflorescence is a raceme to 1 ft long with blue or purple flowers. Lateral sepals are about 0.4-in. long and the spur is from 0.4 to 0.6-in. long. Rare. Barrens. Found in Anderson, Knox, Hamilton and Roane counties in TN, and from PA to NC west to OH and s MO. Jul-Sep.

Dwarf Larkspur
Delphinium tricorne Michaux

Perennial from 8 to 24 in. tall that arises from tuberous roots. The leaves, from 0.8 to 6 in. wide, are long-stalked and mostly basal, palmately and deeply divided into several narrow oblong-linear segments. Several blue or white flowers are borne in a loose terminal raceme to 8 in. long. Lateral sepals are 0.4 to 0.6-in. long, and the spur is 0.5 to 0.75-in. long. The three ovaries of the flower are spreading, and the shiny black seeds are smooth and triangular. Common. Damp to dry woods and barrens. Widespread in the eastern 2/3 of TN and the e U.S. Mar-May. The species name *tricorne* is from the three spreading ovaries.

George Hornal

Jack Carman

Prairie Larkspur
Delphinium virescens Nuttall
Perennial from 1 to 4 ft tall, the stem finely and densely hairy, often glandular. Leaves are chiefly basal or below the middle of the stem, and deeply dissected into numerous linear segments from 0.08 to 0.2-in. wide. The light blue to whitish flowers are borne in a long erect terminal raceme. The spur is from 0.4 to 0.6-in. long and seeds are covered with scales. Occasional. Barrens, plains, cedar glades. Found in the cedar glades and barrens of Middle TN, and also the barrens of Hamilton and Meigs counties. A prairie species that occasionally extends east into central KY, TN and nw GA. May-Jul.

Jack Carman

False Rue Anemone
Enemion biternatum Rafinesque
Smooth perennial from 4 to 16 in. tall with slender stems and fibrous yellowish roots that have small tuber-like thickenings. Basal leaves are long-stalked and divided 2 or 3 times, often with 9 leaflets. Upper leaflets are less than 1 in. wide and broadly obovate with 3 deep, round-tipped lobes. The one to few flowers, from 0.6 to 0.8-in. wide, are without petals but have 5 white sepals and numerous stamens. Occasional. Limestone bluffs, rich woods, thickets, especially near watercourses. Found in Middle TN, also Lauderdale and Loudon counties, and in most of the e U.S. Mar-May. *Isopyrum biternatum* (Raf.) T. & G.

Genus *Hepatica*

Two species are found in TN. The genus name is the feminine of the Latin *hepaticus* (pertaining to the liver), alluding to the shape of the leaves.

Sharp-Lobed Hepatica
Hepatica acutiloba DC.

Perennial to 6 in. tall with only basal leaves, those on hairy stalks. The leaves, from 1 to 3 in. wide, have 3 lobes with pointed tips, and the lobes extend to well past the middle of the leaf. Solitary flowers are borne on long hairy stalks, and are subtended by three green bracts with pointed tips. The flowers, from 0.5 to 1 in. wide, have 5 to 12 sepals (no petals) and numerous stamens and ovaries. Sepal colors vary widely, from white to pink to lavender to purple. Leaves last through winter and the new leaves appear after flowering. Common. Rich upland woods, usually on basic soils. Found in TN from the Western Highland Rim east, also in Haywood County, and in most of the e U.S. and CAN. Feb-Apr. One of the earliest blooming spring wildflowers.

Note: Author Augustin Pyramus de Candolle is usually denoted by the letters "DC."

Jack Carman

Round-Lobed Hepatica

Hepatica americana (DC.) KerGawler

Perennial to 6 in. tall with only basal leaves, those on hairy stalks. The leaves, from 1 to 3 in. wide, have 3 lobes with rounded tips, and the lobes extend to near the middle of the leaf. Solitary flowers are borne on long hairy stalks, and subtended by three green bracts with rounded tips. The flowers, from 0.5 to 1 in. wide, have 5 to 12 sepals (no petals) and numerous stamens and ovaries. Sepal colors commonly only white to pale lavender. Leaves last through winter and the new leaves appear after flowering. Occasional. Rich upland woods, usually on acidic soils. Found in TN from the Western Highland Rim east, and in most of the e U.S. and CAN. Feb-Apr. One of the earliest blooming spring wildflowers.

Jack Carman

Goldenseal   *Hydrastis canadensis* L.
Perennial from 8 to 20 in. tall with a hairy stem, one basal leaf and two leaves near the top of the stem. Leaves are long-stalked, 5-lobed, palmately veined, from 1 to 4 in. wide at flowering, but continue to grow and may be 10 in. wide later. The solitary terminal flower, about 0.5-in. wide, is borne on a hairy stalk. Petals are absent and the three greenish-white sepals fall early, but the white stamens are numerous and showy. The berries are dark red, each with 1 or 2 seeds. Frequent. Rich woods. Widespread in TN and most of the ne U.S. Apr-Jun. Listed for many counties in the state, but populations are declining because the yellow rhizomes are collected for medicinal purposes, including antibiotic, antiseptic and immune stimulant usage. The Latin name was suggested from the leaf of the Broad-Leaf Waterleaf (*Hydrophyllum canadense*) because Goldenseal was early confused with it.

Jack Carman

George Hornal

Genus *Ranunculus*
The flowers of most buttercup species have 5 bright, shiny, waxy, yellow petals, 5 (or less) sepals, and numerous yellow stamens and pistils. There are 23 species found in TN, some quite variable. All species are **poisonous when fresh** and pose a danger to grazing animals. Fortunately, the poison is volatile so dried buttercups mixed in hay are not toxic. The genus name is the Latin name for little frog, alluding that some of these plants grow where frogs abound.

Kidney-Leaf Buttercup
Ranunculus abortivus L.
Erect annual from 8 to 20 in. tall with stem and branches mostly smooth. Basal leaves are normally kidney-shaped and long-stalked, but sometimes are partially lobed or have rounded teeth. Uppermost leaves are mostly sessile and divided into 3 to 5 narrow lobes. Flowers are about 0.25-in. wide, and petals are yellow, shorter than the sepals. Common. Meadows, damp or dry woods, lawns. Widespread across TN, the e U.S. and e CAN. Mar-Jun.

Jack Carman

Early Buttercup *Ranunculus fascicularis* Muhlenberg *ex* Bigelow
Perennial to 1 ft tall with appressed hairy stems and some tuberous roots. Leaves mostly basal, longer than wide, divided into lobed and toothed segments. Flowers glossy yellow with petals to 0.6-in. long. Frequent. Open areas, dry woods. Widespread in TN. Apr-May.
Spearwort (*Ranunculus ambigens* Watson) is a perennial with hollow stems and no basal leaves. Stem leaves are stalked, lance-shaped, to 6 in. long. Flowers glossy yellow, the petals from 0.2 to 0.4-in. long. Infrequent. Marshes. Thinly spread in TN. Apr-Jun.
Bulbous Buttercup (*Ranunculus bulbosus* L.*) is a perennial to 2 ft tall with a bulb-like stem base. Leaves deeply divided into three segments that are cleft and lobed. Yellow flowers to 1 in. wide have reflexed sepals. Occasional. Fields, pastures. Eastern 2/3 of TN. Apr-Jun.

Hispid Buttercup *Ranunculus hispidus* Michaux
Perennial to 3 ft tall with stems that are very hairy below. Leaves are deeply 3-lobed or sometimes trifoliate. Glossy yellow flowers are about 1 in. wide. Common. Dry upland woods, low woods and meadows. Eastern 2/3 of TN and all of the e U.S. Mar-Jun.
Creeping Buttercup (*Ranunculus repens* L.*) is a perennial with creeping stems that root at the nodes, forming dense colonies. Rare. Fields, roadsides, wet meadows. Found in Johnson County, but double-flowered forms are cultivated and often escaped. May-Jul.
Hairy Buttercup (*Ranunculus sardous* Crantz*) is an erect hairy annual to 28 in. tall. Leaves are 3-parted, deeply lobed and cleft. Sepals reflexed and flowers yellow, to 0.8-in. wide. Frequent. Moist fields. Widespread across TN. Apr-Jul. Introduced from Europe.

Jack Carman

Jack Carman

Hooked Buttercup   *Ranunculus recurvatus* Poiret
Few-branched perennial from 8 to 28 in. tall with sparsely hairy stems. Leaves are mostly stalked, hairy, deeply 3-cleft to below the middle, the lateral segments lobed and toothed. Pale yellow petals are shorter than or equal to the sepals. Achene beaks are strongly hooked. Common. Rich, moist woods. Widespread across TN and the e U.S. Apr-Jun.

Swamp Buttercup (*Ranunculus septentrionalis* Poiret) is a perennial with the lower leaves deeply 3-parted or trifoliate. Flowers are about 1 in. wide and the achene beak is straight. Occasional. Wet woods and meadows. Found from the Western Highland Rim east in TN, also Lauderdale County, and from NY to MN south to FL and TX. Apr-Jun. Highly variable.

Jack Carman

Genus *Thalictrum*
Erect herbs having flowers without petals, and 4 or 5 sepals that usually fall early. Flowers are often unisexual with numerous stamens or ovaries. The ovaries have only 1 seed. All species are perennial with twice ternately-divided leaves. Seven species are found in TN.

Early Meadow Rue   *Thalictrum dioicum* L.
Perennial from 12 to 28 in. tall. Leaves are long-stalked, ternately-divided twice, and have smooth, thin, rounded, toothed leaflets. Stamens yellow or yellowish. Plants are either male or female (dioecious). Frequent. Damp woods. Found in the eastern 2/3 of TN, also Obion County, and in most of the eastern U.S. Mar-Apr.
Skunk Meadow Rue (*Thalictrum revolutum* DC.) is a perennial to 6 ft tall. Upper leaves sessile, lower leaves stalked. Leaves are variably divided, leaflets have revolute margins and usually 3 lobes. The lower leaflet surface has finely glandular hairs. Flowers greenish-white. Frequent. Moist or dry woods, meadows, barrens. Found in the eastern 2/3 of TN, also Shelby County, and throughout the e U.S. May-Jul.

Rue Anemone
Thalictrum thalictroides (L.) Eames & Boivin

Slender smooth perennial from 4 to 12 in. tall with tuberous roots. The basal leaves are long-stalked and have 9 rounded leaflets. Stem leaves are sessile and have 3 leaflets. The tips of all leaflets usually have 3 shallow lobes. The flowers, from 0.5 to 1 in. wide, are long-stalked and originate from a single point. The 5 to 10 sepals are white to pinkish and showy. Double flowers are often seen. Common. Rich dry or moist woods. Widespread in TN and the e U.S. Mar-May. One of the earliest blooming spring wildflowers. *Anemonella thalictroides* (L.) Spach. The genus name is an ancient name of some plant mentioned by Dioscorides.

Cliff Meadow Rue (*Thalictrum clavatum* DC.) is a smooth perennial from 12 to 28 in. tall. Leaflets are pale beneath, and the flowers are perfect with broad white stamens. The inflorescence is few-flowered and achenes are curved upward. Occasional. Moist woods and cliffs. Found in the eastern half of TN, and from VA to e KY south to SC and GA. May-Jul.

Jack Carman

Jack Carman

Tassel Rue
Trautvetteria caroliniensis (Walter) Vail

Stout branched perennial from 2 to 5 ft tall. Both stem and basal leaves are palmately (and deeply) divided into 5 to 11 lobes that are irregularly toothed or incised. Basal leaves to 1 ft wide on long petioles, stem leaves much smaller and mostly sessile. The inflorescence is corymb-like, terminating the stem and branches, and extends well above the foliage. Sepals fall early and petals are absent, but the numerous white stamens are broad and showy, to 0.4-in. long. Occasional. Moist woods and barrens. Found from the Eastern Highland Rim east in TN, also in Davidson and Cheatham counties. The U.S. range is from PA and KY to GA, also in s IN, w IL and s MO. Jun-Jul. The genus name is in honor of Ernst Rudolph von Trautvetter, a distinguished 19th century Russian botanist.

Jack Carman

Shrub Yellowroot
Xanthorhiza simplicissima Marshall
Colonial shrub from 12 to 20 in. tall, the roots and stem wood yellow. The leaves are clustered at the top of the stem, alternate, long-stalked, pinnately compound with mostly 5 lance-ovate or broadly ovate leaflets to 3 in. long that are toothed to deeply cleft. The inflorescence consists of several (many) long, narrow, drooping racemes to 5 in. long. The tiny flowers have five maroon (to yellowish-green) sepals to 0.12-in. long and no petals. Occasional. Shaded stream banks. Found from the Cumberland Plateau east in TN, also in Chester, Hardin, Henderson and Lewis counties, and found from s NY to KY south to SC, w FL and MS. Apr-Jun. The genus name is from the Greek *xanthos* (yellow) and *rhiza* (root).

BERBERIDACEAE : BARBERRY FAMILY
Five genera and 7 species are found in Tennessee.

Jack Carman

Blue Cohosh
Caulophyllum thalictroides (L.) Michaux
Erect, grayish-green, smooth perennial from 12 to 32 in. tall. The stem has one large, sessile, triple ternately-compound leaf above the middle, one (rarely two) smaller, twice ternately-compound leaf just below the inflorescence, 1 to 3 terminal inflorescences, and rarely a branch with more leaves and flowers. The leaflets, from 1 to 3 in. long, are irregularly lobed above the middle. Each inflorescence has panicle-like flower clusters (cymes) with small yellow-green to purple-green flowers that are about 0.5-in. wide and have 6 petal-like sepals. Fruit dark blue, **poisonous.** Frequent. Rich woodlands. Found in the eastern 2/3 of TN, it is a mostly northeastern species extending south to north GA and north AL. Apr-May. From the Greek *caulos* (stem) and *phyllon* (leaf).

Giant Blue Cohosh (*C. giganteum* (Farwell) Loconte & Blackwell) is similar, but flowers are mostly purple, larger and fewer. For the same area, it usually will bloom two weeks earlier. Infrequent. Found in Cannon, Greene, Overton, Sullivan, Sumner and Unicoi counties in TN.

Umbrella Leaf
Diphylleia cymosa Michaux
Smooth perennial from 1 to 3 ft tall, arising from a thick rhizome. Flowering stem leaves usually 2, alternate, peltate near the margin, from 1 to 2 ft across, cleft and radially lobed, the lobes pointed and toothed. Non-flowering plants have only one stem leaf. Basal leaves are scattered, erect and centrally peltate. The inflorescence is a solitary cluster, from 2 to 4 in. wide, that extends above the leaves and has white flowers to 0.6-in. wide. Each flower has 6 sepals, 6 petals and 6 stamens, but the sepals fall early. The petals are ovate-elliptic with round tips. Fruits, to 0.4-in. wide, are conspicuous, round, dark blue, fleshy, on red stalks. Infrequent. Rich, cool, mountain woods. Found in Monroe, Blount, Sevier, Greene, Unicoi and Carter counties in TN, and in the Blue Ridge from VA to GA. May-Jun. The genus name is from the Greek *dis* (double) and *phyllon* (leaf).

Jack Carman

Jack Carman

Twinleaf
Jeffersonia diphylla (L.) Persoon
Perennial from 8 to 20 in. tall at maturity that arises from an underground rhizome. The leaves are all basal, on stalks about 6 in. tall at flowering, divided into 2 leaflets that are somewhat kidney-shaped and about 1.5 in. wide (enlarging to 3 to 6 in. wide after flowering). The solitary flowers are borne on leafless stalks, usually extending just above the leaves. The showy white flowers (to 1.8 in. wide) have 8 petals and stamens, and 4 petal-like sepals that fall early. The fruit, from 0.8 to 1.2 in. long, is erect and has a hinged lid. Frequent. Rich moist woods, preferring limestone soils. In TN, found from the Western Highland Rim east. Extended range from w NY to se MN south to MD and AL. Mar-Apr. The genus was named in honor of Thomas Jefferson by his friend and fellow botanist William Bartram.

Jack Carman

BERBERIDACEAE : BARBERRY FAMILY

Mayapple   *Podophyllum peltatum* L.

Smooth colonial perennial from 12 to 20 in. tall. Flowering plants have a forked stem with one leaf on each branch; non-flowering plants have one leaf on an unforked stem. Leaves are large, peltate and palmately divided into 5 to 9 lobes. A single, nodding, white, waxy flower on a short stalk arises from the fork of the stem. The flower, from 1.2 to 2.0 in. wide, has 6 to 9 petals and numerous stamens. The ripe berry is yellow, pulpy, many-seeded, from 1.6 to 2 in. long. Common. Moist woods, meadows. Widespread in TN and the e U.S. Apr-May. **Seeds, leaves, roots are poisonous.** Once used by American Indians and early settlers for several medicinal purposes, it is now a source of medicinal compounds. The ripe fruit pulp is considered by many to be edible raw, and has been used to make preserves.

George Hornal

PAPAVERACEAE : POPPY FAMILY

Six genera with one species each are listed for Tennessee.

Corn Poppy   *Papaver rhoeas* L.*

The red poppy introduced from Flanders that is planted en masse along Tennessee interstates, producing a spectacular display in May.

The Orange Poppy (*Papaver dubium* L.*) is a sparingly-branched, more or less hairy annual to 2 ft tall. Leaves are pinnately divided, the lobes shallowly toothed to deeply cleft. Long-stalked flowers terminate the stem and branches. Petals usually 4, to 1.6 in. long, red to pink or red-orange with a basal dark spot. The anthers are purple. Occasional. Waste places. Thinly scattered in Middle and East TN, and the e U.S. May-Aug. Native of Europe sparingly introduced or escaped.

White Prickly Poppy (*Argemone albiflora* Hornemann*) has large white flowers to 3 in. wide, generally with 6 overlapping petals. Rare. Found as an escape in open, dry, disturbed sites in Jackson County in TN, and scattered throughout the se U.S. May-Aug.

George Hornal

Bloodroot   *Sanguinaria canadensis* L.
Perennial to 6 in. tall from a stout thick rhizome with bright orange-red juice. At flowering, a single, pale green, 3 to 9-lobed leaf encircles the stem that bears a single, showy, white, 8 to 16-petaled flower from 0.8 to 2 in. wide. The leaf has roundish lobes and continues to grow after flowering, sometimes reaching 8 in. wide. Common. Rich woods. Widespread in TN and abundant where found from CAN southward to AL and FL. Mar-Apr. *Sanguinaria* is monotypic, i.e., with only one known species. Experimentally, the alkaloid sanguinarine has shown antiseptic, anesthetic and anticancer tendencies, and is used commercially in toothpaste and mouthwash to inhibit dental plaque. However, the **root or juice may be toxic! Do not ingest!** The genus name is from *sanguinarius* (bleeding), alluding to the color of the root juice.

Jack Carman

Celandine Poppy
Stylophorum diphyllum (Michaux) Nuttall
Showy perennial from 12 to 20 in. tall at flowering, from a rhizome with saffron-colored juice. A pair of stem leaves and several basal leaves are usually present, and all leaves are deeply lobed into 5 to 7 oblong or obovate segments. The flowers, from 1.5 to 2.5 in. wide, have 4 yellow petals and are borne in a terminal, few-flowered, umbel-like cluster. The ovary is egg-shaped and abruptly narrowed into a long style. The seedpods are egg-shaped, bristly-hairy and about 1 in. long. Occasional. Rich moist woods. Mainly a plant of the ne U.S. that extends south into TN, where it is found from the Western Highland Rim east. Mar-May. The genus name is from the Greek *stylos* (style) and *phoros* (bearing), alluding to the long style as one of the distinctive plant characteristics.

Jack Carman

Yellow Corydalis, Harlequin   *Corydalis flavula* (Raf.) DC.
Small green or glaucous annual from 4 to 12 in. tall, the stems branched from the base and erect or reclining. Leaves are divided into many fine segments, and the pale yellow flowers are less than 0.4-in. long. The upper petal has a toothed crest and the corolla a short spur. Frequent. Found in moist soil throughout TN and most of the ne U.S. Apr-May.

Two *Corydalis* species are found in Tennessee. The genus name is the ancient Greek name of the crested lark.

Pale Corydalis (*C. sempervirens* (L.) Persoon) has pink flowers. Infrequent. Dry or rocky woods. Cumberland Plateau east in TN (Fentress, Bledsoe, Monroe, Sevier, Unicoi and Carter counties). A northern species extending south in the mountains to GA. May-Sep.

Jack Carman

Flowers of the Bleeding Heart Family have two sepals, four petals and six stamens, and the leaves are much divided. Three genera and 6 species are found in TN.

Squirrel Corn
Dicentra canadensis (Goldie) Walpers
A handsome perennial to 1 ft tall, arising from a rootstock covered with yellow, pea-shaped bulblets. Leaves are long-stalked and basal, much divided into narrow segments, typically one per flowering stem, somewhat bluish-green and usually covered with a whitish bloom. The inflorescence is a raceme of hanging flowers on a nearly vertical stalk that extends well above the leaves. The flowers are white, from 0.5 to 0.7-in. long, and noticeably fragrant. The 2 outer petals have short, rounded, basal spurs that form a heart-shaped base on the flower. Occasional. Rich woods. A mostly ne U.S. and CAN species extending south to TN, where it is thinly scattered in the eastern half of the state. Apr-May.

George Hornal

Dutchman's Breeches   *Dicentra cucullaria* (L.) Bernhardi

Handsome perennial from 4 to 12 in. tall, arising from a short rhizome covered with small white or pink, tear-shaped bulblets. Leaves are long-stalked and basal, much divided into narrow segments, typically two per flowering stem and somewhat yellowish-green. Inflorescence a raceme of hanging flowers that usually extends well above the leaves. The flowers are white, from 0.6 to 0.8-in. long. The 2 outer petals have tapering basal spurs about 0.35-in. long that are spreading. Occasional. Rich woods. In TN, it is found from the Western Highland Rim east. Extended range from Quebec to ND south to ne OK, AR, n GA and c NC. Mar-Apr.

Jack Carman

Genus *Dicentra*

Three species are found in Tennessee. The genus name is from the Greek *dis* (twice) and *centron* (a spur), alluding to the two basal spurs of the flowers.

Wild Bleeding Heart

Dicentra eximia (KerGawler) Torrey

Handsome perennial from 4 to 20 in. tall, growing from a short scaly rhizome without bulblets. The leaves are long-stalked and much divided into narrow segments, somewhat bluish-green. The inflorescence is a mixed panicle of hanging flowers on a nearly vertical stalk that equals or overtops the leaves. The flowers are dark pink, from 0.75 to 1 in. long. The 2 outer petals have short, rounded, basal spurs that form a heart-shaped base on the flower. Infrequent. Rich wooded slopes or rocky banks. Found in the Appalachians from TN to NY, and in Polk, Blount, Sevier, Unicoi, Carter, Johnson and Union counties in TN. Apr-Sep.

The garden Bleeding Heart (*Dicentra spectabilis**) has beautiful, bright pink, broadly heart-shaped flowers and is often cultivated. Introduced from Asia.

URTICACEAE : NETTLE FAMILY
Five genera and 6 species are found in TN.

Wood Nettle
Laportea canadensis (L.) Weddell
Often colonial perennial to 3 ft tall with fibrous roots and stinging hairs. Leaves are alternate, broadly ovate, sharply toothed, from 3 to 6 in. long. Male flowers arise in clusters from the lower leaf axils; female flowers in loose, widely-spreading, branched clusters, terminal or from the upper leaf axils. Male flowers have 5 sepals and stamens, and female flowers have 4 sepals. Frequent. Rich moist woods. Found throughout TN and the ne U.S. Jun-Aug.

Stinging Nettle (*Urtica dioica* L.*) is similar, but grows to 6 ft tall, has opposite leaves and stinging hairs. Rare. Waste places. Cocke, Greene, Montgomery and Shelby counties. May-Jun. Stinging hairs are present on all *Urtica* and *Laportea* species.

False Nettle (*Boehmeria cylindrica* (L.) Sw.) is similar, but has no stinging hairs, and leaves are long-stalked and opposite. Common. Low moist woods and stream banks. Found throughout TN. Jun-Aug.

Jack Carman

George Hornal

PHYTOLACCACEAE : POKEWEED FAMILY
Tennessee has only one species.

Pokeweed *Phytolacca americana* L.
Coarse smooth perennial from 3 to 10 ft tall that is branched above. The leaves, from 4 to 12 in. long, are alternate, entire, lance-oblong to ovate, on stalks from 0.4 to 2 in. long. The racemes, from 2 to 8 in. long, are borne opposite the leaves and are often erect in flowering, but almost always nodding in fruit. The flowers are about 0.25-in. wide and without petals, but have 5 greenish-white sepals and 5 to 30 stamens. Fruits are nearly round berries to 0.4-in. thick, dark purple and juicy. Frequent. Fields, fence rows, disturbed areas. Found throughout TN and the e U.S. May-Sep. The young leaves are eaten as a spring green, after cooking with 2 changes of water. American Indians used berry tea for rheumatism, arthritis and dysentery. However, the **older leaves, stems, roots and seeds are poisonous.** The genus name is from the Greek *phyton* (plant) and the middle Latin *lacca* (crimson-lake), alluding to the crimson juice obtained from the berries.

Jack Carman

CACTACEAE : CACTUS FAMILY
Tennessee has only one species.

Eastern Prickly Pear
Opuntia humifusa (Raf.) Rafinesque
Prostrate or ascending perennial to 12 in. tall that is usually spreading to form large mats. The green stems are jointed, fleshy and flattened, forming the oblong to almost round pads that are 2 to 6 in. long. Each pad usually has nodes with tufts of fine bristles and occasionally a node may have a long grayish spine. The flowers, from 1.5 to 3 in. wide, are bright yellow with a reddish center, and solitary on swollen ovaries that arise near the tips of joints of the previous year. Stamens are numerous, shorter than the petals. The fruits, from 1 to 2 in. long, are red or purple and edible. Occasional. Sandy or rocky open areas. Thinly spread across TN and found throughout the e U.S. May-Jun. Folk medicinal uses have included treatment of rheumatism, kidney stones, gout, chronic ulcers and wounds. *Opuntia* is an ancient name adopted for this genus.

CHENOPODIACEAE : GOOSEFOOT FAMILY
Four genera and 12 species are found in TN.

George Hornal

Genus *Chenopodium*
Nine species are found in TN. The genus name is from the Greek *chen* (a goose) and *pous* (foot), alluding to the leaf shape.

Lamb's Quarters *Chenopodium album* L.*
Erect annual to 4 ft tall that is often branched above. The leaves are usually white-mealy and coarsely toothed, somewhat diamond-shaped, from 1 to 4 in. long. Small greenish flowers are borne in dense clusters in the upper leaf axils. The seeds are glossy black, and the grayish covering usually remains tightly adherent. Occasional. Cultivated fields, waste places, pastures, barnyards. Scattered throughout TN and the U.S. Aug-Oct. Leaves have been eaten to prevent scurvy and treat stomach aches. A cold tea has been used to treat diarrhea.

Mexican Tea (*C. ambrosioides* L.*) is similar, but is covered with aromatic resinous glands. Occasional. Waste places, roadsides, gardens. Widespread in TN and the e U.S. Aug-Oct. The essential oil distilled from flowering and fruiting plants has been used to treat roundworms, hookworms and intestinal amoeba, but the oil is highly **toxic**.

Jack Carman

AMARANTHACEAE : AMARANTH FAMILY

Cultivated or weedy family representatives that may be familiar are cockscomb, globe-amaranth and pigweed. Although many amaranths are regarded as common weeds, they produce tremendous numbers of seeds and are an important food source for many songbirds. Five genera and 13 species are listed for TN.

Alligatorweed
Alternanthera philoxeroides (Mart.) Griseb.*
Aquatic perennial with stems to 3 ft or more long that are trailing and mat-forming. Leaves are linear-elliptic to obovate, from 2 to 4 in. long. Small, white, clover-like, flower heads (0.6-in. wide) are long-stalked from leaf axils, or terminal on stems. Occasional, but usually locally abundant in shallow water or mud along the Tennessee River and tributaries (east and west). Also found in most of the se coastal states. May-Oct. This native of the tropics is an invasive weed.

Jack Carman

PORTULACACEAE : PURSLANE FAMILY
Four genera and 8 species are listed for Tennessee.

Genus *Claytonia*
Two species are found in TN. The genus is named in honor of John Clayton, an 18th century botanist.

Carolina Spring Beauty
Claytonia caroliniana Michaux
Delicate smooth perennial from 4 to 12 in. tall that arises from a corm. Stem leaves, usually a single opposite pair, are petioled, from 1 to 4 in. long and 0.4 to 1.2 in. wide, and less than 8 times as long as wide. The leaf blade is usually lance-ovate, clearly distinguished from the petiole. From one to few similar basal leaves may also be present. A loose raceme of 2 to 11 showy, long-stalked flowers terminates the stem. The 5 petals, from 0.4 to 0.6-in. long, are white to pale pink with deep pink veins. Occasional. Rich woods. Found from the Eastern Highland Rim east in TN, it is a northern species that extends south to TN and GA in the uplands and mountains. Mar-May, disappearing by early summer.

Virginia Spring Beauty
Claytonia virginica L.

Delicate smooth perennial from 4 to 12 in. tall that arises from a corm. Stem leaves, usually a single opposite pair, are petioled, seldom less than 3 in. long, and more than 8 times as long as wide. The leaf blade is narrow, scarcely distinguished from the petiole. From one to few similar basal leaves may also be present. A loose raceme of 5 to 15 showy, long-stalked flowers terminates the stem. The 5 petals, from 0.4 to 0.6-in. long, are white or pale pink with deep pink veins. Common. Rich woods, roadsides, lawns. Found throughout TN, and most of the eastern U.S. and CAN. Feb-Apr, disappearing by midsummer.

George Hornal

Genus *Talinum*

Three species are listed for Tennessee. The flowers are only open for about 2 hours in the early afternoon on bright sunny days. The derivation of the genus name is somewhat obscure.

Limestone Fameflower
Talinum calcaricum S. Ware

Perennial with many succulent cylindric leaves to 1.5 in. long crowded near the base of the stem. A slender branched scape from 4 to 12 in. tall rises above the leaves, and has few to several flowers. The petals, from 0.3 to 0.4-in. long, are pink to rose-red, and the flowers have 25 to 45 stamens. Infrequent. Thin soil of limestone cedar glades and barrens. Found in the Central Basin in TN, also in nw AL. May-Sep.

Menges' Fameflower (*T. mengesii* W.Wolf) has 50 to 80 stamens. Rare. Thin soil of rocky sandstone outcrops. Found in Rhea County in TN, also in GA and AL. May-Sep.

Appalachian Fameflower (*T. teretifolium* Pursh) has 15 to 20 stamens. Infrequent. Thin soil of rocky sandstone outcrops. Cumberland Plateau in TN, and PA to GA and AL. Jun-Aug.

George Hornal

Pink Family members are perennial or annual herbs with mostly opposite, entire leaves and swollen nodes on the stem. The inflorescence is basically cyme-like. Fifteen genera and 45 species are found in TN.

Corn Cockle   *Agrostemma githago* L.*

Annual to 3 ft tall with the stem and branches thinly hairy. Leaves are opposite, entire, linear to lanceolate, to 5 in. long and 0.4-in. wide. The flowers are solitary at the ends of the branches on stalks to 8 in. long. The calyx-tube is 0.5 to 0.7-in. long with lance-linear lobes from 0.8 to 1.6 in. long, usually longer than the petals. The petals are rose to reddish, oblanceolate, from 0.8 to 1.2 in. long. Occasional. Widely and thinly scattered in TN. A native of Europe now widely established as a weed of grain fields and waste places in most of the e U.S., more abundant north. Jul-Sep. The genus name is from the Greek *agros* (field) and *stemma* (crown).

Genus *Arenaria*

Eight species are listed for Tennessee. The genus name is from *arena* (sand) in which many of the species grow.

Jack Carman

Glade Sandwort   *Arenaria patula* Michaux

Much-branched smooth annual from 4 to 8 in. tall with opposite filiform leaves to 0.8-in. long. The numerous white flowers are about 0.5-in. wide and the 5 petals are notched. Frequent. Limestone cedar glades, barrens, dry limestone cliffs. Found in Middle and East TN, and from IN to MN south to VA, AL and TX. Apr-Jun.

Mountain Sandwort (*Arenaria groenlandica* (Retz.) Spreng.) is similar, but the leaves are linear to linear-oblanceolate, rather soft and fleshy. Rare. Rocky places. A northern species extending south to GA and TN (Carter County) in the mountains. May-Sep.

Thyme-Leaf Sandwort (*Arenaria serpyllifolia* L.*) is a softly-hairy wiry annual to 12 in. tall with oval-shaped leaves to 0.3-in. long, and white flowers about 0.25-in. wide. Frequent. Dry sandy fields and roadsides. Found in Middle and East TN, and in most of the U.S. Apr-Jul.

George Hornal

Jack Carman

Two *Dianthus* species are found in TN. The genus name is from the Greek *Dios* (Jupiter) and *anthos* (flower), with the connotation that this was Jove's own flower.

Deptford Pink   *Dianthus armeria* L.*

Annual or biennial from 8 to 24 in. tall. Basal leaves are numerous and the 5 to 10 pairs of stem leaves are narrow and hairy, to 3 in. long and 0.3-in. wide. The inflorescence is a congested cyme with 3 to 9 flowers that are often surpassed by the slender erect bracts. The rose or pink flowers about 0.4-in. wide are dotted with white and the petals are toothed. Frequent. Fields, roadsides, waste places. Introduced from Europe, it is found throughout TN, the e U.S. and s CAN. May-Aug.

Sweet William (*Dianthus barbatus* L.*) is similar, but perennial. The leaves are 0.4 to 0.8-in. wide and the whitish to red petals are broad and finely toothed around the summit. Rare. Native of Eurasia that sometimes escapes to fields and waste places. Found in Rutherford, Wilson and Blount counties in TN, and here and there in the e U.S., more prevalent northward. Jun-Aug.

Silverling   *Paronychia argyrocoma* (Michaux) Nuttall

Taprooted perennial from 2 to 12 in. tall with numerous silky-hairy, simple or forked stems that usually form mats or tufts. The leaves, from 0.4 to 1.2 in. long, are opposite, entire, linear or lance-linear and smooth to silky. The small flowers are sessile in dense clusters near the top of the stem and mostly hidden by the conspicuous silvery bracts. The sepals are white on the margin and petals are absent. Rare. Open rocky slopes, outcrops, or ledges. Found in Cumberland, Carter and Johnson counties in TN, and from ME to GA, usually at high elevation in the mountains. Jul-Sep. Three *Paronychia* species are found in TN. The genus name is the Greek name for whitlow or felon (a disease of the nails), and for plants with whitish scaly parts that once were supposed to cure the disease.

Jack Carman

Bouncing Bet, Soapwort
Saponaria officinalis L.*

Colonial smooth perennial from 16 to 32 in. tall with elliptic leaves to 4 in. long and 1.6 in. wide. Inflorescence a dense cyme that tops the stem. The flowers are pink to white, about 1 in. wide. Petals with a distinct claw and blade are spreading to reflexed, shallowly notched at the tip. The stamens extend out of the corolla tube. Frequent. Found in waste places and fields, and along roadsides and railroad tracks throughout TN and temperate North America. Jun-Sep. Crushed leaves and roots make lather when mixed with water. American Indians used poulticed leaves for spleen pain and boils. A root tea has been used for several ailments, but large doses may cause **poisoning**.

John MacGregor

Jack Carman

Carolina Pink
Silene caroliniana Walter
ssp. *pensylvanica* (Michaux) R.T.Clausen

Perennial from a taproot with slender stems to 1 ft tall that are usually glandular-hairy. Leaves are oblanceolate, to 5 in. long, the basal stalked but the 2 to 3 pairs of stem leaves usually sessile. The inflorescence is dense with 5 to 13 tubular flowers. Petals, from 0.3 to 0.6-in. long, are pink, wedge-shaped, the margins entire or slightly scalloped. Rare. Shaly soils in dry or rocky woods. Found in Carter, Sullivan and Washington counties in TN, and from NH to e OH south to NC and TN in the mountains. Apr-May.

White Campion, Evening Lychnis
Silene latifolia Poiret*

Short-lived, usually downy perennial from 1 to 4 ft tall that has several pairs of elliptic leaves to 4 in. long. Inflorescence usually much branched, and flowers are white with 5 styles, fragrant, opening in the evening. The petals from 0.8 to 1.6 in. long are deeply notched into 2 segments. Male flowers with stamens and female flowers with pistils occur on different plants. The male calyx to 0.8-in. long is 10-nerved and the female calyx to 1.2 in. long is 20-nerved, becoming much inflated. Occasional. Waste places. Found in Middle and East TN, but introduced and naturalized throughout much of North America. Jun-Sep. *Lychnis alba* Miller*, *Silene pratensis* (Raf.) Godron & Grenier*.

Jack Carman

George Hornal

Round-Leaf Catchfly   *Silene rotundifolia* Nuttall

Perennial to 28 in. tall, the stems weak, freely branched and thinly glandular-hairy. The 5 to 8 pairs of stem leaves are mostly sessile, broadly lanceolate to nearly round, to 4 in. long and 3 in. wide. Inflorescence open with a few tubular flowers. Petals, to 0.9-in. long, are crimson to red, deeply notched into 2 narrow segments. Occasional. Found on sandstone cliffs of the Cumberland Plateau in TN, and from OH to WV south to GA and AL. Jun-Jul.

Sleepy Catchfly (*Silene antirrhina* L.) is a branched annual to 3 ft tall. Basal leaves mostly spatulate to 2.5 in. long, stem leaves reduced. The inflorescence is open, with small white or pink flowers that have 2-lobed petals equaling or barely exceeding the 0.4-in. long calyx. Frequent. Waste places. Found throughout TN, and most of the U.S. Apr-Jul.

Jack Carman

Genus *Silene*

Ten species are found in Tennessee. The genus name is said to have come from the mythological Silenus, the foster-father of Bacchus, and was adopted by Linnaeus from earlier authors.

Starry Campion
Silene stellata (L.) Aiton
Perennial to 4 ft tall with downy stems. The stem leaves, from 1.2 to 4 in. long, are lanceolate to ovate, and usually in whorls of 4. The inflorescence is a loose panicle, and the white flowers are about 0.9-in. wide with 5 fringed petals that are woolly at the base. The calyx is bell-shaped and downy, about 0.5-in. long. Common. Found in rich woods throughout TN, and from OH to ND south to TN and TX. Jul-Sep.

Rough-Leaf Campion (*Silene ovata* Pursh) is similar but taller (to 6 ft). The leaves are usually opposite and the petals are not woolly at the base. Infrequent. Rich woods. Thinly scattered across TN, and found from VA to KY south to GA, AL and AR. Aug-Sep.

Fire Pink   *Silene virginica* L.
Short-lived, erect or ascending perennial from 8 to 32 in. tall, the stems both sticky and downy. The leaves of the basal rosette, to 4 in. long, are stalked, oblanceolate to spatulate. The stem leaves are sessile, opposite and narrow, to 6 or even 12 in. long. The inflorescence is open, with red flowers to 1.5 in. wide that have 5 narrow notched petals, and yellow stamens extending from the center. Common. Rich woods, open woodlands and rocky slopes. Found throughout TN, and from NJ and NY to MI south to GA, AL, AR and OK. Apr-Jun.

Forking Catchfly (*Silene dichotoma* Ehrhart*) is an annual with the pubescent upper stem forked. Flowers are sessile on a one-sided inflorescence. Rare in TN (Union and Carter counties). Introduced, escaped and found in waste places throughout the U.S. Jun-Sep.

George Hornal

Jack Carman

Bladder Campion
Silene vulgaris (Moench) Garcke*
Robust perennial from 8 to 32 in. tall that is usually smooth and glaucous (covered with a whitish bloom). The stem leaves are opposite, lanceolate to oblanceolate, often clasping, to 3 in. long. The flowers are white, from 0.5 to 1.2 in. wide, and the petals are deeply notched. The calyx is smooth, inflated, veined and papery, about 0.4-in. long. Infrequent. Waste places, roadsides. Recorded from Montgomery, Davidson, Cannon, Polk, Jefferson and Carter counties in TN. Introduced from Europe and now naturalized throughout most of temperate North America. Jun-Aug. *Silene cucubalus* Wibel*.

Jack Carman

CARYOPHYLLACEAE : PINK FAMILY

Star Chickweed, Giant Chickweed   *Stellaria pubera* Michaux
Erect or ascending perennial to 16 in. tall, thinly spreading-hairy. Stem leaves are opposite, mostly lanceolate, to 3.5 in. long. The inflorescence is a leafy, open, terminal cyme with numerous white flowers. Flowers to 0.5-in. wide have 5 petals that are very deeply cleft and appear as 10. The sepals are obtuse to acute and shorter than the petals. Common. Rich woods. Found throughout TN, and from NJ to IL south to n FL and AL. Apr-May.

Tennessee Chickweed (*Stellaria corei* Shinners) is similar, but the sepals are acuminate, equal to or longer than the petals. Occasional. Rich woods and seeps. Scattered in Middle and East TN, also found in NC. Apr-Jun. The genus name is from *stella* (a star).

Common Chickweed (*Stellaria media* (L.) Villars*) has white flowers to 0.28-in. wide and blooms most of the year. Frequent. A highly-variable introduced weed of waste places and lawns. Widespread in TN.

POLYGONACEAE : SMARTWEED FAMILY
Six genera and 35 species are found in TN.

Buckwheat Vine
Brunnichia ovata (Walter) Shinners
High-climbing woody vine. Leaves, from 2 to 6 in. long, are alternate, stalked and ovate to oblong-ovate with a truncate or heart-shaped base. The flowers are borne in panicle-like clusters and have 5 greenish lobes, 8 white stamens. The showy fruiting calyx is 0.8 to 1.2 in. long, mostly hanging, somewhat leathery, greenish-yellow, the stalk winged on one side. Occasional. Wet woods and margins of wet areas. Found in almost every county in West TN and adjacent Middle TN, but not recorded further east. U.S. range from SC to FL to TX on the Coastal Plain and north in the interior to s IL and MO. Jun-Jul. *Brunnichia cirrhosa* Gaertner. The genus name is in honor of M. T. Brunnich, an 18th century Norwegian naturalist.

Jack Carman

Harper's Umbrella Plant
Eriogonum harperi Goodman

Coarse erect perennial from 3 to 7 ft tall that arises from a taproot. The stem is freely branched above and has long, soft, spreading hairs. The leaves are numerous, alternate, lanceolate or lance-elliptic, sessile, hairy beneath, smooth above, from 4 to 6 in. long. The inflorescence is terminal, large and showy. The flowers are softly hairy and have white tepals that are yellowish inside. Rare. Found in Middle TN, mostly on cliffs of the Caney Fork River in DeKalb, Smith, Wilson and Putnam counties. It ranges from MO and KS to LA and TX, and irregularly east to KY, TN, AL and FL. Jun-Aug. Many species of *Eriogonum* are found in western North America. The genus name is from the Greek *erion* (wool) and *gonu* (knee), from the woolly stems and leaves, and the swollen joints of the plant.

Jack Carman

Jack Carman

Genus *Polygonum*

Twenty two species are found in Tennessee including weeds, knotweeds, climbing buckwheats and smartweeds. The fresh sap of some species may cause skin irritation, and leaf teas of several species have had several traditional folk medicine uses.

Pennsylvania Smartweed
Polygonum pensylvanicum (L.) Small

Erect or sprawling, freely-branched annual from 1 to 6 ft tall that arises from a taproot. The leaves are alternate, mostly smooth, lance-shaped, tapering to the tip. The base of the leaf forms a short sheath (ocrea) around the stem, with the sheath usually tattered but not fringed or bristly on the upper margin. Racemes, from 0.6 to 1.2 in. long, are numerous, cylindric, dense, terminal on the stem and branches. Flowers have 5 bluntly-rounded, rose or white tepals about 0.1-in. long. Common. Fields, waste areas, disturbed areas, especially in moist rich soil. Found throughout TN, and from Nova Scotia to SD south to FL and TX. May-Oct.

Jack Carman

False Buckwheat
Polygonum scandens L.

Perennial twining vine to 17 ft long, the stem sharply angled and often rough on the angles. The leaves, from 2 to 5 in. long, are oblong-ovate to ovate with a heart-shaped or sagittate base. The flowers are borne in racemes and the calyx is greenish to white or pinkish with a distinctly wavy or tattered margin and wing-keeled in fruit. The perianth is white, less than 0.1-in. long, and the achene is a very glossy black. Common. Moist woods, thickets, roadsides. Found throughout TN, and from Quebec to ND south to FL and TX. Jul-Oct. The genus name is from *poly* (many) and *gonu* (knee or joint) in reference to the many thickened joints of the stem.

Jack Carman

Virginia Knotweed, Jumpseed
Polygonum virginianum L.

Erect rhizomatous perennial to 3 ft tall. The leaves, to 6 in. long, are alternate, lanceolate to ovate and tapered to the tip, and have short stalks to 1 in. long. The base of the leaf stalk forms a short sheath (ocrea) around the stem with the sheath both hairy and fringed above. The inflorescence is a very slender terminal raceme to 2 ft long with the base of each flower or its stalk in a sheath (ocreola). The ocreola are 1 to 3 flowered, well separated below but becoming nearly overlapping above. Each flower has 4 greenish-white to pinkish tepals about 0.1-in. long. Common. Moist woods, low wet areas. Found throughout TN and the eastern U.S. Jul-Oct. When pressure is applied to the style tips of mature fruit, the achenes "jump" from the plant.

Jack Carman

POLYGONACEAE : SMARTWEED FAMILY

Sheep Sorrel   ***Rumex acetosella*** L.*

Dioecious, colonial, branched, weedy perennial from 4 to 16 in. tall. Leaves, from 0.8 to 2 in. long, are alternate, stalked, and 3-lobed with a large elliptic-to-oblong central lobe and 2 small spreading basal lobes (ears). The inflorescence sometimes occupies half of the plant. The greenish, yellow, pink or red flowers grow in clusters and have 6 tepals about 0.08-in. long. The achene is about 0.06-in. long. Common. Acid soils. Fields, lawns, waste areas and pastures. Found throughout TN and most of North America. Apr-Aug. Leaf teas have had several medicinal uses in the past, but large doses are potentially **toxic**.

Curly Dock (*Rumex crispus* L.*) is unbranched and has large crisped leaves. Frequent. Waste areas. Found throughout TN. May-Jul. Seven *Rumex* species occur in TN.

Jack Carman

CLUSIACEAE : ST. JOHNSWORT FAMILY
Two genera and 27 species are found in TN.

Genus *Hypericum*
There are 23 species listed for the state. The genus is characterized by entire, paired leaves, and pale to bright yellow flowers. For several species, the flowers last less than one day, being open in the morning, but wilting rapidly in full sun. The genus name is adapted from the ancient Greek *Hypericon*.

St. Peterswort
Hypericum crux-andreae (L.) Crantz
Perennial, branching, woody shrub to 40 in. tall. Leaves are elliptic-oblong, rounded at the tip, clasping at the base, and from 0.6 to 1.4 in. long. The flowers have 4 sepals (the 2 outer broadly round-ovate, the 2 inner narrowly lanceolate), 4 broad petals about 0.7-in. long, and numerous stamens. Occasional. Sandy areas. Mainly found in the Eastern Highland Rim and Cumberland Plateau in TN, but also Lawrence, Lewis, Dickson, Hamilton and Polk counties. U.S. range from s NY to e OK south. Jul-Aug. *H. stans* (Michaux) Adams & Robson, *Ascyrum stans* Michaux.

Coppery St. Johnswort
Hypericum denticulatum Walter

Erect perennial to 28 in. tall with a 4-angled stem branched above. Leaves are elliptic to nearly round, to 0.8-in. long, often erect or ascending. The 5 petals are coppery yellow, 0.4-in. long, and asymmetric with the flower shape resembling a pinwheel. Stamens 50-80. Frequent. Wet areas. Mostly Highland Rim and Cumberland Plateau in TN. U.S. range from MD to s IL south. Jul-Sep.

Shrubby St. Johnswort (*H. prolificum* L.) is a highly-branched shrub to 80 in. tall with narrow, petioled leaves and small petals (0.4-in. long). Usually 3 to 7 flowers in each cyme. Frequent. Wet or dry areas. Found mostly in the eastern 2/3 of TN, and from the ne U.S. south to GA and LA. Jul-Sep.

Creeping St. Johnswort (*H. adpressum* Barton) is an erect, mostly unbranched perennial to 3 ft tall. Stem leafy, leaves mostly narrowly elliptic, to 2.5 in. long and 0.4-in. wide, the margins revolute. The inflorescence is terminal with many flowers, the petals to 0.33-in. long. Rare. Marshes. Coffee, Warren and Marion counties in TN, and found from MA to GA and TN. Jul-Aug.

Jack Carman

Golden St. Johnswort
Hypericum frondosum Michaux

Perennial, branching, woody shrub to 40 in. tall. The leaves are sessile, oblong to elliptic to ovate-lanceolate, 1.2 to 2.5 in. long and 0.4 to 0.6-in. wide. Inflorescence 1 to 3-flowered cymes with broad leaf-like bracts, the inflorescence thus appearing leafy. The flowers have 5 wide petals about 1 in. long and numerous stamens. Frequent. Cedar glades and rocky areas. Found in Middle TN (scattered east and west), and the east-central U.S. May-Jul.

Naked St. Johnswort (*H. nudiflorum* Michaux) is a branching shrub to 80 in. tall with many flowers in an open cyme, minute bracteal leaves and small petals (0.4-in.), the inflorescence appearing naked. Infrequent. Wet areas. Found in the Cumberland Plateau, also Carter and Humphreys counties in TN. Extended range includes most of the se U.S. Jun-Aug.

Jack Carman

Jack Carman

Pineweed, Orange Grass
Hypericum gentianoides (L.) BSP.
Erect annual to 12 in. tall, repeatedly branched into numerous, filiform branches. Leaves are scale-like, appressed, to 0.1-in. long. The flowers are 5-petaled, nearly sessile, solitary at the stem nodes, and about 0.3-in. wide. Frequent. Sterile, sandy soil. Found from the Western Highland Rim east in TN, and throughout most of the eastern U.S. Jun-Sep.

Nits-and-Lice (*H. drummondii* (Greville & Hooker) T. & G.) is similar, but taller (to 24 in.) with less branching, longer linear leaves (to 0.6-in.), and larger flowers (0.4-in.). Occasional. Dry soil. Widely scattered in TN. U.S. range from MD and OH to se KS south. Jul-Sep.

Note:

BSP. denotes authors Nathaniel Britton, Emerson Sterns, and Justus Poggenburg.

T. & G. denotes authors John Torrey and Asa Gray.

St. Andrew's Cross   *Hypericum hypericoides* (L.) Crantz
Perennial woody shrub to 48 in. tall with a single main stem, freely branched above. Leaves are linear to oblanceolate, narrowed to the base, rounded at the tip, 0.8 to 1.2 in. long. The flowers have 4 sepals (the 2 outer broadly rounded, the 2 inner much smaller), 4 narrow pointed petals to 0.5-in. long (forming an "X"), and numerous stamens. Frequent. Dry or moist areas. Found throughout TN and from NJ to OK south. Jun-Aug.

Reclining St. Andrew's Cross (*H. stragulum* Adams & Robson) is similar, but a decumbent shrub with prostrate branches and short erect flowering stems, giving a compact mat appearance. Common. Dry or moist areas. Found throughout TN, and from NY to n GA west to e OK. Jul-Aug.

Jack Carman

Dwarf St. Johnswort
Hypericum mutilum L.

Annual or perennial to 32 in. tall with an erect stem, much branched above the middle and appearing delicate. Leaves are lanceolate to elliptic or ovate, rounded at the base, pointed at the tip, to 1.6 in. long. Inflorescence usually highly branched with numerous flowers that are 5-petaled, about 0.2-in. across. Sepals broadest near the middle. Common. Moist areas. Found throughout TN, and the e U.S. and CAN. Jul-Sep.

Clasping-Leaf St. Johnswort (*Hypericum gymnanthum* Engelmann & A.Gray) is an erect annual to 28 in. tall with a few branches above. Leaves are mostly deltoid-ovate, broadly rounded at the base and sessile. Inflorescence loose and open with long internodes, the cymes well above the uppermost foliage. Flowers small with 10 to 14 stamens, and petals to 0.15-in. long. Sepals broadest well below the middle. Rare. Loose soil. Found in Coffee, Franklin, Hickman, Lawrence and Van Buren counties in TN. A Coastal Plain species scattered inland. Jun-Sep.

Jack Carman

Common St. Johnswort   *Hypericum perforatum* L.*

Branching, leafy perennial to 32 in. tall. Leaves are sessile and linear-oblong, 0.8 to 1.6 in. long. The inflorescence has many flowers in a compound cyme. The flowers have numerous stamens, and the 5 petals to 0.4-in. long are black-dotted near the margin. Frequent. Fields, meadows, roadsides. Found in the eastern 2/3 of TN, also Henry, Hardin, and McNairy counties, and throughout the U.S. and s CAN. Jun-Sep.

Mountain St. Johnswort (*Hypericum graveolens* Buckley) is an erect perennial to 2 ft tall, mostly unbranched. Leaves ovate and black-spotted, about 1 in. wide, sessile or clasping. Cymes few-flowered. Petals are 0.4 to 0.7-in. long, often black-lined or black-dotted. Rare. Balds and wet seeps at high elevation in the mountains of NC and TN (Carter, Johnson, Sevier and Unicoi counties). Jul.

Jack Carman

Spotted St. Johnswort
Hypericum punctatum Lamarck

Erect perennial to 40 in. tall, branched below the inflorescence. Leaves are oblong-elliptic to oblong-ovate, blunt-tipped, 1.2 to 2.6 in. long, to 0.7-in. wide. Leaves, stems, sepals and petals are conspicuously black-dotted. Inflorescence terminal on the stem and branches, small and crowded with short-stalked flowers. The 5 petals are about 0.25-in. long. Common. Wet or dry areas. Widespread in TN and the e U.S. Jun-Aug.

False Spotted St. Johnswort *(H. pseudomaculatum* Bush) is similar, but leaves more pointed, petals over 0.3-in. long. Infrequent. Wet or dry areas. Found in counties near the Tennessee River west and east, and from IL to OK south. Jun-Aug.

Blue Ridge St. Johnswort (*Hypericum mitchellianum* Rydberg) is a sparingly-branched perennial to 3 ft tall. Leaves are sessile, somewhat clasping, ovate-oblong, to 2.5 in. long and half as wide. Flowers few in small crowded cymes. Sepals to 0.4-in. long and marked with black lines, petals to 0.5-in. long, scarcely black-dotted. Rare. Moist slopes at high elevation from sw VA to NC and TN. Jul.

Jack Carman

Jack Carman

Rough-Fruited St. Johnswort
Hypericum sphaerocarpum Michaux

Erect perennial to 30 in. tall, often branched from the base. Leaves are linear-oblong to narrowly elliptic, tapering to the base, 1.2 to 2.8 in. long and 0.2 to 0.6-in. wide, often with evident lateral veins. Inflorescence compact and much branched with many flowers. The sepals are lanceolate to ovate, uniform or nearly so, from 0.1 to 0.2-in. long. The 5 petals are 0.2 to 0.35-in. long. Stamens 45 to 85. Occasional. Cedar glades and barrens. Found in Middle TN, also Benton, McNairy, Rhea and Knox counties. U.S. range from OH to IA south to AL and AR. Jun-Aug.

Straggling St. Johnswort (*H. dolabriforme* Ventenat) is similar, with narrower and shorter leaves from 0.8 to 1.6 in. long without evident lateral veins. Inflorescence compact with few flowers. Sepals very unequal, the outer pair 0.28 to 0.5-in. long, the others much smaller. Petals longer than 0.35-in., stamens 120 to 200. Occasional. Barrens. Central Basin, Sequatchie Valley, and Ridge and Valley in TN. U.S. range from s IN and KY to GA. Jun-Aug.

Genus *Triadenum*

There are 4 species listed for the state. The genus is characterized by entire, paired leaves, and the flowers are 5-petaled. The flowers open in mid-to-late afternoon and are closed by morning.

Lesser Marsh St. Johnswort

Triadenum tubulosum (Walter) Gleason
Perennial with erect stems to 40 in. tall. The leaves are without translucent glands, oblong or elliptic-oblong to elliptic-oblanceolate, sessile, cordate at the base, and to 5 in. long and 2 in. wide. The flowers are greenish-white (about 0.5-in. across) in a terminal cyme or in the leaf axils. Infrequent. Wooded swamps. Found in Fayette, Hardeman, Decatur, Lewis, Montgomery, Coffee, Bledsoe and Polk counties in TN. A mostly Coastal Plain species found from VA to TX, occasionally inland to s MO and s OH. Jul-Sep.

Jack Carman

George Hornal

Greater Marsh St. Johnswort

Triadenum walteri (Gmelin) Gleason
Perennial with erect stems to 40 in. tall. The leaves are dotted with translucent glands, lance-elliptic to oblong or oblong-lanceolate, tapering to a short petiole, and to 5 in. long and 1.2 in. wide. The flowers are pinkish (about 0.5-in. across) in a terminal cyme or in the leaf axils. Occasional. Swamps, marshes. Found in the western 2/3 of TN, also Knox and Polk counties. A mostly Coastal Plain species found from MD to TX, occasionally inland to s MO and s IN. Jul-Sep.

Virginia Marsh St. Johnswort (*T. virginicum* (L.) Rafinesque) is similar, but less robust (to 24 in. tall) with smaller leaves (to 2.4 in. long) which are cordate at the base. Infrequent. Swamps, marshes. Found in Fentress, Hamilton, Johnson, Overton, Warren and White counties in TN. A mostly Coastal Plain species found from Nova Scotia to MS, occasionally inland to IL. Jul-Aug.

Jack Carman

Velvet Leaf   *Abutilon theophrasti* Medikus*

Stout branching annual from 3 to 5 ft tall that is softly hairy throughout. Leaves are long-stalked, heart-shaped, entire or obscurely toothed, from 4 to 6 in. long and wide. The flowers are yellow, from 0.6 to 1 in. across. Numerous stamens surround the style, united at the base but free at the tips, forming a showy tube-like structure that protrudes from the center of the flower. The fruit, from 0.8 to 1.2 in. wide, is erect, cylindric but flat-topped and tapered to the base, ridged down the side, densely hairy, topped with conspicuous horizontally-spreading beaks. Occasional. Native of Asia now established as a weed in fields and waste places. Widespread in TN and the e U.S., but more abundant southward. Jul-Oct. The species name is in honor of Greek scientist Theophrastus (370-285 B.C.)

Cultivated members of the Mallow Family include cotton, hollyhock and okra. The flowers have 5 petals. Eight genera and 17 species are listed for TN.

Halberd-Leaf Rose Mallow   *Hibiscus laevis* Allioni

Smooth perennial from 3 to 7 ft tall with few to many stems. Leaves are toothed, long-stalked, mostly halberd-shaped with the basal lobes tapered. Flowers are crowded at the end of the stems, pink with a red-purple center, the petals from 2.4 to 3.2 in. long. Numerous stamens surround the style, united at the base but free at the tips, forming a showy tube-like structure that protrudes from the center of the flower. Seedpod roundish with a pointed tip, about 1 in. long. Seeds have reddish-brown hairs. Occasional. Ditches, river banks. Widespread in the e U.S. and TN (mostly West TN). Jul-Sep. *Hibiscus militaris* Cavanilles.

George Hornal

Genus *Hibiscus*

Four species are found in Tennessee. *Hibiscus* is an old Greek and Latin name for some large mallow.

Swamp Rose Mallow
Hibiscus moscheutos L.

Perennial from 4 to 7 ft tall with few to many stems that are downy above. Leaves are long-stalked, downy beneath, somewhat toothed, lanceolate to heart-shaped or lobed. The flowers are 4 to 8 in. wide, white (to pink) with a red-purple center, crowded at the end of the stems. Numerous stamens surround the style, united at the base but free at the tips, forming a showy tube-like structure that protrudes from the center of the flower. Seedpod roundish with a pointed tip, about 1 in. long. Seeds are smooth, dark brown. Frequent. Swamp edges, meadows, ditches. Widespread in TN and the e U.S. Jun-Sep.

Rose-of-Sharon (*Hibiscus syriacus* L.*) is similar, but flowers are smaller, white to lavender with a red-purple center. A cultivated shrub that sometimes escapes.

Jack Carman

Carolina Mallow, Bristly Mallow   *Modiola caroliniana* (L.) G. Don*

Annual or biennial herb with ascending or prostrate downy stems to 2 ft long, often rooting at the nodes. The roundish leaves are palmately divided into 3 to 5 lobes that are irregularly incised. The flowers, about 0.4-in. wide, are borne singly on long stalks from the leaf axils, and have brilliant orange-red petals with a blackish-purple base. Numerous stamens surround the style, united at the base but free at the tips, forming a showy tube-like structure that protrudes from the center of the flower. The flowers are open only in sunlight. Rare. Roadsides, lawns and pastures. Found throughout the se U.S. Officially recorded only from Knox and Shelby counties in TN, but likely more prevalent. Mar-Jun. *Modiola* is a monotypic (single species) genus, from *modiolus* (nave of a wheel) and alluding to the shape of the fruit.

Jack Carman

Coastal Plain Sida   *Sida elliottii* T. & G.
Branching perennial to 3 ft tall with firm, linear to narrowly oblong leaves from 0.8 to 2.4 in. long that are short-stalked to sessile, sharply toothed to almost entire. The flowers are solitary in the leaf axils and borne on stalks from 0.2 to 1 in. long. The petals are bright yellow, about 0.6-in. long. Numerous stamens surround the style, united at the base but free at the tips, forming a showy tube-like structure that protrudes from the center of the flower. Rare. Dry to moist soils, fields, barrens. Found in Decatur, Davidson, Rutherford, Hamilton and Meigs counties in TN, and widespread in most of the se U.S. Jun-Aug.

Flower-of-an-Hour (*Hibiscus trionum* L.*) is a hairy annual to 20 in. tall. Leaves are long-stalked, deeply 3-parted, the segments oblong to obovate and coarsely lobed or toothed. The calyx is conspicuously veined and hairy. Petals, to 1.6 in. long, are pale yellow with a purple base. Flowers only open for a few hours. Rare. Roadsides, fields, waste places. Found in Henry, Knox, Grainger, Hawkins, and Greene counties in TN, and throughout the e U.S. Jul-Sep.

Jack Carman

Four *Sida* species are found in Tennessee. *Sida* was a name used by Theophrastus for some related plant.

Prickly Mallow   *Sida spinosa* L.*
Softly-hairy, branching, weedy annual from 1 to 2 ft tall. The leaves are lance-ovate to oblong or elliptic, toothed, from 0.8 to 1.6 in. long on slender stalks from 0.4 to 1.2 in. long. Stipules of the lower leaves are usually reduced to hard spines. The flowers are pale yellow, to 0.5-in. wide, usually borne singly in the leaf axils, but sometimes in a small cluster. Numerous stamens surround the style, united at the base but free at the tips, forming a showy tube-like structure that protrudes from the center of the flower. Frequent. Waste places, fields, roadsides. Widespread in TN and the e U.S. Jul-Oct.

Jack Carman

Dwarf Sundew *Drosera brevifolia* Pursh
Basal rosette mostly prostrate with red to green leaves that have smooth dilated petioles, and wedge-shaped blades that are rounded at the tips. A glandular-hairy flower scape rises from the rosette center to 3 in. tall, bearing 1 to 10 small flowers. The petals are pink or white and obovate. Rare. Sandy, bare soil. A mostly Coastal Plain species found in Coffee, Franklin, Lewis and Warren counties in TN. May. An average rosette is about the size of a quarter, and the leaves wither soon after flowering.

Pink Sundew (*Drosera capillaris* Poiret) has a smooth scape with pink flowers, and the prostrate leaf rosette remains all year. Rare. Low wet areas. Found in Cumberland, Bledsoe, McNairy and Van Buren counties in TN. May-Aug.

Round-Leaf Sundew (*Drosera rotundifolia* L.) is similar to Spatulate-Leaf Sundew except the leaf blades are nearly round. Rare. Marshes. Found in Carter, Fentress, Sevier and Johnson counties in TN. A northern species extending south to SC, GA, TN, IL and CA. Jul-Sep.

Jack Carman

Sundews are carnivorous plants. Small insects are caught by red, mucilage-tipped, tentacle-hairs on the basal-leaf rosette. The insects are attracted by both the color and the aroma. When an insect touches a leaf, the leaf rolls the nearby hairs toward the victim and traps it. Flowers are open for about 2 hours a day, midday to early afternoon, and usually only in full sun. Four species are found in TN. The genus name is from the Greek *droseros* (dewy).

Spatulate-Leaf Sundew   *Drosera intermedia* Hayne
Basal rosette with shallowly arching, red to green leaves (to 2.5 in. long) composed of short oval blades and long narrow petioles. The flower scape rises from the rosette center to 4 in. tall, bearing 1 to several small flowers. Petals white and obovate. Infrequent. Wet bare places. Cumberland Plateau and Eastern Highland Rim in TN. May-Jun.

George Hornal

CISTACEAE : ROCKROSE FAMILY
Two genera and 8 species are found in TN.

Low Frostweed
Helianthemum propinquum E. P. Bicknell
Erect perennial with stems from 4 to 12 in. tall scattered along a creeping rhizome. Leaves are linear-spatulate to oblong-linear, from 0.4 to 1.2 in. long. Branching hairs are present on the stem, leaves and calyx. From 2 to 6 yellow, 5-petaled flowers about 1 in. wide are borne in terminal cymes. Some flowers remain closed and are self-pollinating. Rare. Dry open areas. Coffee, Cumberland, Monroe and Van Buren counties. A ne U.S. species with disjunct populations in TN. May-Jul. The genus name is from the Greek *helios* (the sun) and *anthemon* (flower).

Canada Frostweed (*H. canadense* (L.) Michaux) is similar, but several stems arise from a caudex, and long simple hairs are also found on the calyx. Rare. Dry sandy soil. Blount and Sevier counties. A northeastern species extending south to TN and GA. May-Jul.

Jack Carman

Jack Carman

VIOLACEAE : VIOLET FAMILY
Two genera and 24 species with 3 additional varieties are found in Tennessee.

Genus *Hybanthus*
Green Violet flowers only vaguely resemble other violets, but the shape and form of the stamens and pistil are characteristic of the family. The genus name, from the Greek *hybos* (hump-like) and *anthos* (flower), likely refers to the drooping flowers. Only one species is found in TN.

Green Violet
Hybanthus concolor (T.Forster) Sprengel
Leafy-stemmed, rather coarse and usually hairy perennial to 3 ft tall. The leaves are alternate, from 3 to 6 in. long, broadly elliptic to ovate-oblong with an abruptly acuminate tip, and tapering at the base into a short stalk from 0.4 to 0.8-in. long. The flowers, about 0.2-in. long, hang on drooping stalks from the leaf axils, and the sepals and petals are both greenish-white. Common. Rich woods and ravines. Found throughout TN, and the e U.S. from TN and GA north. Apr-Jun. The species name *concolor* (of one color) reflects the green of both sepals and petals.

Jack Carman

Sweet White Violet   ***Viola blanda*** Willdenow
Low perennial with creeping rhizomes. Leaves, from 0.8 to 4 in. long, are all basal, long-stalked, broadly heart-shaped, and dark green with a satiny sheen. White flowers are on separate long stalks extending just above the leaves, and petals are longer than 0.4-in. The lower 3 petals are usually purple-veined near the base. Both flower and leaf stalks are tinged with red. Occasional. Rich woodlands. Found in the eastern half of TN and the northeastern U.S. Apr-May.

The Northern White Violet (*V. macloskeyi* Lloyd ssp. *pallens* (Banks *ex* DC.) Baker) is similar, but the petals are less than 0.4-in. Rare. Rich wet places. A northern species that extends south to TN and n GA in the Blue Ridge. Apr-Jul.

Jack Carman

Violets   **Genus V*iola***
Violets have either an obviously leafy, above-ground stem (caulescent) or almost no above-ground stem such that leaves appear as being all basal (acaulescent). Most species produce the normal 5-petaled flowers (2 upper and 3 lower petals) in the spring, and very fertile cleistogamous (without petals) flowers in the summer. There are 23 species and 3 varieties known to occur in TN. *Viola* is the classical name for violet.

Canada Violet   ***Viola canadensis*** L.
Perennial with a leafy stem from 8 to 16 in. tall. Basal leaves, from 1.2 to 5 in. long, are narrowly to broadly heart-shaped and long-stalked. The stem leaves are similar and numerous. The flowers, from 0.8 to 1.2 in. wide, are terminal and on long stalks from the leaf axils, white with a yellow center. Petals are purple-veined near the base, and usually purple-tinted on the back. Frequent. Moist woodlands. Found in the eastern half of TN, and from Newfoundland to AK south to AL, AR and AZ. Apr-Jul.

Jack Carman

Dog Violet   *Viola conspersa* Reichenbach

Smooth caulescent perennial with numerous leafy stems to 12 in. tall, arising from an occasionally-branched rhizome. Basal leaves are long-stalked, mostly reniform to orbicular. Stem leaves are long-stalked, mostly heart-shaped, to 1.6 in. long, and have prominent stipules that are narrow and deeply fringed. Flowers, from 0.4 to 0.8-in. wide, are terminal or from leaf axils, on slender long stalks that surpass the leaves. The petals are light blue-violet with darker veins, the two lateral ones bearded. The lower petal spur is about 0.2-in. long. Occasional. Moist woodlands. Found in the eastern half of TN, it is a mostly northeastern species extending south in the uplands to TN and AL. Apr-Jun.

Jack Carman

Marsh Blue Violet   *Viola cucullata* Aiton

Low, smooth, acaulescent perennial with leaves that are all basal, heart-shaped, long-stalked, from 1.6 to 4 in. long. Flowers, mostly 0.6 to 1.2 in. wide, are blue-violet (to white), and borne on tall, very erect flower stalks that usually extend well above the leaves. All petals have dark veins near the base, forming an eye-zone at the center of the flower, and the two lateral petals are densely bearded. Common. Rich wet or moist places in shade or sun. Found throughout TN and most of the e U.S. from TN and GA north. Apr-Jun.

Jack Carman

Glade Violet
Viola egglestonii Brainerd

Low, smooth, acaulescent perennial. The leaves, from 2 to 4 in. long, are all basal, quite variable, usually divided into 5 to 9 narrow segments, toothed at the tip, and with a few, long, narrow teeth along the margin. Flowers to 1.0 in. wide are borne on long stalks, and are blue-violet with the 3 lower petals bearded. Occasional. Limestone barrens and cedar glades in the Central Basin, also in Hamilton and Meigs counties in TN. Extended range from s IN south to n AL and nw GA. Mar-May. Closely related to the Wood Violet (*Viola palmata* L.), and often considered a variety of it.

Jack Carman

Halberd-Leaf Yellow Violet
Viola hastata Michaux

Caulescent perennial from 2 to 10 in. tall that arises from a long branching rhizome. The 2 to 4 leaves, from 2 to 4 in. long, are mostly halberd-shaped, on short stalks near the top of the stem, and occasionally one on a long stalk from the base of the stem. The upper surfaces of the leaves are often mottled with silver. Flowers, from 0.6 to 0.8-in. wide, are bright yellow and borne on slender erect stalks extending above the leaves. Occasional. Rich woods. Found from the Eastern Highland Rim east in TN, and from PA and OH south to SC, n GA and e TN. Apr-May.

Lance-Leaf Violet   *Viola lanceolata* L.
Smooth acaulescent perennial with creeping
stolons in the summer. Leaves are basal,
erect, narrowly lanceolate and tapering to
the usually reddish stalks, to 4 in. long, and
generally more than 3 times as long as wide
(see *Viola primulifolia*). Flowers, from 0.4 to
0.8-in. wide, are on long reddish stalks and
are white. The 3 lower petals have
brownish-purple veins near the base, and all
are beardless. Infrequent. Wet places.
Widely scattered from the Western Highland
Rim east in TN (Montgomery, Robertson,
Overton, Fentress, Scott, Morgan, Sevier,
Warren, Coffee and Franklin counties), and
found in most of the e U.S. Apr-Jun.

Jack Carman

Jack Carman

Wood Violet   *Viola palmata* L.
Smooth or hairy, acaulescent perennial. The
leaves, from 2 to 4 in. wide, are all basal,
long-stalked, palmately 3 to 11 lobed with
the segments variously toothed or cleft and
usually hairy, but the earliest leaves are
often heart-shaped. The flowers are long-
stalked, large (to 1 in. wide), blue-violet to
white, or sometimes streaked or blotched
violet and white. Common. Woods,
clearings and glades. Found throughout TN
and most of the e U.S. Apr-May. *Viola
triloba* Schwein.

Bird's-Foot Violet   *Viola pedata* L.

Low, smooth, acaulescent perennial. The leaves are all basal, long-stalked, more or less palmately divided into 3 principal parts, with the lateral segments again 3 to 5 cleft into narrow lanceolate or linear segments that often are toothed at the tip. The flowers are large (to 1.2 in. across), borne on long stalks extending above the leaves. Petal colors vary from blue-violet to lavender or white, or they may be bi-colored (the upper 2 a deep satiny purple). All petals are beardless, and the large orange stamens are conspicuous at the center of the flower. Frequent. Roadsides, open woods. Found in the eastern 2/3 of TN, also Hardin, McNairy and Carroll counties. U.S. range from ME to MN south to n FL and e TX. Apr-Jun. The common name is from the leaves with narrow segments, said to resemble a "bird's foot." The bi-colored form has been considered as the most beautiful violet in the world.

Primrose-Leaf Violet
Viola primulifolia L.

Acaulescent perennial with creeping stolons. The leaves are all basal, long-stalked, oblong to ovate to obovate, rounded to truncate to wedge-shaped at the base, tapering to the broadly-winged summit of the stalk, and generally less than 3 times as long as wide (see *Viola lanceolata*). The flowers, from 0.4 to 0.8-in. wide, are borne on long stalks usually surpassing the leaves, and are white. The 3 lower petals have brownish-purple veins near the base. Occasional. Moist open areas. Found from the Eastern Highland Rim east in TN, also in Lawrence, Hardin, McNairy, Benton, Carroll and Henry counties, and in most of the e U.S. Apr-Jun.

Yellow Woodland Violet
Viola pubescens Aiton
Smooth or downy, caulescent perennial from 4 to 18 in. tall. Leaves, from 1.2 to 3.6 in. long, are long-stalked, broadly ovate to round-ovate, several arising from the stem and 1 to several from the stem base. The flowers, from 0.6 to 1 in. wide, are on smooth or downy stalks from the leaf axils that rise little above the leaves. The petals are yellow with brownish-purple veins near the base, and the lateral ones are bearded. Common. Rich woods. Found throughout TN and most of the e U.S. Apr-May. *Viola pensylvanica* Michaux, *Viola eriocarpa* Schweinitz.

Jack Carman

Field Pansy   *Viola rafinesquii* Greene
Slender, smooth, caulescent annual from 2 to 16 in. tall with leafy stems, often branched from the base. Leaves, from 0.2 to 1.2 in. long, are short-stalked, spatulate to oblanceolate with very noticeable stipules at the base. Flowers, from 0.4 to 0.8-in. wide, are long-stalked and blue to bluish-white to ivory. The sepals are about half as long as the petals. Common. Fields, open woods, roadsides. Found throughout TN and most of the e U.S. Mar-Apr.

The European Field Pansy (*Viola arvensis* Murray*) is similar, but the stem is more robust. The flowers are all pale yellow (ivory), and the broadly lanceolate sepals are longer than the petals. Infrequent. Fields and roadsides. Found in Knox, Lawrence, Maury, Sumner, Williamson and Wilson counties in TN, and in most of the e U.S. Apr-Sep.

Jack Carman

Long-Spurred Violet
Viola rostrata Pursh

Smooth, caulescent perennial with several erect or spreading stems, from 2 to 10 in. tall, arising from a short rhizome. The stem and basal leaves, from 0.8 to 3 in. long, are long-stalked and heart-shaped. The flowers, from 0.6 to 1 in. wide, are on long stalks, terminal or from the leaf axils, rising well above the leaves. The petals are beardless and light violet with dark veins that form an "eye" in the center. The aft-extending spur is from 0.6 to 0.8-in. long. Frequent. Rich shady slopes and woodlands. Found from the Eastern Highland Rim east in TN, also in Williamson, Davidson, Cheatham and Stewart counties. Extended range from ME and se CAN to WI south to GA and AL. Apr-Jun.

Walter's Violet (*Viola walteri* House) is similar, but stems are smaller (to 4 in. tall) and mostly prostrate, and the lateral petals are bearded. Infrequent. Dry or moist woods and ledges. Found in Bedford, Blount, Cumberland, Hamilton, Jefferson, Sevier and White counties in TN, and from OH to VA south to FL and TX. Apr-Jun.

Jack Carman

Round-Leaf Yellow Violet
Viola rotundifolia Michaux

Acaulescent perennial from a long wiry rhizome that appears to be stout and jagged because of the hardened bases of old leaves. The leaves are all basal, long-stalked, and broadly cordate-ovate or nearly round, about 1 in. long at flowering and almost as wide, much enlarged later (to 5 in. wide). The flowers, from 0.6 to 0.8-in. wide, are on short stout stalks and bright yellow. The lateral petals are bearded, and the 3 lower ones brown-veined at the base. Occasional. Rich woods. Found from the Cumberland Plateau east in TN, it is a northeastern species extending south to SC and GA in the mountains. Mar-Apr.

Jack Carman

Arrow-Leaf Violet   *Viola sagittata* Aiton
Smooth or hairy perennial. The leaves, from 1.6 to 4 in. long, are basal, on erect stalks usually longer than the blades, mostly ovate or narrower, and often with a sagittate toothed base. The flowers are long-stalked, purple-violet, and from 0.8 to 1 in. wide. The lower petals usually are prominently dark-veined at the base. Frequent. Dry to moist open woods and clearings. Found from the Western Highland Rim east in TN, also in Henry and Obion counties, and throughout most of the e U.S. Apr-Jun.

Southern Wood Violet (*Viola hirsutula* Brainerd) has ovate leaves with silvery-pubescent upper surfaces, and purplish and smooth lower surfaces. Flowers are blue-purple. Frequent. Woodlands. Found from the Western Highland Rim east in TN, it is a more southeastern species extending north into TN and KY. Apr-Jun.

Jack Carman

Common Blue Violet   *Viola sororia* Willdenow var. *sororia*
Smooth to hairy, acaulescent perennial from a stout horizontal rhizome. Leaves, from 1.6 to 4 in. long, are basal, long-stalked, more or less heart-shaped. Flowers are large (to 1.2 in. wide) and violet to white. Common. Woodlands, thickets, lawns. Found throughout TN and most of the U.S. Apr-Jun. A showy white color form with a blue "eye" is known as the Confederate Violet (*Viola priceana* Pollard). *Viola papilionacea* Pursh.

Missouri Violet (*Viola sororia* Willd. var. *missouriensis* (Greene) L.E. McKinney) is similar, but the leaves are triangular-shaped and flowers are pale violet. Occasional. Low woods, bottomlands. Found throughout TN. Apr-Jun.

George Hornal

Jack Carman

Cream Violet
Viola striata Aiton

Smooth caulescent perennial to 12 in. tall with leafy stems. Both stem and basal leaves, from 0.8 to 3 in. long, are long-stalked, ovate to heart-shaped. Prominent slender stipules are deeply fringed. Flowers, from 0.8 to 1 in. wide, are numerous, on stalks rising well above the leaves, and cream-colored or ivory. The petals have prominent brownish-purple veins near the base, and the lateral ones are strongly bearded. The spur is well developed and thick, to 0.16-in. long. Frequent. Rich woodlands and stream banks, often weedy. Found from the Western Highland Rim east in TN. U.S. range from MA to s WI south to GA and AR. Apr-Jun.

Jack Carman

Three-Parted Yellow Violet
Viola tripartita Elliott **var. *tripartita***

Perennial from 6 to 18 in. tall that arises from a short rhizome, and is usually downy above. Usually 2 to 4 leaves are borne near the top of the stem that are 1.2 to 4 in. long and deeply cleft into 3 divisions with the central division the largest. Solitary flowers, from 0.6 to 0.8-in. wide, are borne on slender erect stalks from the leaf axils. The bright yellow petals have brown-purple lines toward the base and the lateral ones are bearded. The upper two petals are sometimes marked with purple on the back. Rare. Rich woods. Found in Franklin, Marion, Hamilton and Cumberland counties in TN. Mar-May. **var. *glaberrima*** (DC.) Harper is similar, but the leaves are ovate, not divided. Occasional. Rich woods. Found from the Western Highland Rim east in TN. Mar-May. The U.S. range for both varieties is from sw PA and s OH south to GA, AL and ne MS.

George Hornal

Passionflower, Maypops, Apricot Vine   *Passiflora incarnata* L.
Climbing or trailing vine with soft-hairy stems to 25 ft long. The leaves (to 6 in. long) are
deeply and palmately 3-lobed, soft-hairy underneath, rounded to the base and petioled. The
leaf lobes are lance-ovate with constricted bases and pointed tips. The unusual blossoms
are usually solitary, on stalks 2 to 4 in. long arising from the leaf axils. The flowers are large,
about 3 in. wide with whitish sepals and petals (green on the back), lavender filiform corona
segments with purple bands, 5 recurved stamens with large white anthers, and 3 long styles
with knobby stigmas. Fruit a yellow (green) edible berry. Common. Fields, thickets, fence
rows. Widespread in TN and most of the e U.S. from s PA south. Jun-Sep. Passionflower is
the "Official State Wildflower" of Tennessee.

The Passionflower Family is represented by one genus and 2 species in Tennessee.

Yellow Passionflower   *Passiflora lutea* L.
Climbing or trailing vine with soft-hairy (to smooth) stems to 15 ft long. The leaves (1 to 3 in.
wide) are shallowly and palmately 3-lobed, wider than long, shallowly cordate at the base
and petioled. Leaf lobes are blunt and rounded at the tip. Showy blossoms are on 1 to 2 in.
stalks, with 1 to 3 arising from the leaf axils. Flowers are about 1.5 in. wide with pale green
sepals, narrow whitish-green petals, yellowish-green filiform corona segments, 5 recurved
stamens with large tan anthers, and 3 long styles with knobby stigmas. Fruit a small black
berry. Common. Woods, thickets. Widespread in TN and found in the e U.S. from PA to
WV south to FL and AL. Jun-Sep.

Jack Carman

CUCURBITACEAE : GOURD FAMILY

A family of mostly herbaceous or softly woody, twining or high-climbing vines. Five genera with one species each are found in Tennessee.

Creeping Cucumber
Melothria pendula L.

Slender, smooth, climbing, annual vine from 40 to 80 in. long. Leaves, from 1.2 to 3 in. long, are alternate, stalked, shallowly to deeply and palmately 5-lobed, toothed, deeply cordate at the base. The flowers are few, yellow, 5-lobed. The female flowers, to 0.3-in. wide, are solitary on long slender stalks, and the male flowers, from 0.08 to 0.25-in. wide, are borne in a short raceme that terminates a long slender stalk. The fruit is green, melon-like, about 0.4-in. long. Occasional. Moist woods, thickets, fields, roadsides. Widely scattered throughout TN, and found from s VA to s IN to s MO south to FL and northern Mexico. Jun-Aug. The genus name was adapted from *melothron*, an ancient name for some fruiting vine.

BRASSICACEAE : MUSTARD FAMILY

Flowers of the Mustard Family usually have 4 sepals, 4 petals diagonal to the sepals, and 4 inner stamens that are longer than the 2 outer stamens. The petals are usually narrowed at the base and spreading at the tip, forming a cross. It is represented by 32 genera and 78 species in TN.

Garlic Mustard
Alliaria petiolata (Bieb.) Cavara & Grande*

Mostly smooth, erect biennial to 3 ft tall with few branches. The leaves have the odor of garlic, and are mostly deltoid, coarsely-toothed, stalked, from 1.2 to 2.4 in. long and wide. Flowers are borne in racemes to 12 in. long that are terminal or from the leaf axils. The 4 petals to 0.25-in. long are white, spatulate, and gradually narrowed to a claw. Fruit pods are narrow, 4-angled, and erect or ascending. Occasional. A native of Europe found as a weed in gardens and woods. Thinly scattered in TN, and found throughout most of the e U.S. Apr-May. The genus is derived from *allium* (onion or garlic), alluding to the odor of the plant.

George Hornal

Smooth Rock Cress
Arabis laevigata (Muhlenberg) Poiret
Erect smooth biennial to 40 in. tall that may have a few branches above. Stem leaves, from 2 to 6 in. long, are narrowly lanceolate, glaucous (covered with a whitish bloom), sessile with a sagittate base and sometimes clasping. The flowers have 4 white petals to 0.25-in. long. Narrow fruits to 4 in. long are flat and widely spreading. Common. Woods and hillsides. Found throughout TN, and from Quebec to SD south to GA and OK. Apr-May. The genus was named after the country Arabia, according to Linnaeus.

Sicklepod (*Arabis canadensis* L.) is similar, but stem leaves are hairy, not sagittate or clasping at the base. Occasional. Woods. Found mostly in Middle and East TN, and from ME to MN south to GA and TX. May-Jul.

Lyre-Leaf Rock Cress (*Arabis lyrata* L.) is somewhat similar, but is only 4 to 16 in. tall and branched from the base. Fruit pods are ascending. Infrequent. Dry woods and fields. Found in East TN, it is a northern species extending south to GA and TN in the mountains. May-Jul.

Lake Cress
Armoracia lacustris (A.Gray) Al-Shehbaz & Bates
Fibrous-rooted aquatic perennial with lax, submersed or prostrate stems. Submersed leaves are pinnately dissected into many needle-like segments. Leaves (if any) above the waterline are lanceolate to narrowly oblong, toothed, to 2.8 in. long. The white flowers are borne in a loose raceme on spreading short stalks. The four petals to 0.33-in. long are obovate and narrowed to the claw. The fruit is egg-shaped and about 0.3-in. long. Infrequent. Quiet water and muddy shores. Found in Lauderdale, Lake, Obion, Stewart, Montgomery and Grundy counties in TN, and from Quebec to MN south to FL and TX. May-Aug. *Armoracia* is the ancient name of Horseradish.

Horseradish (*Armoracia rusticana* (Lamarck) Gaertner, Meyer & Scherbius*) is somewhat similar, but an erect perennial to 40 in. tall with oblong, long-stalked, lower leaf blades from 4 to 12 in. long. Rare. Commonly cultivated and often escaped into wet areas. Recorded from Stewart, Montgomery and Robertson counties in TN. May-Jul.

Jack Carman

Winter Cress, Yellow Rocket
Barbarea vulgaris R. Brown*

Dark green, smooth, erect, winter annual or biennial to 3 ft tall. The basal leaves to 6 in. long are stalked, and have from 1 to 4 pairs of small lateral lobes and a large terminal lobe. Stem leaves similar, but progressively reduced upward and mostly sessile or clasping. The yellow flowers are borne in a crowded terminal raceme and have 4 petals to 0.4-in. long. Mature fruits, to 1.25 in. long, are borne on thin stalks that are ascending or spreading. Frequent. Fields, roadsides, wet meadows. Found in Middle and East TN (also Lake and McNairy counties), and throughout most of the e U.S. Apr-Jun. Native of Eurasia. The genus name was adapted from the ancient name of the plant, Herb of St. Barbara.

Early Winter Cress (*Barbarea verna* (Miller) Aschers*) is similar, but basal leaves have 4 to 10 pairs of lateral lobes. The fruits are from 1.8 to 2.8 in. long, and borne on stalks almost as thick as the fruit. Frequent. Damp soil, fields, roadsides. Found in Middle and East TN, and throughout most of the U.S. and s CAN. Apr-Jun.

Jack Carman

Jack Carman

Genus *Brassica*

Three species are found in Tennessee. The genus name is the Latin name of cabbage.

Field Mustard, Turnip
Brassica rapa L.*

Winter annual to 3 ft tall (sometimes taller in robust plants). The leaves, to 12 in. long and 4 in. wide, are usually bristly-hairy on the margins and midvein below. The lower leaves are stalked and pinnately lobed, and the upper leaves are reduced, toothed and clasping. The inflorescence is a terminal cluster of 4-petaled yellow flowers to 0.4-in. wide. Fruits are ascending. The cultivated turnip was derived from this species. Frequent. Fields, waste places. Cultivated, escaped, and found throughout TN and the se U.S. Mar-Jun. *Brassica campestris* L.*

Black Mustard (*Brassica nigra* (L.) Koch*) is similar, but both the upper and lower leaves are stalked. Rare. Fields, waste places. In TN, recorded in Shelby, Lauderdale, Obion, McNairy and Davidson counties. Naturalized from Europe and a principal source of table mustard. May-Aug.

Shepherd's Purse
Capsella bursa-pastoris (L.) Medikus*
Sparingly-branched winter annual from 4 to 24 in. tall that arises from a basal rosette of oblong, lobed leaves from 2 to 4 in. long. The stem leaves are linear to lanceolate, clasping, much reduced. The inflorescence is a terminal raceme of small white flowers that are scarcely noticeable. The mature racemes, to 12 in. long, have spreading fruit stalks. Fruits are heart-shaped, attached at the point rather than the notch, strongly flattened, to 0.33-in. long. Frequent. Fields, waste places. Introduced and naturalized as a cosmopolitan weed, it is found throughout TN and the e U.S. Mar-Jun. Dried or fresh herb tea made from seeds and leaves has been used to stop bleeding, and the dried herb is a useful styptic against hemorrhage. The genus name is the diminutive of *capsa* (a box). The common name comes from the shape of the fruit that was thought to resemble a medieval shepherd's purse.

Jack Carman

Jack Carman

Genus *Cardamine*
Eight species are found in Tennessee. The genus name is adapted from the Greek *kardamon*, the ancient name of some cress.

Hoary Bitter Cress
Cardamine hirsuta L.*
Mostly smooth, weedy, winter annual from 4 to 16 in. tall. Basal leaves, from 1.2 to 3.2 in. long, are numerous and conspicuous in a prominent rosette, pinnately divided with 1 to 4 leaflet pairs. The lateral leaflets are rounded to elliptic with wavy or toothed margins, and the terminal leaflet is larger and usually reniform. The few stem leaves are similar but much smaller, and the petioles are hairy at the base. The flowers are borne on narrowly ascending stalks and the 4 petals are white, from 0.08 to 0.12-in. long. Fruits are erect, from 0.6 to 1 in. long. Common. Naturalized in lawns, waste places, disturbed areas. Found throughout TN, and from s NY to IL south to AL. Mar-Apr. Introduced from the Old World.

Jack Carman

Spring Cress
Cardamine rhomboidea (Persoon) DC.

Perennial to 24 in. tall from a stout rhizome, the herbage sparsely or densely covered with very short hairs. Basal leaves are green beneath, and have roundish blades to 1.6 in. long on petioles to 3.5 in. long. The 4 to 8 stem leaves are reduced, narrowly oblong or ovate, the upper ones usually sessile. The inflorescence is a terminal raceme of white (rarely pink) flowers on stalks about 0.4-in. long. The 4 petals are about 0.5-in. long and the sepals are green, turning yellow after flowering. Common. Moist alluvial woods. Found throughout TN, and from Quebec to SD south to FL and TX. Apr-Jun. *Cardamine bulbosa* (Schreber) BSP.

Purple Cress (*Cardamine douglassii* (Torrey) Britton) is similar, but basal leaves are purplish beneath, flowers are lavender to pink, and sepals are purple turning brown with age. Occasional. Rich moist wooded slopes. Found in Middle TN, also Knox, Loudon, Claiborne and Scott counties. U.S. range from NH to s MN south to VA, TN and MO. Apr-May.

Jack Carman

Crinkleroot, Pepperroot, Broad-Leaf Toothwort
Dentaria diphylla Michaux

Perennial with stems from 8 to 16 in. long, arising from a long rhizome of uniform diameter. The mostly evergreen basal leaves have stalks from 4 to 6 in. long, and are dissected into 3 segments to 4 in. long that are toothed, ovate, prominently-veined. The stem leaves (a single pair) have short stalks and 3 ovate segments, to 3 in. long and half as wide, that have coarse rounded teeth. The flower cluster is terminal and the 4 petals, from 0.4 to 0.6-in. long, are dull white but often turning pinkish with age. Common. Rich wooded slopes and coves. Found in Middle and East TN, and from New Brunswick to MN south to GA and AL. Apr-May. Toothwort rhizomes are edible and have a pungent or peppery taste, somewhat like radishes.

Jack Carman

Genus *Dentaria*
Four species are found in Tennessee. The genus name is derived from *dens* (a tooth) and refers to the toothed rhizomes of some species. According to the Doctrine of Signatures, the rhizomes could be used to cure toothaches. Root tea has been used as a gargle for sore throat and hoarseness.

Slender Toothwort
Dentaria heterophylla Nuttall
Perennial with stems from 8 to 16 in. long, arising from a rhizome that is constricted into segments at intervals of 0.8 to 1.6 in. Basal leaves have long stalks and are dissected into 3 segments to 3 in. long that are toothed and mostly obovate. Stem leaves (a single pair) have short stalks, and 3 linear to narrowly oblong segments that are entire or toothed, to 3 in. long. The flower cluster is terminal and the 4 petals are white to pinkish, from 0.4 to 0.6-in. long. Occasional. Rich woods. Found in Middle and East TN, and from NJ to IN south to GA and MS. Mar-May. *Cardamine angustata* O.E.Schulz.

Jack Carman

Cut-Leaf Toothwort
Dentaria laciniata Muhl. *ex* Willd.
Perennial with stems from 8 to 16 in. long, arising from a rhizome that is constricted into segments at intervals of 0.8 to 1.2 in. Stems are short-hairy above and have a whorl of 3 leaves above the middle, each palmately divided into 3 narrow, toothed segments. The central segment is occasionally deeply divided, such that the leaves appear to have 5 segments. Basal leaves are long-stalked and similar to the stem leaves, but are almost always absent at flowering. The flower cluster is terminal and the 4 petals are white (sometimes pinkish to pale lavender), 0.5 to 0.8-in. long. Common. Rich moist woods. Found throughout TN, and from ME to MN south to FL, LA and OK. Mar-May. *Cardamine concatenata* (Michx.) H.E.Ahles, *Cardamine laciniata* (Muhl. *ex* Willd.) A.W.Wood.

Fine-Leaf Toothwort
Dentaria multifida Muhlenberg
Smooth perennial with stems from 8 to 16 in. long, arising from a rhizome that is constricted into segments at intervals of 0.4 to 0.8-in. Stem leaves (usually a single pair) are divided numerous times into narrow, linear, entire segments from 0.04 to 0.12-in. wide. Basal leaves are long-stalked, similar to the stem leaves and usually present at flowering. The flower cluster is terminal and the 4 petals are white (sometimes pinkish to pale lavender), from 0.5 to 0.7-in. long. Occasional. Rich moist woods. Found in Middle TN, also Hamilton, Polk, Union and Claiborne counties, and from c OH and c IN south to north GA and north AL. Mar-Apr. *Cardamine multifida* Muhlenberg, *Cardamine dissecta* (Leavenworth) Al-Shehbaz.

Genus *Draba*
Four species are found in Tennessee. The genus name is from *drabe* (acrid), the ancient name of a cress.

George Hornal

Jack Carman

Vernal Whitlow Grass
Draba verna L.*
Winter annual from 1 to 8 in. tall. The hairy leaves are all crowded in a basal rosette, mostly oblanceolate, from 0.4 to 0.8-in. long. The inflorescence of lax racemes occurs on slender, wiry, branched scapes. The flowers are 0.1 to 0.2-in. wide, and have 4 white petals cleft nearly halfway, thus appearing as 8 petals. The fruit is smooth, flattened and egg-shaped, from 0.16 to 0.4-in. long. Common. Fields, lawns, open dry places. A native of Eurasia introduced and naturalized throughout TN and much of North America. Feb-Apr.

Short-Fruited Whitlow Grass (*Draba brachycarpa* Nuttall *ex* T. & G.) is similar, but the stem is leafy and the few basal leaves disappear quickly. The petals may be yellow or white, and are rounded or notched at the tip. The fruit is oblong-elliptic, from 0.1 to 0.16-in. long. Occasional. Dry woods and fields. Thinly scattered in TN, and found from VA to IN to KS south to FL and TX. Mar-May.

Western Wallflower
Erysimum capitatum (Douglas) Greene

Erect biennial from 6 to 36 in. tall that may be unbranched or branched in the upper portion. The basal and stem leaves, from 1 to 5 in. long, are lanceolate and usually toothed. The flowers, to 0.8-in. wide, are borne in a dense terminal raceme and have 4 orange petals that are quite showy. The fruit pods, from 2 to 4 in. long, are slender and erect. Infrequent. Limestone bluffs, open rocky areas. Primarily a western species found in Davidson, Smith, DeKalb, Putnam, Scott and Roane counties in TN. May-Jul. The genus name is from the Greek *eryomai* (help or save), alluding to the supposed medicinal properties of some species.

Jack Carman

George Hornal

Dame's Rocket
Hesperis matronalis L.*

Erect biennial or perennial from 20 to 40 in. tall, often branched above. The leaves are lanceolate to deltoid-lanceolate, sessile to short-stalked, toothed, and hairy. Fragrant flowers are borne in showy terminal racemes on the stem and branches. The four petals, from 0.8 to 1.0 in. long, are usually purple but vary to pink or white. The fruits are narrow, to 4 in. long, somewhat constricted between the seeds. Infrequent. Roadsides, open woods, moist bottomlands. Thinly scattered in East TN, but also found in Cumberland, Macon and Montgomery counties in Middle TN. Extended range from se CAN to MI and IA south to KY and GA. May-Jul. The genus name is from the Greek *hesperos* (evening or evening-star), alluding to the evening fragrance of the flowers.

Purple Rocket
Iodanthus pinnatifidus (Michaux) Steudel
Mostly smooth perennial to 40 in. tall. Leaves are thin, lanceolate to elliptic or oblong, commonly sharply toothed, the lower or larger leaves pinnatifid at the base. The flowers are borne in a terminal raceme, and the four petals are pale violet to nearly white, about 0.5-in. long. The fruit is slender, from 0.8 to 1.6 in. long. Occasional. Moist or wet alluvial woods. Widespread throughout Middle TN, and also found in Knox and Loudon counties east, and Lake and Obion counties west. U.S. range from w PA to MN south to TN and OK. May-Jun. The genus name is from the Greek *iodes* (violet-colored) and *anthos* (flower).

Jack Carman

Pasture Glade Cress *Leavenworthia exigua* Rollins **var. *exigua***
Smooth winter annual. Leaves are all basal, to 2 in. long, pinnatifid, the terminal lobe much larger than the lateral lobes. Flowers (and pods) are solitary on stalks to 6 in. long. Petals, to 0.4-in. long, are white to pale lavender with a light yellow base, and have tips with shallow notches. The style is 0.04 to 0.12-in. long. Seedpods strongly flattened, oblong, to 0.8-in. long and 0.2-in. wide. Occasional. Wet limestone glades, roadside ditches. Found in Bedford, Davidson, Decatur, Giles, Marshall, Maury, Perry, Rutherford, Trousdale, Wayne, Williamson and Wilson counties. U.S. range from s KY to n AL and nw GA. Mar-Apr. The **var. *lutea*** Rollins is similar, but has flowers that are all yellow. Rare. Found in Maury and Bedford counties in TN.

Jack Carman

Jack Carman

Long-Styled Glade Cress   *Leavenworthia stylosa* A. Gray
Smooth winter annual. Leaves are all basal, pinnatifid, the terminal lobe much larger than the lateral lobes. Flowers (and pods) are solitary on long stalks. Petals, from 0.4 to 0.65-in. long, may be white or lavender with a yellow base or all yellow, and have tips with deep notches. The style is 0.12 to 0.3-in. long and persists on the tip of the seedpod. Seedpods are thick or somewhat flat, about 1 in. long and 0.2-in. wide, sometimes weakly bead-like. Wings of the seeds are well developed. Infrequent. Wet limestone glades, ditches, low fields. Endemic to Middle TN (Sumner, Smith, Wilson, Davidson, Rutherford, Bedford and Maury counties). Mar-May. The yellow color form appears more prevalent north, and the white color form more prevalent south, but all color variations sometimes occur in the same population.

Genus *Leavenworthia*
Four species occur in TN with three species found primarily in the Central Basin. Usually, the flowers are open only on sunny days. The genus name is in honor of Dr. Melines Leavenworth, a 19th century southern botanist.

Beaded Glade Cress
Leavenworthia torulosa A. Gray
Smooth winter annual. Leaves are all basal, to 2 in. long, pinnatifid, the terminal lobe much larger than the lateral lobes. The flowers (and pods) are solitary on stalks from 2 to 6 in. long. Petals, from 0.25 to 0.4-in. long, are white to pale lavender with yellow bases, and have tips with shallow notches. The styles are short, to 0.2-in. long. The seedpods, to 1.2 in. long and 0.16-in. wide, are linear, strongly bead-like (torulose) even when young. Wings of the seeds are very narrow or absent. Occasional. Wet ditches, wet limestone glades, low areas. Found in Middle TN, East TN, s KY and nw GA. Mar-May.

Jack Carman

Small Glade Cress
Leavenworthia uniflora (Michaux) Britton
Smooth winter annual. Leaves are all basal, from 0.8 to 4 in. long, pinnatifid, the terminal lobe only slightly larger than the adjacent lateral lobes. Flowers (and pods) are solitary on stalks from 2 to 6 in. long. Petals, from 0.2 to 0.3-in. long, are white and have rounded tips without a notch. The style is from 0.06 to 0.12-in. long. The seedpods are thick and somewhat fleshy, cylindric, to 1.2 in. long and 0.2-in. wide. The seeds are broadly winged. Occasional. Limestone glades, fields, ditches, wet areas, barrens. Found in Middle and East TN. The U.S. range is from sw OH to nw GA and nw AR. Feb-May. Of the four Glade Cress found in TN, it is the first to bloom.

Genus *Lepidium*
Three species are found in Tennessee. The genus name is from the Greek *lepidion* (little scale), alluding to the fruit.

Jack Carman

Jack Carman

Field Peppergrass
Lepidium campestre (L.) R. Brown*
Densely short-hairy annual or biennial from 4 to 20 in. tall. Basal leaves are long, oblanceolate, entire to shallowly lobed, and stem leaves are erect or ascending, lanceolate to narrowly oblong, entire or toothed, clasping, to 1.6 in. long. The terminal racemes are dense, to 6 in. long. Flowers, to 0.2-in. wide, are white with yellow anthers. Fruit stalks, to 0.3-in. long, are widely spreading, and the oblong-ovate fruit is broadly winged, convex below and concave above, to 0.25-in. long. Frequent. Roadsides, waste places, fields. Found in Middle and East TN, and throughout most of the e U.S. Apr-Jun. Native of Europe.

Poor-Man's Pepper *(Lepidium virginicum* L.) is similar, but smooth. The stem leaves are not clasping and the fruit is notched at the tip. Common. Fields, rocky glades, waste places. Found throughout TN and the U.S. Feb-Nov. American Indians used bruised fresh plants or leaf tea for poison ivy rash or scurvy. Leaves have been poulticed on the chest for croup, but application may cause skin irritation or blisters.

Genus *Lesquerella*
Bladderpods are distinguished by the pods which are spherical or egg-shaped, but internally partitioned into 2 distinct halves. The preferred habitat for the annual species is disturbed ground, particularly agricultural fields. Five species are found in TN and four are listed as state rare plants.

Duck River Bladderpod
Lesquerella densipila Rollins
Winter annual mostly 6 to 12 in. tall. Stem leaves are alternate, toothed to shallowly lobed, mostly elliptic to lance-shaped, and have bases that clasp the stem. Flowers, about 0.6-in. wide, are borne in a long terminal raceme and have 4 yellow petals. Seedpods are mostly rounded and usually smooth, but may be densely covered with short, simple or branched hairs. Infrequent. Areas disturbed by flooding or agriculture. Found in Bedford, Cheatham, Davidson, Giles, Lincoln, Marshall, Maury, Rutherford and Williamson counties in TN, but mainly in the Duck River drainage basin. Endemic to Middle TN and adjacent n AL. Mar-May.

Jack Carman

Jack Carman

Short's Bladderpod
Lesquerella globosa (Desv.) S. Watson
Slender erect perennial from 8 to 20 in. tall, often branched near the base. The stems are hairy and very leafy to the inflorescence. The basal leaves, from 1 to 2 in. long and 0.2 to 0.6-in. wide, are obovate to oblanceolate, short-stalked, usually wavy margined. Stem leaves are smaller, not clasping, oblanceolate to linear. As many as 50 flowers are borne in terminal racemes to 4 in. long. The flowers have 4 yellow petals from 0.16 to 0.3-in. long. The seedpod is almost round, loosely hairy, about 0.1-in. wide, and the persistent style is usually longer than the pod. Infrequent. Limestone rocky cliffs, river bluffs, barrens. Found in Cheatham, Davidson, Maury, Montgomery, Smith and Trousdale counties in TN. U.S. range from Middle TN north to s IN. Apr-May. The genus name is in honor of Leo Lesquereux, a distinguished 19th century bryologist and paleobotanist.

Jack Carman

Nashville Mustard
Lesquerella lescurii (A. Gray) S. Watson
Winter annual usually 6 to 12 in. tall. The stem leaves are alternate, toothed to shallowly lobed, mostly elliptic to lance-shaped, and have bases that clasp the stem. The flowers, about 0.6-in. wide, are borne in a long terminal raceme, and have 4 yellow petals. The seedpods are mostly roundish with the 2 halves somewhat saucer-shaped, and covered with a mixture of long, bulbous-based hairs and an understory of small branched hairs. Infrequent. Wet fields, lawns, roadsides, usually near limestone outcrops. Endemic to Middle TN, and found in Stewart, Montgomery, Sumner, Dickson, Cheatham, Davidson, Wilson, Smith, Williamson and Rutherford counties. Mar-May.

Nashville Mustard can usually be observed as what appears to be a "yellow carpet" at the I-24 and Haywood Lane interchange in south Nashville in late March.

George Hornal

Spring Creek Bladderpod
Lesquerella perforata Rollins
Gray-green winter annual usually 6 to 12 in. tall. The leaves are alternate, narrowly oblong to oblanceolate, and have bases that clasp the stem. The flowers, about 0.6-in. wide, are borne in a long terminal raceme and have 4 white petals. The style is smooth. Seedpods are somewhat pear-shaped with a papery wall, about 0.25-in. long, mostly smooth to sparsely hairy on the outside but densely hairy on the inside. Rare. Federally endangered and endemic to Wilson County in TN. Found mainly in fields and disturbed areas along major creeks in the vicinity of Lebanon. Mar-Apr.

Stones River Bladderpod
Lesquerella stonensis Rollins

Gray-green winter annual usually 6 to 12 in. tall. The leaves are alternate, narrowly oblong to oblanceolate, and have bases that clasp the stem. The flowers, about 0.6-in. wide, are borne in a long terminal raceme and have 4 white petals. The style is densely hairy. The seedpods are mostly roundish, about 0.25-in. long, slightly depressed where the 2 halves are joined, densely hairy on the outside but smooth on the inside. Rare. Endemic to Rutherford County in TN. Found mainly in fields and disturbed areas along the Stones River. Mar-Apr.

Jack Carman

Watercress   *Nasturtium officinale* R. Brown*

Aquatic mat-forming perennial with smooth, submerged or partly-floating stems. The dark green leaves are pinnately compound with 3 to 9 leaflets, the terminal leaflet much larger and round. The flowers are white, about 0.2-in. wide, and clustered at the stem tips. The petals are twice as long as the sepals. The fruit, from 0.4 to 1 in. long, is slender and has a short beak. Frequent. Clear water streams and spring heads. Found in Middle and East TN, and throughout the U.S. and s CAN. Apr-Oct. *Rorippa nasturtium-aquaticum* (L.) Hayek*. A most successful immigrant from Europe where it is cultivated and the young sprouts are eaten in salads. The leaves are rich in Vitamin C and slightly pungent. In fact, the genus name is from *nasus tortus* (a wry or twisted nose), alluding to the effect of the pungent qualities of the plant.

Jack Carman

George Hornal

The Heath Family is often regarded as typical of northern temperate and arctic regions. Most members are trees or shrubs, and many are cultivated for their handsome flowers. Sixteen genera and 42 species are found in TN, all native.

Spotted Wintergreen, Pipsissewa
Chimaphila maculata (L.) Pursh

Low evergreen perennial from 4 to 8 in. tall that arises from a creeping rhizome. Stem leaves, from 0.8 to 3 in. long, are opposite or often almost whorled, lance-shaped, thick, toothed, striped with white along the midvein and often along the lateral veins, smooth, short-stalked. From 1 to 5 fragrant, nodding, waxy flowers, from 0.5 to 0.7-in. wide, are borne in an umbel-like cluster well above the leaves. The 5 petals are white or pinkish, and the stigma is rounded and green. Although the flowers nod, the fruit capsule is erect. Common. Dry woods, especially sandy soils. Widely scattered in TN and found from ME to MI south to SC, GA and AL. Jun-Jul. Some botanical treatments place this genus in the Shinleaf Family (Pyrolaceae). Genus name from the Greek *cheima* (winter) and *philein* (to love).

Trailing Arbutus, Mayflower
Epigaea repens L.

Prostrate, creeping, evergreen shrub with branched, spreading-hairy, reddish-brown stems to 16 in. long. Leaves, from 0.8 to 4 in. long, are alternate, entire, leathery, ovate to oblong, rounded or heart-shaped at the base, on hairy stalks half as long as the blade. The flowers are borne in clusters at the branch tips, and are pink to white, from 0.3 to 0.6-in. long, salverform with 5 rounded lobes, densely hairy within. Occasional. Dry, sandy, acid woods and rocky banks. Found from the Cumberland Plateau east in TN, and from Newfoundland to Saskatchewan south to FL, MS and IA. Mar-May. Although leaf tea is a folk remedy for bladder and kidney disorders, it is potentially **toxic**. The genus name is from the Greek *epi* (upon) and *gaea* (the earth), alluding to the trailing growth habit.

Jack Carman

Jack Carman

Wintergreen, Teaberry, Checkerberry   *Gaultheria procumbens* L.
Diminutive, evergreen, colonial shrub with erect stems from 4 to 8 in. tall that arise from a horizontal rhizome. The leaves, from 0.8 to 2 in. long, are alternate, usually elliptic or oblong, glossy, smooth, entire or shallowly toothed, stalked, few and crowded near the top of the stem. The solitary flowers, from 0.3 to 0.4-in. long, hang from the leaf axils on stalks from 2 to 4 in. long, and are waxy, white, barrel-shaped with 5 short rounded lobes. The fruit is dry or mealy, berry-like, bright red and has the characteristic flavor of wintergreen. Occasional. Dry or moist acid woods. Found in the eastern half of TN, and from Newfoundland to Manitoba south to VA, KY and MN, and in the uplands to TN, AL and GA. Jul-Aug. Traditionally, a leaf tea was used for colds, headaches, fevers and kidney ailments. The entire plant has the odor of wintergreen when crushed.

George Hornal

Mountain Laurel   *Kalmia latifolia* L.
Evergreen shrub to 10 ft tall that often forms dense thickets. The leaves, from 2 to 4 in. long, are mostly alternate, entire, rich green, leathery, smooth, elliptic-oblanceolate or elliptic, on stalks from 0.4 to 0.8-in. long. Flowers are borne in clusters that terminate the stem and branches, and are white to rose with purple spots, bowl-shaped, from 0.8 to 1 in. wide on stalks to 1.6 in. long. Common. Dry woods, chiefly in sandy or rocky acid soil. Found from the Western Highland Rim east in TN. U.S. range from se ME south to GA and w FL west to s IN and se LA. May-Jun. **The entire plant is highly poisonous**, and even honey made from the flowers is reported to be **toxic**.

Carolina Sheep Laurel (*Kalmia carolina* Small) is a branched shrub to 5 ft tall with narrow elliptic leaves that are dull to bluish green. Flowers are borne in lateral clusters and are deep pink, from 0.25 to 0.5-in. wide. Rare. Swamps, bogs, acid soils. Found in Johnson County in TN, it is a mountainous and Coastal Plain species of the se U.S. May-Jun. **Highly poisonous. Do not ingest.**

Alan S. Heilman

Sand Myrtle   *Leiophyllum buxifolium* (Bergius) Elliott
Low, freely-branched, evergreen shrub from 4 to 20 in. tall. Leaves, from 0.25 to 0.5-in. long, are alternate or opposite, entire, lustrous, leathery, ovate to oblong, numerous, crowded. Numerous flowers are borne in dense clusters from the upper leaf axils. The 5 petals are white or pinkish, about 0.15-in. long, and the 10 stamens have purple anthers. Rare. Sandy barrens of the Atlantic Coastal Plain (NJ, NC and SC), exposed outcrops in the high mountains (Blue Ridge and Smokies). Found in Carter, Greene, Sevier and Blount counties in TN. May. *Leiophyllum* is a monotypic genus, i.e., it has only one species. The genus name is from the Greek *leios* (smooth) and *phyllon* (leaf).

Jack Carman

Genus *Leucothoe*
Three species are found in Tennessee. The genus name is in honor of Leucothoe, the daughter of Orchamus, King of Babylon.

Dog Hobble
Leucothoe fontanesiana (Steudel) Sleumer
Colonial, evergreen, spreading shrub to 5 ft tall often found in dense thickets. Leaves, from 3 to 6 in. long, are alternate, leathery, sharply toothed, mostly elliptic, pointed at the tip, on stalks from 0.4 to 0.6-in. long. From 20 to 60 flowers are borne in dense racemes to 4 in. long that hang from the leaf axils. Flowers are urn-shaped, about 0.25-in. long. Occasional. Mountain streams. Found from the Cumberland Plateau east in TN, and in the southern highlands from VA to GA and AL. Apr-Jun.

Fetterbush (*Leucothoe recurva* (Buckley) A.Gray) is somewhat similar, but taller and more upright. The leaves are deciduous and the flower racemes are one-sided. Infrequent. Dry ridges and rocky slopes at high elevation. Found from WV to TN and GA. Apr-Jun.

Jack Carman

Pinesap   *Monotropa hypopithys* L.

Saprophytic erect perennial from 4 to 12 in. tall with a downy stem, often found in small colonies. Both stem and flowers are yellow, tawny, pink or reddish. Several flowers, from 0.3 to 0.7-in. long, are nodding, urn-shaped, and borne in a one-sided terminal raceme. Although the flowers are nodding, the mature fruits are erect. Occasional. Moist or dry acid woods. Scattered throughout TN, and found in most of the U.S. and CAN. May-Sep.

Sweet Pinesap (*Monotropsis odorata* Schweinitz), is similar, but only 2 to 5 in. tall. The stem is smooth but has numerous, crowded, overlapping scales. The flowers are pink to rose to purple, about 0.4-in. long, and have the odor of violets. Mature fruits are nodding. Rare. Dry woods. Found in Grundy, Polk, Monroe, Blount and Sevier counties in TN, and in the eastern highlands, from ME to KY south to SC and AL. Feb-Apr. The genus name is from *Monotropa* and *opsis* (appearance), for the resemblance to that genus.

Genus *Monotropa*

Two species are found in Tennessee. The genus name is from the Greek *monos* (one) and *tropos* (turn), in reference to the summit of the flower stem being turned to one side. Some botanical treatments place this genus in the Indian Pipe Family (Monotropaceae).

Indian Pipe   *Monotropa uniflora* L.

Saprophytic erect perennial from 4 to 8 in. tall with a smooth stem, either solitary or sometimes growing in small colonies. Both stem and flowers are waxy-white, rarely pink or reddish. A lone flower, from 0.4 to 0.7-in. long, is borne at the top of the stem, and is nodding, urn-shaped, odorless. Although the flower is nodding, the mature fruit is erect. Frequent. Rich woods. Found throughout TN and most of the U.S. and CAN. Jun-Sep.

Jack Carman

Jack Carman

Flame Azalea   *Rhododendron calendulaceum* (Michaux) Torrey

Freely-branched, erect shrub to 10 ft tall. Leaves, from 2 to 4 in. long, are deciduous, not full-grown at flowering, mostly elliptic, usually pale-hairy beneath, short-stalked. Flowers, from 1.6 to 2 in. wide, are borne in clusters of 5 to 15, scarcely fragrant, yellow to orange or red, tubular with 5 spreading and pointed lobes, the upper lobe only slightly wider. Occasional. Dry open woods. Found in the Blue Ridge in TN, also Hawkins County, and in the Appalachians from PA to GA and AL. Apr-May (Jun at high elevation).

Cumberland Azalea (*R. cumberlandense* Braun) is similar, but leaves are fully grown at flowering. The upper flower lobe is much wider and marked with orange. Occasional. Upland woods. Cumberland Plateau east in TN, also in WV and e KY. Jun.

Swamp Azalea (*R. viscosum* (L.) Torrey), to 6 ft tall, has hairy twigs and leaves. Flowers are white (pink) and hairy. Stamens extend past the floral tube less than the tube length. Rare. Wet areas. Found in the eastern half of TN, and from ME to OH south to FL. Jun-Jul.

Mountain (Piedmont) Azalea   *Rhododendron canescens* (Michaux) Sweet

Erect shrub to 10 ft tall, usually not colonial. Leaves are deciduous, mostly pale-hairy beneath. Flowers are 5-lobed, white to deep pink. Corolla lobes are much shorter than the corolla tube, and stamens are about 3 times as long as the corolla tube. Frequent. Swamps, moist woods. Widespread in TN and the se U.S., except the Blue Ridge. Apr-May.

Pinxter Flower (*R. periclymenoides* (Michx.) Shinners) is similar, but colonial and leaves are mostly smooth beneath. Corolla tube about as long as the lobes. Occasional. Apr-May.

Jack Carman

Jack Carman

Catawba Rhododendron   *Rhododendron catawbiense* Michaux
Erect woody shrub to 10 ft (or more) tall. Leaves are alternate, smooth, leathery, evergreen, somewhat glaucous beneath, elliptic or oval, from 2 to 6 in. long. The flowers, to 2 in. wide, are borne in clusters at the branch tips, and are deep pink to purple, tubular with 5 rounded lobes. Occasional. Rocky ridges, slopes and balds at high elevation. Found from the Cumberland Plateau east in TN, and from VA and KY south to AL and GA. May-Jun.

Carolina Rhododendron (*R. minus* Michaux) is similar, but leaves have reddish-brown scales beneath, and flowers are white to pink, slightly smaller. Infrequent. Stream banks, open wooded slopes in the uplands. Found in Monroe, Polk, Roane, Loudon, Blount, Sevier, Greene, Unicoi, Washington and Carter counties in TN, also GA and AL. May-Jun.

Jack Carman

Genus *Rhododendron*
Eleven species are found in Tennessee that may be grouped into two classes: eight are **azaleas** with deciduous leaves, and three are **rhododendrons** with evergreen leaves. Rhododendron is the Greek name for rose-tree.

Great Rhododendron
***Rhododendron maximum* L.**
Erect woody shrub to 20 ft (or more) tall that is often found in dense colonies. Leaves are alternate, evergreen, leathery, smooth above but scurfy-hairy beneath, from 4 to 12 in. long and 1 to 3 in. wide. The flowers, about 1.5 in. wide, are borne in clusters at the branch tips, and are tubular with 5 rounded lobes, white (rarely pink) with the largest lobe spotted with green, yellow or orange. Occasional. Moist or wet woods, stream banks. Found from the Cumberland Plateau east in TN, also in Smith and Benton counties. A northeastern U.S. and adjacent CAN species that extends south in the uplands and mountains to GA and AL. Jun-Jul.

Jack Carman

ERICACEAE : HEATH FAMILY

Farkleberry   *Vaccinium arboreum* Marshall
Freely-branched shrub to 18 ft tall. Leaves, from 0.8 to 2 in. long, are firm, deciduous, entire, shining above but dull and sometimes downy beneath, oblanceolate to obovate, narrowed to a short stalk. Several flowers, on drooping stalks to 0.4-in. long, are borne near the summit of numerous lateral branches such that the combined inflorescence is large and showy. The corolla, about 0.2-in. long, is white, bell-shaped with 5 short lobes. The stamens are included, but the style protrudes slightly outside the corolla. The berry is black and lustrous, but dry and mealy, inedible. Common. Dry, sandy or rocky woods. Found throughout TN, and from se VA to s IN to se KS south to FL and TX. May-Jun.

Jack Carman

DIAPENSIACEAE : DIAPENSIA FAMILY

Two genera with one species each are found in Tennessee.

Beetleweed, Galax
Galax urceolata (Poiret) Brummitt
Smooth, colonial, evergreen perennial with a tuft of scaly creeping rhizomes and fibrous red roots. The veiny and shining leaves are all basal, long-stalked, orbicular to ovate, deeply cordate at the base, toothed, from 1.5 to 6 in. wide. The slender flowering scapes are 8 to 32 in. tall, and terminated by a long spike-like raceme from 2 to 4 in. long. The flowers have 5 white petals from 0.15 to 0.25-in. long. Occasional. Moist or dry open woods on acidic soils. Found in the Blue Ridge Mountains and adjacent counties in the Ridge and Valley Province in TN. Found chiefly in the mountains from w MD to KY south to GA and AL, and extending to the Coastal Plain of NC and se VA. May-Jul. *Galax* is a monotypic genus, i.e., having only one species, and the name is from the Greek *gala* (milk), presumably from the milk-white flowers. *Galax aphylla* L.

Jack Carman

Most members of this family have simple, unlobed and undivided leaves, corollas with 5 radially symmetric, petal-like lobes joined at the base, and 5 stamens. Six genera and 16 species are found in TN.

Scarlet Pimpernel
Anagallis arvensis L.*

A much-branched annual to 12 in. tall, erect or sprawling with a 4-angled stem. Leaves are opposite, elliptic to ovate, sessile, from 0.4 to 0.8-in. long. Flowers, to 0.4-in. wide, are solitary from the leaf axils, on slender stalks that usually surpass the leaves. Flowers are usually scarlet to brick-red (rarely white). Occasional. Roadsides, lawns, fields, waste places. Thinly spread across TN and practically throughout North America. May-Aug. Native of Eurasia. Known as Poor-Man's Weatherglass in England because the flowers close at the approach of bad weather. In fact, the genus name is from the Greek *ana* (again) and *agallein* (to delight in), from the habit of the flowers closing in bad weather and opening again in sunshine. Contact with leaves may sometimes cause a skin rash.

Jack Carman

Shooting Star
Dodecatheon meadia L.

Smooth perennial with a leafy basal rosette, erect scapes from 6 to 20 in. tall, and a terminal umbel of handsome nodding flowers on erect or ascending stalks. The mostly oblong to oblanceolate leaves (to 8 in. long) are usually tinged with red at the base. The 5 corolla lobes are narrow, white to lilac, and bent sharply back. The 5 stamens are united and converge, appearing cone-like. Frequent. Meadows, open woods, barrens, and limestone bluffs. In TN, it is found from the Western Highland Rim east. Its extended range is from WI to PA south to GA and TX. Apr-Jun. The common name is derived from the resemblance of the flower to a celestial shooting star. The genus name is from the Greek *dodeca* (twelve) and *theos* (god), alluding to the primrose which was believed to be under the care of twelve superior gods.

Featherfoil, Water Violet
Hottonia inflata Elliott

An unusual, smooth, aquatic, winter annual with a whorl of leaves at the water surface or sometimes emersed when the water level recedes. Pale green leaves, from 1 to 7 in. long, are divided into long, linear, very narrow, lateral divisions and have a feathery appearance. The flowers are borne on a thick, hollow, jointed stem that rises above the leaves, and has 3 to 10 flowers whorled around each joint. The corolla is white and 5-lobed, the lobes less than 0.2-in. long. Rare. Quiet shallow pools, swamps, ditches, occasionally wet soil. In TN, found in Lake, Marion, Montgomery, Obion and Stewart counties. Chiefly an Atlantic and Gulf Coastal Plain species that extends north in the Mississippi River valley. May-Aug. The genus name is in honor of Petrus Hotton, a late 17th and early 18th century Dutch botanist and professor at Leiden.

Jack Carman

Jack Carman

Lance-Leaf Loosestrife
Lysimachia lanceolata Walter

Erect perennial from 8 to 36 in. tall, the lateral branches scarcely exceeding the leaves. The leaves, to 6 in. long and 0.6-in. wide, are opposite, mostly sessile, linear to lanceolate or narrowly oblong, and often folded along the midrib. The long-stalked yellow flowers, from 0.4 to 0.8-in. wide, are somewhat nodding. The corolla lobes have finely-toothed margins and a pointed tip. Frequent. Moist or wet woods, barrens. Found throughout TN, and from NJ to WI south to FL and TX. Jun-Aug.

Fringed Loosestrife (*L. ciliata* L.) is similar, but has ovate to lanceolate leaves with obvious stalks from 0.2 to 2 in. long that are hairy along the entire margin. Frequent. Moist or wet ground in shade or sun. Found throughout TN and most of the U.S. Jun-Aug.

Appalachian Loosestrife (*L. tonsa* (Wood) Knuth) is similar to Fringed Loosestrife, but has mostly smooth leaf stalks. Occasional. Cumberland Plateau east in TN, and from KY to WV south to GA and n AL. Jun-Aug.

Jack Carman

Genus *Lysimachia*

Ten species are found in Tennessee. The genus was named for Lysimachus, a king of ancient Sicily, who is said to have used a genus member to pacify a maddened bull. Colonists fed these plants to oxen so they would work together peacefully.

Whorled Loosestrife
Lysimachia quadrifolia L.

Erect perennial to 3 ft tall with a smooth to sparsely hairy stem that is usually not branched. The stem leaves occur in whorls of 3 to 7, and are broadly to narrowly lanceolate, hairy beneath, widely spreading, to 4 in. long. The flowers are borne on spreading stalks to 2 in. long from the leaf axils. The petals are about 0.3-in. long, yellow with dark lines and red at the base. Frequent. Dry upland soil, open woods. In TN, found from the Western Highland Rim east. U.S. range from ME to MN south to AL. May-Jul.

Swamp Candles
Lysimachia terrestris (L.) BSP.

Erect smooth perennial from 16 to 32 in. tall, often branched, but usually with a single flowering raceme that terminates the stem. Leaves are opposite, narrowly lanceolate, from 2 to 4 in. long. The raceme is erect, from 4 to 12 in. long and many flowered. The individual flowers about 0.5-in. wide are borne on short stalks (to 0.6-in.), and have narrowly elliptic, yellow, corolla lobes with dark lines and red at the base. Rare. Moist meadows and open areas. A mostly northern species extending south to TN, where it is found in Coffee, Unicoi and Warren counties. Jun-Aug.

Moneywort (*L. nummularia* L.*) is a creeping perennial with small, opposite, almost round, semi-evergreen leaves. The yellow flowers grow on slender stalks from the leaf axils. Occasional. Introduced from Europe, now naturalized in moist areas of roadsides and lawns throughout TN and the e U.S. Jun-Aug.

Jack Carman

PRIMULACEAE : PRIMROSE FAMILY

Water Pimpernel
Samolus parviflorus Rafinesque

Erect perennial from 4 to 12 in. tall, usually branched above. Leaves, from 0.8 to 4 in. long, are spatulate to obovate with those on the stem alternate and basal ones forming a rosette. The inflorescence extends above the leaves and is raceme-like. White flowers to 0.12-in. wide are borne on spreading stalks to 0.6-in. long. Common. Muddy banks of streams and ditches. Found throughout TN and most of the U.S. May-Aug. *Samolus floribundus* HBK. The genus name is an ancient name, probably of Celtic origin, and is said to refer to the curative properties of this genus in diseases of cattle and swine.

Note: HBK. denotes authors Friedrich von Humboldt, Aime Bonpland, and Carl Kunth.

CRASSULACEAE : SEDUM FAMILY

Two genera and seven species are found in Tennessee.

Jack Carman

Elf Orpine
Diamorpha smallii Britton

Smooth winter annual from 1.5 to 4 in. tall that is branched at the base and has red stems and leaves. The leaves are alternate, sessile, cylindric, to 0.25-in. long. The flowers are borne in compound cymes that are terminal on the stem and branches. The flowers have 4 white petals to 0.12-in. long and 8 stamens. The fruits, borne in a group of 4, are erect, pointed, united at the base. Infrequent. Sandstone outcrops of the Cumberland Plateau (found in Cumberland, Franklin, Grundy, Hamilton, Marion, Putnam and Rhea counties in TN). Also found in NC and GA (on granite) and in AL. Apr. *Diamorpha cymosa* (Nuttall) Britton, *Sedum smallii* (Britton) Ahles.

Jack Carman

Jack Carman

Widow's Cross   ***Sedum pulchellum*** Michaux
Smooth winter annual from 4 to 12 in. tall that is often branched at the base. The leaves are
numerous, alternate, mostly cylindric, from 0.4 to 1.2 in. long. The inflorescence atop the
stem has from 3 to 7 widely-spreading branches to 4 in. long. Flowers are crowded on the
upper side of each branch, and have 4 spreading, pink to white petals from 0.12 to 0.25-in.
long and red anthers. Frequent. Exposed limestone of cedar glades, bluffs and roadbeds.
Found in Middle and East TN, also Decatur and Henderson counties. Also found in KY and
west to MO, OK and TX. Apr-May.

Genus *Sedum*
Six species are found in Tennessee. The genus name is from *sedere* (to sit), alluding to the
ability of many species to grow on rocks or walls.

Mountain Stonecrop   ***Sedum ternatum*** Michaux
Smooth spreading perennial with creeping stems and several erect, leafy, sterile shoots and
a single flowering stem to 7 in. tall. Lower leaves are evergreen, in whorls of 3 (or 4), and
usually obovate, from 0.4 to 0.8-in. long. The flowering stem has alternate and oblanceolate
leaves, and is topped by a spreading inflorescence with 2 to 4 branches. The flowers are
crowded on the upper side of each branch, and have 4 spreading, white petals from 0.2 to
0.4-in. long and dark anthers. Common. Rocks, logs, moist soil of open woodlands. Found
from the Western Highland Rim east in TN, also in Fayette County. Extended range includes
most of the e U.S. Apr-May.

George Hornal

The Saxifrage Family is represented by 14 genera and 35 species in Tennessee.

Brook Saxifrage
Boykinia aconitifolia Nuttall
Perennial from 1 to 2 ft tall, stems glandular-hairy above. The basal and stem leaves, from 2 to 4 in. wide, are long-stalked, broadly reniform, 5 to 9-lobed to the middle with the lobes narrowly and unequally toothed. Cymes at first are compact, later elongating and raceme-like. The flowers have 5 white petals that are obovate, short-clawed, from 0.12 to 0.2-in. long. Infrequent. Moist mountain woods. Found in Franklin, Polk, Hamilton, Rhea, Blount, Cumberland, Scott, Morgan and Fentress counties in TN, and from VA to KY south to GA and AL. Jun-Jul. The genus name is in honor of Samuel Boykin, an early active botanist of Georgia.

Jack Carman

Common Alumroot
Heuchera americana L.
Perennial from 16 to 56 in. tall. Basal leaves (shown left) are long-stalked, unequally 5 to 9-lobed, palmately veined, and often white-mottled. Small non-showy flowers are borne on a naked scape rising well above the leaves. The calyx is glandular-hairy, and the stamens and style extend well past the pink, white, or greenish petals. Common. Dry upland woods. Found throughout TN and the e U.S. Apr-Jun.

Four *Heuchera* species are found in TN. Genus name in honor of Johann Heinrich Heucher, an 18th century German botanist.

Jack Carman

Maple-Leaf Alumroot
Heuchera villosa Michaux
Perennial from 8 to 32 in. tall. Basal leaves are long-stalked and the blades are toothed, rough-hairy and sharply lobed. Tiny pink to white flowers are borne in a congested cluster that terminates a hairy leafless stalk and extends well above the leaves. The calyx is covered with long white hairs and the seeds have small sharp projections. Common. Moist shaded ledges and cliffs. Found throughout Middle and East TN, and irregularly in the mountains from VA to TN west to s IN and AR. Jun-Sep.

Small-Flowered Alumroot (*Heuchera parviflora* Bartling) is similar, but 4 to 18 in. tall with soft-hairy leaves that have rounded lobes. The seeds are nearly smooth. Occasional. Shaded rocks and ledges in the Cumberland Plateau. U.S. range from WV to NC and AL west to s IL and AR. Jul-Sep.

Jack Carman

Wild Hydrangea   *Hydrangea arborescens* L.

Straggling shrub from 3 to 10 ft tall with brown flaking bark on old stems. Leaves are opposite, sharply toothed, oblong-ovate to round-ovate, from 2 to 7 in. long. The white flowers are borne in flat or rounded clusters from 2 to 4 in. wide that terminate the branches. The central flowers are small and fertile, and produce seeds. The showy marginal flowers with 3 or 4 petal-like sepals to 0.4-in. long are sterile. Common. Dry or moist, often rocky woods and hillsides. Found throughout TN and most of the e U.S. May-Jul. The genus name is from the Greek *hydor* (water) and *aggeion* (a vessel), from the shape of the fruit.

Oak-Leaf Hydrangea (*Hydrangea quercifolia* Bartram) leaves are woolly beneath, have 5 to 7 sharp lobes, and somewhat resemble oak leaves. The flowers are born in terminal pyramidal clusters that have many sterile, showy, white flowers that age purplish. Occasional. Dry woods. A southern species extending north to the southern border counties of West and Middle TN, also Benton, Perry and Moore counties. Spread from cultivation northward. Jun.

Sweet Spire   *Itea virginica* L.

Shrub from 3 to 10 ft tall with hairy twigs. Leaves, from 1.2 to 3.6 in. long, are alternate, smooth, sharply toothed, elliptic to obovate, pointed at the tip, on stalks from 0.12 to 0.4-in. long. Flowers are borne in slender, downy racemes from 1.6 to 6 in. long that terminate the stem and branches. The 5 petals are white, about 0.25-in. long. Frequent. Swamps, wet woods. Found throughout TN, it is chiefly a Coastal Plain species found from s NJ and e PA to FL to LA, and inland in the Mississippi River valley to s IL. May-Jun.

Jack Carman

Jack Carman

Bishop's Cap, Miterwort
Mitella diphylla L.

Perennial from 4 to 16 in. tall that arises from a rhizome. Long-stalked basal leaves have blades from 1.8 to 3 in. long that are palmately-veined, round-ovate with a heart-shaped base, shallowly 3 to 5-lobed, roundly toothed, hairy. Stem leaves (a single pair) are sessile, mostly 3-lobed and smaller than the basal leaves. Small white flowers are borne in a raceme from 2 to 6 in. long that terminates the slender stem. The calyx tube is mostly cup-shaped, and petals are small (to 0.1-in. long) and deeply fringed. The beauty of the flowers is evident when viewed with a 10X lens. The seeds are black and shining. Frequent. Rich woods, moist rocks, mossy banks. Found from the Western Highland Rim east in TN, it is a more northern species extending south to GA and TN. Apr-Jun. The genus name is a diminutive of *mitra* (a cap), alluding to the shape of the young fruit.

Genus *Parnassia*

Two species are found in Tennessee. The genus was named in ancient times after Mount Parnassus.

Kidney-Leaf Grass-of-Parnassus
Parnassia asarifolia Ventenat

Smooth perennial from 8 to 16 in. tall. Basal leaves are long-stalked, thin and flexible, kidney-shaped, from 1 to 2 in. wide. Each flowering stem has a terminal flower and a single sessile leaf near the middle of the stem that is similar to the basal leaves but smaller. The 5 white petals are prominently veined, narrow-stalked, from 0.5 to 0.7-in. long. The 5 stamens with anthers are alternate with 5 shorter, sterile staminodes. Occasional. Swamps, bogs, stream banks, seepage slopes. Found from the Cumberland Plateau east in TN. The U.S. range is from AR and e TX east to VA and GA, chiefly in the uplands. Sep-Oct.

Jack Carman

Large-Leaf Grass-of-Parnassus
Parnassia grandifolia DC.
Smooth perennial from 8 to 16 in. tall. Basal leaves are long-stalked, palmately veined, broadly round-ovate, from 2 to 3 in. long. Each flowering stem has a terminal flower and a single sessile leaf near the middle of the stem that is similar to the basal leaves but smaller. The 5 white petals, from 0.6 to 0.9-in. long, have prominent green veins and are sessile. The 5 stamens with reddish anthers are alternate with 5 longer, sterile staminodes. Infrequent. Wet limestone seeps. Thinly spread in TN from the Western Highland Rim east (Lewis, Maury, Williamson, DeKalb, Anderson, Campbell, Claiborne and Carter counties), and found throughout most of the se U.S., chiefly in the uplands. Sep-Oct.

Jack Carman

Jack Carman

Ditch Stonecrop
Penthorum sedoides L.
Smooth erect perennial from 8 to 28 in. tall that arises from a rhizome and is sometimes branched above. Leaves, from 2 to 4 in. long, are alternate, lance-shaped, sharply toothed. The inflorescence is a terminal cyme with 2 to 4 branches. Small greenish flowers are arranged along one side of each branch. The fruit is a capsule about 0.25-in. wide that has 5 to 7 horn-shaped lobes. Common. Ditches, marshes, muddy soil. Found throughout TN and the e U.S. Jun-Oct. The genus name is from the Greek *penthos* (five) and *horos* (a mark) alluding to most plant characteristics being based on the number 5. The species name is derived from the resemblance of the flowers to those in the genus *Sedum* of the Sedum Family.

Carey's Saxifrage
Saxifraga careyana Gray

Perennial from 8 to 20 in. tall with a basal rosette of leaves and a widely-branched inflorescence. The leaves, to 4 in. long, are ovate to slightly obovate, coarsely serrate, usually smooth above and hairy beneath. Flowers are regular and white. The 5 petals are mostly elliptic, to 0.16-in. long, often with a few yellow spots near the base. Stamens have slender filaments and red anthers. Occasional. Moist rocky places. Found from the Cumberland Plateau east in TN (at low elevation), also in the mountains of s VA and NC. May-Jul.

Carolina Saxifrage (*S. caroliniana* Gray) is similar, but the petals are clawed at the base and have more yellow spots. Rare. Moist rocky woods. Found in Carter, Cocke and Johnson counties in TN, also in the mountains of VA and NC. May-Jun.

Jack Carman

Jack Carman

Genus *Saxifraga*

Five species are found in Tennessee. The genus name is from *saxum* (a stone) and *frangere* (to break). It was early applied, through the Doctrine of Signatures, to European species bearing granular bulblets which were supposed to dissolve kidney stones.

Mountain Saxifrage
Saxifraga michauxii Britton

Hairy perennial from 4 to 20 in. tall that has most leaves in a basal rosette, and is branched above into a large open inflorescence. Leaves are coarsely-serrate, obovate to oblanceolate, from 2 to 6 in. long. The irregular white flowers have 2 small unspotted petals, and 3 larger stalked petals to 0.16-in. long that are dotted with yellow. Infrequent. Moist or wet ledges and rocky woods. In TN, found at high elevation in the eastern mountains, also in Scott, Fentress and Pickett counties. U.S. range in the mountains from VA and KY south to GA. Jun-Aug. The species name is in honor of its discoverer, Andre Michaux.

Jack Carman

Mountain Lettuce, Brook Lettuce
Saxifraga micranthidifolia (Haw.) Steudel
Perennial from 12 to 32 in. tall, arising from a stout rhizome and branched above, forming a large open inflorescence. Blades of the basal leaves are sharply toothed, oblanceolate to oblong, from 3 to 8 in. long, gradually tapering to a winged petiole. The flowers are about 0.25-in. wide with 5 oval petals, white with a yellow spot near the base. Infrequent. Wet cliffs and mountain brooks, chiefly in the Blue Ridge from TN and NC to WV and e PA. Found in Polk, Monroe, Blount, Sevier, Cocke, Unicoi, Carter and Johnson counties in TN. Commonly seen in the Great Smoky Mountains National Park during spring. Apr-Jun.

Early Saxifrage
Saxifraga virginiensis Michaux
Perennial with all leaves in a basal rosette. The leaves, from 1 to 3 in. long, are oblong or ovate and usually toothed. A branched inflorescence, from 4 to 16 in. tall, arises from the center of the basal rosette, and is at first compact but later lax and open. The flowers have 5 white petals to 0.2-in. long that are spatulate to obovate, and stamens barely extend beyond the petals. The calyx tube is bell-shaped. Frequent. Moist or dry open woods, rock ledges, stream banks. Found from the Western Highland Rim east in TN, also in Madison County, and from New Brunswick to Manitoba south to GA, LA and OK. Mar-May.

Jack Carman

George Hornal

SAXIFRAGACEAE : SAXIFRAGE FAMILY

Foamflower *Tiarella cordifolia* L.
Erect perennial from 4 to 14 in. tall that
arises from a rhizome. The leaves, from 2 to
4 in. long, are all basal, long-stalked, broadly
heart-shaped, toothed, palmately veined,
shallowly 3 to 5-lobed, hairy. The flowers
are borne in a raceme to 4 in. long that
terminates a leafless stalk and extends well
above the leaves. The 5 petals are white,
from 0.12 to 0.2-in. long, and the 10 stamens
are long and showy. Common. Rich woods.
Found from the Western Highland Rim east
in TN, and throughout most of the e U.S.
Apr-Jun. The genus name means "little
tiara," in reference to the odd form of the
fruit. A tiara was the head-dress of the
classical Persians – a kind of turban.

ROSACEAE : ROSE FAMILY

Genus *Agrimonia*
Five species are found in Tennessee. The
genus name is a corruption of *Argemone*.

Jack Carman

Woodland Agrimony
Agrimonia rostellata Wallroth
Perennial with smooth stems to 3 ft tall. The
compound leaves have 3 to 9 large leaflets
that are mostly wider above the middle, thin,
coarsely and bluntly toothed, smooth on the
upper surface, but conspicuously glandular
(and often with hairs on the veins) on the
lower surface. The inflorescence is a long,
interrupted, spike-like raceme with the axis
glandular, and sometimes with a very few
spreading bristles. The yellow flowers are
about 0.3-in. wide and 5-petaled. Frequent.
Moist rich woods. Widely scattered in TN,
and found in most of the e U.S. Jul-Aug.

Southern Agrimony (*A. parviflora* Aiton) is
quite similar, but the inflorescence axis is
densely short-hairy, and leaves have 11 to
23 leaflets. Frequent. Damp woods. Found
throughout TN and most of the e U.S. Jul-
Aug.

Downy Agrimony (*A. pubescens* Wallroth) is
also similar, but has densely pubescent
stems, and the inflorescence axis is not
glandular. Frequent. Dry woods. Found
mostly in Middle and East TN, and from ME
to se SD south to GA and OK. Jul-Aug.

George Hornal

Goatsbeard   *Aruncus dioicus* (Walter) Fernald
Erect or ascending perennial from 3 to 7 ft tall with several smooth stems arising from a crown. Leaves are alternate, large, 2 or 3 times ternately divided into toothed, lance-shaped leaflets from 2 to 6 in. long. A large and wispy inflorescence of tiny white flowers terminates the stem. The female and male flowers are borne on separate plants. Frequent. Slopes in rich moist open woods. Found from the Western Highland Rim east in TN, also in Lauderdale and Tipton counties, and from PA to IA south to NC, AL and AR. May-Jun.
False Goatsbeard (*Astilbe biternata* (Ventenat) Britton) is similar, but stems are coarse and hairy, and the terminal leaflet usually has 3 lobes. Occasional. Slopes in rich moist woods. Found in the eastern half of TN, and in the uplands from VA to KY south to GA. Jun. A member of the Saxifrage Family (Saxifragaceae).

George Hornal

Familiar fruits of the Rose Family include almond, apple, blackberry, cherry, peach, pear, plum, raspberry and strawberry. The flowers commonly have 5 petals and many stamens. There are 23 genera and 105 species listed for TN.

Indian Strawberry
Duchesnea indica (Andrzejowski) Focke*
Low hairy perennial with creeping stems that root at the nodes. Leaves are long-stalked and compound with 3 ovate to elliptic, bluntly-toothed leaflets from 0.8 to 1.6 in. long. Solitary flowers arise from the leaf axils on stalks from 1 to 4 in. long. The flowers, about 0.6-in. wide, are yellow with 5 petals and 20 stamens. The floral bracts are large, green, 3-toothed and slightly longer than the petals. The mature fruit is bright red and fleshy, but not juicy or edible. Occasional. Lawns, moist waste areas. Widespread in TN and the e U.S. Feb-Oct. Native of India. The genus name honors Antoine Nicolas Duchesne, an early 18th century botanist.

George Hornal

Wild Strawberry   *Fragaria virginiana* Duchesne
Low perennial usually spreading freely by runners. Leaves are long-stalked and compound with 3 leaflets that are thick and firm, dark green, bluntly toothed, elliptic to oblanceolate, from 1 to 5 in. long. Flower clusters are long-stalked, but usually borne below the leaves. Flowers, about 0.75-in. wide, are white with 5 petals and 20 stamens. The fruit, about 0.6-in. wide, is roundish, edible, fleshy and juicy with seeds set in pits on the surface. Frequent. Roadsides, barrens, woodland borders. Scattered throughout TN and the e U.S. Apr-May.

Wood Strawberry (*Fragaria vesca* L.) is similar, but flowers are about 0.5-in. wide, and the flower clusters may rise above the leaves. Seeds are set on the fruit surface instead of pits. Rare. Rich woods. Found in the ne U.S. and south to TN (Blount County). May-Jun.

Jack Carman

White Avens   *Geum canadense* Jacquin
Perennial with a smooth to downy, slender stem to 40 in. tall. Lower leaves are long-stalked, compound with 3 obovate toothed leaflets, but upper leaves are usually simple and almost sessile. Flowers, about 0.6-in. wide, have 5 white petals about as long as the sepals. The many beaked achenes form the densely bristly fruiting head. Common. Dry or moist open woods. Found throughout TN and the e U.S. May-Jul.

Spring Avens (*Geum vernum* (Raf.) T. & G.) is similar, but flowers are yellow or cream, about 0.3-in. wide. Lower stem and basal leaves are pinnately dissected or compound. Frequent. Rich open woods. Found from the Western Highland Rim east in TN, and in most of the eastern U.S. Apr-May.

Pale Avens or Rough Avens (*Geum virginianum* L.) is also similar, but the stem is densely hairy below. Flowers are cream to pale yellow, about 0.6-in. wide, and petals are much shorter than the sepals. Frequent. Moist upland woods. Found throughout TN, and from MA to IN south to TN and NC. Jun-Jul.

George Hornal

Genus *Geum*
Seven species are found in Tennessee. The genus name is the ancient name for avens.

Spreading Avens
Geum radiatum Michaux
Erect perennial from 8 to 20 in. tall with densely hairy stems. Basal leaves are long-stalked, compound with small lateral leaflets and a reniform terminal leaflet, from 3 to 6 in. wide, that is sharply toothed. Stem leaves are sessile, rounded to obovate with tattered margins, much smaller than the basal leaves. One to few showy flowers are borne at the top of the stem. The 5 petals, from 0.5 to 0.8-in. long, are bright yellow and notched on the rounded tip. Stamens and pistils are numerous. Rare. High elevation balds and exposed rocky outcrops. Found in Blount, Carter and Sevier counties in TN, and endemic to the border area of NC and TN. Jun-Jul.

Genus *Porteranthus*
Two species are found in Tennessee.

Jack Carman

American Ipecac, Indian Physic
Porteranthus stipulatus (Muhlenberg *ex* Willdenow) Britton
Erect perennial to 40 in. tall with a thinly hairy stem that is branched above. Leaves are alternate, almost sessile, trifoliate (with 3 leaflets), and have 2 stipules at the base. Leaflets are lance-shaped, sharply toothed, from 2 to 3 in. long, and stipules are broadly ovate, sharply toothed, from 0.4 to 1.2 in. long. The lower leaflets are sometimes both pinnately lobed and toothed. Loose clusters of flowers on long stalks terminate the stem and branches. The petals are narrow, white, pointed, about 0.75-in. long but sometimes with slightly different lengths. Frequent. Rich woods. Widespread in TN, and found from w NY to KS south to GA and TX. May-Jun. *Gillenia stipulata* (Muhlenberg) Baillon.

Bowman's Root (*Porteranthus trifoliatus* (L.) Britton) is similar, but stipules are linear, entire and usually not present at flowering. Occasional. Rich woods. Found from the Eastern Highland Rim east in TN, and in most of the e U.S. May-Jun. *Gillenia trifoliata* (L.) Moench.

Jack Carman

Dwarf Cinquefoil *Potentilla canadensis* L.

Low perennial with long, slender, creeping, silky-hairy stems that often root at the nodes. Leaves are palmately compound. The 5 wedge-shaped leaflets, from 0.4 to 1.6 in. long, have rounded tips, toothed only along the outer half. Solitary flowers, from 0.4 to 0.6-in. wide, arise from the leaf axils on slender silky-hairy stalks to 2.4 in. long. The 5 petals are yellow and obovate. Frequent. Dry fields and woods. Found from the Central Basin east in TN, also in Cheatham County, and throughout the e U.S. and e CAN. Mar-May.

Three-Toothed Cinquefoil (*Potentilla tridentata* (Solander) Aiton) leaves have 3 lance-shaped, evergreen leaflets, each with only three teeth at the blunt tip. Flowers have 5 white petals. Rare. Rock crevices, balds at high elevation. Found in Carter, Johnson and Unicoi counties in TN, it is a northern species that extends south to GA in the mountains. Jun-Aug.

Sulphur Cinquefoil
Rough-Fruited Cinquefoil
Potentilla recta L.*

Jack Carman

Erect hairy perennial from 16 to 32 in. tall. Leaves are palmately compound, the lower long-stalked with 5 to 7 leaflets, the upper short-stalked with often only 3 leaflets. The leaflets, from 0.8 to 4 in. long, are narrowly oblanceolate and deeply toothed. Loose clusters of flowers terminate the stem and branches. The 5 petals, from 0.3 to 0.6-in. long, are pale yellow and shallowly notched on the rounded tip. The seeds (achenes) have low curved ridges. Frequent. Waste areas, roadsides, dry fields. Found from the Western Highland Rim east in TN, also in Carroll and Shelby counties, and throughout the e U.S. May-Jul.

Rough Cinquefoil (*Potentilla norvegica* L.) has similar but smaller flowers (about 0.5-in. wide), and the compound leaves have only 3 deeply-toothed leaflets. Occasional. Fields, waste places, roadsides. Found from the Western Highland Rim east in TN, also in Shelby County, and in most of the e U.S. May-Sep.

Jack Carman

Common Cinquefoil   *Potentilla simplex* Michaux
Low coarse perennial to 12 in. tall, at first erect, but soon arching to the ground as the stem continues to grow, often forming tangled mats. The stems are slender with long internodes, softly-hairy to almost smooth. The 5 radial leaflets to 3 in. long are mostly elliptic with teeth extending from the tip to near the base. The flowers, from 0.4 to 0.6-in. wide, are yellow with five rounded petals, and solitary on long slender stalks from the leaf axils, with the lowest flower occurring at the second leaf node. Common. Fields, lawns, dry woods, waste places. Found throughout TN, the e U.S. and e CAN. Apr-Jun. The cinquefoils are also called "five fingers," obviously comparing the five spreading leaflets to the fingers of a hand. Genus name from *potens* (powerful), alluding to the reputed medicinal powers of one species.

Jack Carman

Roses   **Genus *Rosa***
Flowers of wild roses have only 5 petals, in sharp contrast to those of cultivated roses that have many petals in overlapping layers. Seven wild rose species are found in TN. *Rosa* is the ancient Latin name for rose.

Multiflora Rose
Rosa multiflora Thunberg *ex* Murray*
Vigorously colonial perennial with slender, arching or climbing stems to 10 ft long that have curved thorns. Leaves are alternate, pinnately compound and usually have 7 elliptic to obovate, toothed leaflets to 1 in. long. Fringed stipules are found at the base of the leaf. The flowers are borne in dense clusters just above the leaves. The 5 petals are white (pink), from 0.4 to 0.8-in. long. The hips are red. Occasional. Roadsides, fence rows, open woods, pastures. Widespread in TN. Escaped, naturalized and scattered throughout the e U.S. May-Jun. Introduced from east Asia to be used as a living hedge. It forms unpenetrable masses and provides excellent wildlife cover, but has become a pest in many areas.

Jack Carman

Swamp Rose   ***Rosa palustris*** Marshall

Upright, freely-branched shrub to 7 ft tall, the stems with stout curved thorns. Leaves are pinnately compound with usually 7 finely-toothed, elliptic to oblanceolate leaflets from 0.8 to 2.5 in. long. Stipules at the leaf base are entire with hairy margins. Flowers are solitary or few and borne at the branch tips. The 5 petals are pink, from 0.8 to 1.2 in. long. Hips are red. Frequent. Swamps, wet areas. Found throughout TN and in all of the e U.S. Jun-Aug.

Virginia Rose (*Rosa virginiana* Miller) is similar, but the leaflets are coarsely toothed, glossy. The stipules are usually toothed and glandular. Rare. Moist or dry areas. Found in Sumner, Maury, and Montgomery counties in TN, and from e CAN to VA inland to MO. May-Jun.

Jack Carman

Prairie Rose   ***Rosa setigera*** Michaux
Perennial with smooth, climbing, arching or trailing stems from 7 to 14 ft long with curved thorns. The leaves are pinnately compound with usually 3 (rarely 5) glossy, dark green, coarsely-toothed, lance-shaped leaflets from 1 to 4 in. long. The stipules at the leaf base are narrow with glandular-hairy margins. Flowers are borne in small terminal clusters. The petals are pink, from 0.8 to 1.2 in. long, and hips are small, brown-green. Frequent. Open woods, thickets, fence rows. Found throughout TN and in most of the se U.S. May-Jun.

Carolina Rose or Pasture Rose (*Rosa carolina* L.) is similar to the Swamp Rose, but only grows to 3 ft tall and the stems have straight thorns. The leaflets are coarsely toothed, and stipules are toothed to entire. Common. Dry woods, pastures, fence rows. Found throughout TN and in most of the eastern U.S. May-Jun.

George Hornal

Southern Blackberry   *Rubus argutus* Link
Perennial with erect or arching, angled stems to 7 ft long and numerous curved thorns. Leaves are palmately lobed with 3 or 5 leaflets that are coarsely toothed, oblanceolate-oblong, from 1 to 5 in. long, less than half as wide. Flower clusters terminate the stem and branches. The 5 white petals are 0.8 to 1 in. long. The fruit is black, seedy, very juicy, edible. Frequent. Thickets, woods edges. Widespread in TN and the se U.S. May-Jun.

Black Raspberry (*Rubus occidentalis* L.) has erect or arching, strongly glaucous stems with curved thorns. Sepals, to 0.35-in. long, are longer than the white petals. Fruit purple-black, seedy, edible. Frequent. Disturbed areas. Widespread in TN and the e U.S. May-Jun.

Wineberry (*Rubus phoenicolasius* Maximowicz*) is densely covered with long, purple, bristly, glandular hairs. The petals are white and shorter than the sepals. Fruit red. Occasional. Found in the eastern half of TN, also Stewart County, and throughout the e U.S. May-Jun. Native of e Asia. Fourteen *Rubus* species are found in TN.

Purple-Flowering Raspberry   *Rubus odoratus* L.
Widely-branched shrub from 3 to 5 ft tall without thorns and densely covered with glandular hairs above. Leaves are large, palmately lobed with 3 or 5 triangular divisions that are irregularly toothed. Small clusters of flowers are borne at the branch tips. The 5 petals are rose-purple, obovate, from 0.6 to 1 in. long. The fruit is red, dry and tasteless. Occasional. Rich woodland borders, roadsides. Found in the Blue Ridge in TN, also Hancock and Marion counties, the ne U.S. and se CAN, and south in the mountains to GA. Jun-Jul.

Jack Carman

Jack Carman

Japanese Spiraea   *Spiraea japonica* L.f.*
Shrub to 5 ft tall. The leaves are lance-shaped, sharply toothed, tapered to the tip, from 3 to 6 in. long and 1 to 2 in. wide. The flower clusters, from 2 to 8 in. wide, are terminal, corymb-like, flat-topped or slightly rounded. Numerous flowers about 0.2-in. wide have 5 pink to reddish petals and a finely-hairy hypanthium. Occasional. Moist low areas, stream banks. Found from the Eastern Highland Rim east in TN, also in Davidson and Cheatham counties, and often escaped from cultivation in the e U.S. Jun-Jul. Native of Japan.
Appalachian Spiraea (*Spiraea virginiana* Britton) is similar, but the leaves are oblanceolate, the hypanthium is glaucous and the flowers are white. Infrequent. Damp rocky stream banks. Found in Hamilton, Sequatchie, Van Buren, Cumberland, Morgan, Scott, Roane and Blount counties in TN, and from WV and VA south to NC and GA in the highlands. Jun-Jul.

Note: L.f. denotes author Carl von Linne, the son of Linnaeus.

Genus *Spiraea*
Six species are found in Tennessee. The genus name is from the Greek *speira* (a wreath).

Steeplebush, Hardhack
Spiraea tomentosa L.
Shrub to 4 ft tall with few branches. Leaves, from 1 to 2 in. long, are toothed, lance-shaped, smooth above but the underside prominently veined and densely covered with white or tan hairs. The flowers are borne in a dense, terminal, branched cluster to 6 in. long. The 5 petals are pink, rarely white, about 0.15-in. long. Occasional. Moist low areas, wet meadows, swamps. Found from the Eastern Highland Rim east in TN, also in Rutherford, Stewart and Montgomery counties, and throughout the e U.S. (except deep South) and e CAN. Jun-Aug.

Jack Carman

124

George Hornal

ROSACEAE : ROSE FAMILY

Barren Strawberry   *Waldsteinia fragarioides* (Michaux) Trattinick

Low perennial arising from a woody rhizome. Leaves, on hairy stalks from 1 to 7 in. long, are all basal, compound with 3 leaflets, to 3 in. long, that are rounded at the tip, wedge-shaped at the base, sharply toothed and often shallowly lobed. Small flower clusters are borne on long naked stalks, usually at the same level of the leaves or slightly under. The 5 yellow petals, from 0.2 to 0.4-in. long, are longer than the sepals, and stamens are 50 or more. The fruit is a hairy achene, inedible. Occasional. Rich moist or dry woods. Found from the Eastern Highland Rim east in TN, also in Davidson County, and from ME to western Quebec to MN south to PA and IN, and south in the highlands to AL and GA. Apr-May. The genus name is in honor of Francis Adam, Count of Waldstein-Wartenburg, a German botanist.

Jack Carman

FABACEAE : BEAN FAMILY

Most members of the Bean Family are easily recognized by the pea-like flowers. The large upper petal is called the *standard*, two smaller lateral petals are known as the *wings*, and the lower two petals which are usually fused are called the *keel*. Leaves often have noticeable stipules, and are pinnately (less often palmately) compound with 3 (trifoliate) to numerous leaflets. The fruits are bean-like pods. There are 44 genera and 129 species listed for TN.

Hog Peanut
Amphicarpaea bracteata (L.) Fernald

Twining annual, or short-lived perennial vine to 5 ft long. The leaves are compound with 3 leaflets. Leaflets, from 1 to 3 in. long, are mostly ovate with broadly-rounded bases and straight appressed hairs on both surfaces. The inflorescence is a simple nodding raceme on long stalks from the leaf axils. Flowers pale purple to white, from 0.5 to 0.7-in. wide. Other flowers are found at the base of the stem that often produce fruit below ground. Common. Woods, thickets, roadsides, stream banks. Found throughout TN and most of the e U.S. Aug-Sep.

Jack Carman

Groundnut   ***Apios americana*** Medikus

Twining, herbaceous, perennial vine from 3 to 10 ft long. Leaves are pinnately compound with 5 to 7 leaflets that are ovate to lanceolate, entire, to 2.4 in. long. The sweetly-fragrant, brown-purple flowers to 0.5-in. wide occur in dense racemes that arise from the leaf axils. Common. Moist woods, bottomlands, thickets. Found throughout TN and most of the e U.S. Jul-Aug. The edible and delicious tubers, known as "Turkey Peas," were used as food by Pilgrims during the first bleak winters. The tubers can be used in soups or stews, or fried like potatoes. A favorite Indian food with 3 times the protein of potatoes.

Jack Carman

Genus *Apios*

Two species are found in Tennessee. The genus name is the Greek *apios* (a pear), alluding to the somewhat pear-shaped tuberous enlargements of the rootstock.

Price's Potato Bean

Apios priceana B.L. Robinson

Twining perennial vine to 10 ft (or more) long. The leaves are pinnately compound with 5 to 9 leaflets that are ovate-lanceolate, entire, to 2.5 in. long. Flowers about 1 in. long occur in axillary racemes, and are pinkish-purple to greenish-white. The standard terminates in a spongy projection at the apex. Infrequent. Rocky slopes. In TN, recorded from Montgomery, Williamson, Hickman, Davidson, Grundy and Marion counties. Known only from n AL, TN and KY. Jul-Aug. The species name is in honor of its discoverer, Sarah Frances Price.

Jack Carman

Pyne's Ground Plum
Astragalus bibullatus Barneby & Bridges
Low spreading perennial about 4 to 8 in. tall. The leaves are alternate and pinnately compound, and have about 25 leaflets. Pale purple flowers, from 0.6 to 0.8-in. long, are borne in dense racemes that arise from the leaf axils. The smooth pods have a ridge around the middle, are red above and yellow below, somewhat resemble a plum, and lie on the ground. Rare. Central Basin cedar glade endemic, currently only found in Rutherford County. Apr.

Pyne's Ground Plum is recently described and related to the Prairie Ground Plum (*Astragalus crassicarpus* Nuttall) of the upper midwest, southwest and plains states.

Genus *Astragalus*
Three species are found in Tennessee. The genus name is an ancient Greek name of a leguminous plant.

Canada Milk Vetch
Astragalus canadensis L.
Robust perennial from 2 to 5 ft tall that arises from a rhizome. The leaves are alternate and pinnately compound, and have 15 to 35 oblong to elliptic leaflets from 0.4 to 1.6 in. long that are hairy beneath. The white or yellowish-white flowers, from 0.5 to 0.7-in. long, are borne in dense, long-stalked racemes from 2 to 6 in. long. Pods are numerous, crowded, erect, from 0.4 to 0.6-in. long. Occasional. Open woods, riverbanks, moist soil. It is thinly scattered from the Western Highland Rim east in TN, and found throughout most of the U.S. and s CAN. Jul-Aug.

Jack Carman

Tennessee Milk Vetch
Astragalus tennesseensis A.Gray *ex* Chapman

Perennial from 4 to 20 in. tall. The stems are clustered on a stout taproot and covered with soft spreading hairs. The leaves are alternate and pinnately compound, and have from 23 to 33 narrowly oblong to elliptic leaflets from 0.4 to 0.8-in. long that are smooth above and long-hairy beneath. The yellowish-white flowers, from 0.6 to 0.8-in. long, are borne in dense, long-stalked racemes that arise from the leaf axils. The pods, from 1 to 1.6 in. long, are hairy and yellow, and usually lie on the ground. Infrequent. Cedar glades and calcareous barrens. Found in Robertson, Davidson, Wilson, Williamson, Rutherford, Maury, Marshall and Bedford counties in TN, and from IL to n AL. Apr-May.

Genus *Baptisia*

Five species are found in Tennessee. The genus name is taken from the Greek *baptizein* (to dye). Some *Baptisia* species have been used as an inferior substitute for true indigo dye.

Jack Carman

Jack Carman

White Wild Indigo
Baptisia alba (L.) R. Brown

Mostly smooth, erect perennial from 2 to 5 ft tall with the branches mostly horizontal. The leaves are alternate and trifoliate with oblong-lanceolate or oblanceolate leaflets from 0.8 to 1.6 in. long. The inflorescence is a long raceme that extends above the leaves, and has numerous white flowers from 0.5 to 0.75-in. long. Occasional. Dry sandy woods. Found from the Western Highland Rim west in TN, and from VA to TN south to AL and w FL. May.

Spiked Indigo (*Baptisia albescens* Small) is quite similar, but only grows to 3 ft tall and the branches are mostly ascending. The raceme is shorter, and has fewer but larger flowers. Infrequent. Rich woods. Found from the Cumberland Plateau east in TN (Van Buren, Bledsoe, Cumberland, Fentress, Johnson and Polk counties), and from VA to TN south to FL and AL. May. Often considered not distinct from *Baptisia alba*.

Blue False Indigo, Blue Wild Indigo
Baptisia australis (L.) R. Brown
Smooth erect perennial from 2 to 5 ft tall that is highly branched. The leaves are alternate and trifoliate with obovate or oblanceolate leaflets from 1 to 3 in. long. Stipules, from 0.3 to 0.8-in. long, are usually persistent until flowering. The inflorescence is a long raceme that extends well above the leaves, and has blue-violet flowers from 0.8 to 1 in. long. Infrequent. Moist open woods and barrens. Found in Middle and East TN (Davidson, Rutherford, Maury, Marshall, Coffee, Hamilton, Scott and Hancock counties). U.S. range from s NY to n GA west to NB and TX. May-Jun.

Yellow Wild Indigo (*Baptisia tinctoria* (L.) R. Brown) has numerous small racemes of bright yellow flowers to 0.5-in. wide. Occasional. Dry, open woods and fields. Found from the Eastern Highland Rim east in TN, also in Maury County. A mostly northeastern U.S. species extending south to TN and GA. Apr-Aug.

Jack Carman

Climbing Butterfly Pea   *Centrosema virginianum* (L.) Bentham
Climbing or trailing, downy, perennial vine to 5 ft long. Leaves are compound with 3 leaflets that are entire, oblong to ovate or elliptic, from 1.2 to 2.4 in. long. From 1 to 4 flowers in a short-stalked raceme are borne in the leaf axils. Flowers, from 0.8 to 1.4 in. long, are deep pink to lavender, the center mostly white. The standard is spreading, roundish and much larger than the other petals. Occasional. Dry upland woods and barrens. Found throughout TN (but more prevalent east), and from s NJ to KY and AR south to FL and TX. Jul-Aug. The genus name is from the Greek *centron* (a spur) and *sema* (a standard), alluding to the small median spur at the base of the standard.

Jack Carman

Partridge Pea
Chamaecrista fasciculata (Michx.) Greene
Annual to 3 ft tall with erect or ascending, rarely spreading downy stems. The leaves are pinnately compound with 5 to 18 leaflet pairs. Leaflets to 0.8-in. long are oblong, light sensitive, and fold at night. Short racemes of 1 to 6 flowers arise from the upper leaf axils. The flowers have 10 stamens and 5 petals to 0.8-in. long that are bright yellow and about equal in size. Four petals are red-marked at the base. Common. Open, disturbed habitats. Found throughout TN and most of the e U.S. Jun-Sep. *Cassia fasciculata* Michaux.

Jack Carman

Jack Carman

Genus *Chamaecrista*
Two species are found in Tennessee.

Wild Sensitive Plant
Chamaecrista nictitans (L.) Moench
Erect annual from 4 to 20 in. tall. Leaves are pinnately compound with 7 to 20 leaflet pairs. The leaflets are oblong, both light and touch sensitive, from 0.25 to 0.6-in. long. Flowers are yellow with 5 stamens and are usually solitary (or 2 to 3 together) on short stalks from the upper leaf axils. The petals are unequal, one about 0.3-in. long and nearly (or fully) twice as long as the other 4. Common. Dry upland woods and disturbed sites. Found throughout TN and most of the e U.S. Jul-Sep. *Cassia nictitans* L.

Butterfly Pea   ***Clitoria mariana*** L.
Twining smooth perennial to 40 in. long. Leaves are compound with 3 leaflets that are entire, ovate to oblong-lanceolate, to 2.4 in. long. Flowers, from 1.6 to 2.4 in. long, are light blue to pink-lavender (dark purple in the center) and are borne in the leaf axils, either singly or in a small cluster of 2 or 3 flowers. The standard is obovate, much larger than the other petals and slightly rolled rather than spreading. Common. Dry upland woods and barrens. Found throughout TN and most of the e U.S. Jun-Aug.

Jack Carman

Crown Vetch   *Coronilla varia* L.*
Loosely-ascending, vine-like perennial from 12 to 40 in. tall. The leaves are alternate and pinnately compound, and have 11 to 25 oblong to obovate leaflets from 0.4 to 0.8-in. long. The inflorescence consists of long-stalked umbels that arise singly from numerous leaf axils, and have 10 to 20 pink, rose or purplish flowers from 0.4 to 0.6-in. long. Occasional. Roadsides, waste places. Recorded from the Western Highland Rim east in TN, and found throughout most of the e U.S. May-Sep. Introduced from Europe and planted as a ground cover for erosion control. The genus name is a diminutive of *corona* (a crown), alluding to the shape of the inflorescence.

Genus *Crotolaria*
Three species are found in Tennessee. The genus name is from the Greek *crotalon* (a rattle).

Jack Carman

Weedy Rattlebox
Crotalaria sagittalis L.
Erect annual from 4 to 16 in. tall with a spreading-hairy stem that may be branched above. Leaves are simple, alternate, downy, sessile, lanceolate to linear, from 1 to 3 in. long. The inflorescence is a few-flowered raceme of pale yellow flowers from 0.25 to 0.5-in. tall. Seeds are loose and rattle in the inflated black pod. Occasional. Dry open woods, waste areas. Found throughout TN and most of the e U.S. Jun-Sep.

Coastal Plain Rattlebox (*Crotalaria purshii* DC.) is similar, but the upper leaf surface is smooth. Rare. Sandy clearings. Recorded only from Blount County in TN, but more common along the Gulf Coast and eastern seaboard from se VA south. May-Jul.

Showy Rattlebox (*Crotalaria spectabilis* Roth*) is a **poisonous** annual to 4 ft tall with a long showy raceme of deep yellow flowers to 1 in. tall. Infrequent. Fields, roadsides. Found in Shelby, Madison, Henry, Knox, Jefferson and Grainger counties in TN, and the s U.S. Jul-Sep.

Jack Carman

Genus *Dalea*
Five species are found in TN. The genus name is in honor of Samuel Dale, an 18th century English botanist.

White Prairie Clover
Dalea candida Michaux *ex* Willdenow
Erect smooth perennial to 40 in. tall with pinnately compound leaves having 5 to 9 leaflets. Leaflets from 0.4 to 1.4 in. long may be narrow to fairly broad, flat or folded. Inflorescences from 1 to few with white flowers borne in a cylindric head from 0.6 to 2.4 in. long. Rare. Dry barrens and margins of upland woods. In TN, found in Davidson, Wilson, Rutherford, Overton and Meigs counties. A mostly western species extending east into TN and AL. Jun-Jul. *Petalostemum candidum* (Willdenow) Michaux.

Jack Carman

Leafy Prairie Clover
Dalea foliosa (A. Gray) Barneby
Smooth perennial from 1 to 2.5 ft tall that has pinnately compound leaves with 19 to 31 leaflets. The leaflets are oblong to elliptic, mostly flat, from 0.2 to 0.4-in. long. Flowers are roseate, fading to white, borne in a dense cylindrical head from 0.8 to 2 in. long. Infrequent. Cedar glades and calcareous barrens. Found in the TN Central Basin (Sumner, Davidson, Wilson, Williamson, Rutherford, Maury and Marshall counties), and from northeast IL to north AL. Jul-Sep. *Petalostemum foliosum* A. Gray.

Hare's-Foot Prairie Clover (*Dalea leporina* (Aiton) Bullock) is an erect leafy annual from 1 to 5 ft tall that may be unbranched to much branched above. The leaves are pinnately compound with 15 to 35 oblong to obovate leaflets to 0.5-in. long. Erect dense spikes from 0.6 to 3.2 in. long have white or cream flowers about 0.25-in. long. Rare. Barrens, open woods, disturbed areas. Found in Davidson and Humphreys counties in TN, and from Latin America north to ND, MN and IN. Jun-Aug.

George Hornal

Gattinger's Prairie Clover   ***Dalea gattingeri*** (A.Heller) Barneby
Sprawling perennial with many branches to 20 in. long. Leaves pinnately compound with 5 to 7 narrow leaflets. Flowers rose-purple in a long cylindric head on a wiry reddish stem. Occasional. Dry calcareous, rocky glades. In TN, found in the Central Basin and surrounding counties, also Hamilton and Meigs counties. A southeast U.S. endemic also found in n AL and nw GA. Jul-Sep. *Petalostemum gattingeri* (A.Heller) A.Heller.

Purple Prairie Clover (*Dalea purpurea* Ventenat) is upright, from 8 to 40 in. tall. Leaves have 3 to 7 (usually 5) leaflets. Flowers rose-purple in a dense cone-like head that becomes cylindric with age. Rare. Dry barrens, open glades. A more northern and western species extending south and east to TN in Davidson, Wilson and Rutherford counties. Jun-Jul.

Prairie Mimosa   ***Desmanthus illinoensis*** (Michx.) MacMillan *ex* Robinson & Fernald
Erect perennial with clustered stems from 1 to 4 ft (or more) tall that arise from a taproot. Leaves are alternate and bipinnately compound, and have numerous oblong leaflets from 0.06 to 0.2-in. long. Small white flowers are borne in 0.5-in. rounded heads that are terminal on long stalks from the leaf axils. Dark thin pods to 1 in. long are strongly curved and somewhat twisted together into a distinctive rounded cluster. Occasional. Dry soil, fields, barrens, cedar glades. Scattered throughout TN. U.S. range from OH to ND south to FL and NM. Jun-Jul. The genus name is from the Greek *desme* (a bundle) and *anthos* (flower).

George Hornal

Genus *Desmodium*
Seventeen species are found in Tennessee.

Small-Leaf Tick Trefoil
Desmodium ciliare (Muhl. *ex* Willd.) DC.
Erect perennial from 1 to 3 ft tall with slender stem(s) having few to many long spreading hairs. Leaves are compound with 3 leaflets to 1 in. long that are mostly ovate-oblong, very blunt, and sparsely hairy. Inflorescence a large terminal panicle with pinkish flowers to 0.2-in. long on stalks to 0.4-in. long. Occasional. Dry, sandy soil, found in the eastern 2/3 of TN. Jul-Aug.

Naked-Flowered Tick Trefoil (*D. nudiflorum* (L.) DC.) is perennial, the stem forked at the base. One branch is sterile, to 12 in. tall with leaves crowded at the top that have ovate to obovate leaflets to 4 in. long. The other branch is a leafless scape to 40 in. tall that extends well above the leaves and has pink to purple flowers about 0.3-in. long. Common. Rich woods. Statewide. Jul-Aug.

Panicled Tick Trefoil (*D. paniculatum* (L.) DC.) is branched above, 2 to 4 ft tall with many purplish flowers in large panicles. Common. Dry woods. Statewide. Jul-Aug.

Jack Carman

Prostrate Tick Trefoil (*D. rotundifolium* DC.) is prostrate with stems to 5 ft long. Leaves are round, petals purple. Common. Dry woods. Found throughout TN and the e U.S. Jul-Sep. Genus name from the Greek *desmos* (a bond or chain), from the constricted seedpods.

Hairy Milk Pea   ***Galactia volubilis*** (L.) Britton
Perennial with climbing and twining, hairy stems to 5 ft long. Leaves are compound, often 2 to 3 at a node, each with 3 ovate to oblong or elliptic leaflets to 2 in. long. The flowers are borne in loose racemes to 4 in. long with 1 to 3 flowers at each node, and are 0.3 to 0.4-in. wide, pink-purple, on stalks about 0.15-in. long. Common. Dry upland woods and barrens. Found throughout TN and most of the e U.S. Jul-Aug. The genus name is adapted from *gala* (milk) since it was originally believed that the branches had a milky sap.

Jack Carman

Jack Carman

Everlasting Pea   *Lathyrus latifolius* L.*
Trailing or climbing perennial with broadly-winged stems to 7 ft long. Leaves have 2 elliptic to lanceolate leaflets to 3 in. long. Flowers, to 1.2 in. long, are reddish-purple to pink or white and occur in a raceme of 4 to 10 flowers each. Fruit smooth. Occasional. A native of southern Europe, escaped and well established in waste places. It is scattered throughout TN (more prevalent central and east), and the se U.S. Jun-Aug. The genus name is reputed to be from *la* (very) and *thuros* (passionate), the original plant supposedly an aphrodisiac.

Hairy Pea (*Lathyrus hirsutus* L.*) is similar, but an annual with smaller flowers (to 0.6-in. long) and hairy fruit. Occasional. A native of Europe, introduced and escaped to roadsides and waste places. Widely scattered in TN, more prevalent west. Apr-Jul.

Marsh Pea, Vetchling   *Lathyrus palustris* L.
Slender climbing perennial to 4 ft long from a rhizome, the stem often winged. Leaves are compound with 2 to 4 pairs of elliptic to linear leaflets from 1 to 3 in. long. Flowers, from 0.6 to 0.8-in. long, are red-purple to whitish and borne in small racemes of 2 to 6. Rare. Meadows, wet thickets, bottomland woods. A mostly northern species extending south to TN, and found in Coffee, Warren, Knox and Anderson counties. Jul-Sep.

Forest Pea (*Lathyrus venosus* Muhl. *ex* Willd.) has 4 to 6 leaflet pairs. Flowers are purplish, 0.5 to 0.8-in. long, occurring in dense racemes of 10 to 20 flowers. Infrequent. Woods and thickets. In TN, found in Chester, Cheatham, Hamilton, Rhea, Blount, Cocke and Sullivan counties. A mostly northeastern species extending south to TN and GA. Jun-Jul.

Jack Carman

Jack Carman

Narrow-Leaf Lespedeza
Lespedeza angustifolia (Pursh) Elliott
Erect perennial from 20 to 40 in. tall that is sometimes branched above. Leaves are compound and nearly sessile with 3 linear leaflets from 0.8 to 2.5 in. long. The inflorescence is a dense spike to 1.2 in. long on an ascending stalk from 0.4 to 2 in. long. Flowers about 0.3-in. wide are white with a purple spot. Rare. Barrens and open areas. Found mostly in the Coastal Plain from MA to FL to LA with disjunct populations in Lincoln, Coffee and Warren counties in TN. Aug-Sep.

Bicolor Lespedeza (*Lespedeza bicolor* Turczaninow*) is shrub-like with many spreading to ascending branches to 10 ft long. Many rose-purple flowers are borne in a leafy inflorescence at the top of the branches. Occasional. A Japanese native that has been planted or escaped. It is scattered throughout TN and the se U.S. Jul-Oct.

Lespedezas are useful for improving soil fertility, and seeds are an important food source for bobwhite quail. Eleven species are found in Tennessee.

Jack Carman

Dusty Bush Clover
Lespedeza capitata Michaux
Erect perennial to 5 ft tall that is densely covered with long soft hairs which give the plant its "dusty" appearance. Leaves compound with 3 leaflets to 2 in. long that are oblong to elliptic. Numerous dense racemes are borne in the upper leaf axils. Flowers to 0.5-in. wide are pale yellow with a purple spot. Occasional. Dry woods, barrens, and fields. Found in Middle and East TN, and in most of the e U.S. Aug-Sep.

Three other Lespedezas are frequent in TN. Sericea Lespedeza (*Lespedeza cuneata* (Dum.Cours.) G.Don*), to 4 ft tall, has white flowers marked with purple borne in the leaf axils. An Asian native planted on roadsides and escaped to waste places. Aug-Sep.

Wand-Like Bush Clover (*Lespedeza intermedia* (S.Watson) Britton), less than 3 ft tall, has purple flowers in the upper leaf axils. Dry upland woods. Aug-Sep.

Slender Bush Clover (*Lespedeza virginica* (L.) Britton), to 3.5 ft tall, has purple flowers in a crowded leafy inflorescence along the stem. Dry upland woods. Aug-Sep.

Jack Carman

Smooth Creeping Bush Clover   *Lespedeza repens* (L.) Barton
Perennial with many trailing, nearly smooth stems to 40 in. long. Leaves are compound with 3 elliptic, ovate or oblong leaflets from 0.4 to 1 in. long and half as wide. Loose racemes of 3 to 12 pink-purple flowers to 0.3-in. wide occur at the end of long stalks. Frequent. Dry woods and thickets. Found throughout TN and most of the e U.S. Aug-Sep. Andre Michaux named the genus in honor of Vincente Manuel de Cespedes, Spanish Governor of East Florida in the 18th century. The name was later misspelled as de Lespedez.

Downy Creeping Bush Clover (*Lespedeza procumbens* Michaux) is similar, but is sparsely to densely covered with spreading hairs. Frequent. It is widely scattered in TN, but is less prevalent in West TN. Found throughout most of the e U.S. Aug-Sep.

Jack Carman

Birdsfoot Trefoil
Lotus corniculatus L.*
Taprooted, more or less smooth perennial with reclining or ascending stems to 2 ft tall. The leaves are pinnately compound with 5 leaflets, the lower pair evidently displaced from the 3 terminal ones and resembling stipules. The leaflets, from 2 to 6 in. long, are elliptic to oblanceolate, 1.5 to 2.5 times as long as wide. Terminal, umbel-like heads of 4 to 8 flowers are borne on long stalks from the upper leaf axils. The corolla, from 0.4 to 0.6-in. long, is bright yellow and the standard is marked with faint red lines. Infrequent. Meadows, roadsides, disturbed areas. Found in Montgomery, Rutherford, Putnam, Cumberland, Scott, Loudon, Knox and Washington counties in TN. A native of Europe that is widely established in the U.S. Jun-Aug.

The large colony found in the I-24 median about 5 miles east of Murfreesboro is quite showy in June. *Lotus* was an ancient Greek plant name used in many senses. However, its use was restricted by Linnaeus to this clover-like genus.

Jack Carman

White Sweet Clover *Melilotus alba* Medikus*

Erect, highly-branched biennial from 3 to 6 ft (or more) tall that arises from a taproot. The leaves are alternate, stalked and trifoliate with lance-shaped leaflets from 0.4 to 1 in. long. The narrow, long, loose racemes of 0.25-in. white flowers are terminal on long stalks from the leaf axils. Frequent. Fields, waste places, roadsides. Found throughout TN, the U.S. and CAN. Apr-Oct. Introduced from Europe. The genus name is from the Greek *meli* (honey) and *lotos*, which was an ancient Greek plant name used in many senses.

Yellow Sweet Clover (*Melilotus officinalis* (L.) Pallas*) (also shown above) is quite similar, except the flowers are yellow. Frequent. Fields, roadsides, waste places. Found throughout TN and the e U.S., though less prevalent south. Apr-Oct. Introduced from Europe.

Jack Carman

Genus *Orbexilum*
Two species are found in Tennessee.

Sampson's Snakeroot
Orbexilum pedunculatum (Miller) Rydberg
Erect branched perennial from 12 to 32 in. tall. Leaves are compound with 3 lance-linear to narrowly oblong leaflets that are 1.25 to 2.75 in. long, less than 0.8-in. wide, and gradually narrowed to a blunt tip. Spike-like racemes to 2.5 in. long extend well above the leaves, and consist of pale-purple flowers about 0.25-in. wide. Frequent. Dry open woods, barrens, and fields. Found throughout most of TN and from OH to KS south. May-Jun. *Psoralea psoralioides* (Walter) Cory.

Sainfoin (*Orbexilum onobrychis* (Nuttall) Rydberg) is similar, but leaflets are 2 to 4 in. long and 1 in. or more wide. Infrequent. Open woods and moist barrens. Found from the Ridge and Valley east in TN, also in Montgomery County. U.S. range from OH to IA south to MO and SC. Jun-Jul. *Psoralea onobrychis* Nuttall.

Nashville Breadroot
Pediomelum subacaule (T. & G.) Rydberg
Spreading perennial, usually about 6 in. tall with many hairy branches arising from the base that have a single terminal leaf or a dense (to loose) raceme of flowers. The dark green to blue-green leaves are palmately compound. The flowers are purple-blue (rarely white). Infrequent. Limestone cedar glades and barrens. Found in the TN Central Basin in Davidson, Wilson, Williamson, Rutherford, Maury, Marshall, and Bedford counties, also in Meigs County in East TN, and in KY and AL. Apr-May. *Psoralea subacaulis* T. & G.

Jack Carman

George Hornal

Kudzu
Pueraria lobata (Willdenow) Ohwi*
Trailing or climbing, semi-woody, perennial vine to 100 ft long, the younger parts hairy. Leaves are compound, usually with 3 leaflets from 4 to 6 in. long that are broadly ovate to almost round, hairy beneath and often lobed. Flowers are reddish-purple, about 1 in. wide, and occur in clusters from 4 to 8 in. long. Occasional. Roadsides, woods and fields. Widespread in TN and the se U.S. Jul-Oct. This fast-growing Japanese native has been used for erosion control, but it is aggressive and invasive. In China, a root tea is used for headaches and various stomach disorders. Experimentally, it lowers blood sugar and blood pressure. The genus name is in honor of M. W. Puerari, a 19th century Swiss botanist.

George Hornal

Sensitive Brier   ***Schrankia microphylla*** (Dryander) J.F. Macbride
Perennial with prostrate to weakly arching stems from 3 to 7 ft long that are strongly ribbed
and covered with small hooked prickles. The leaves are alternate, prickly and bipinnately
compound, and have numerous oblong or elliptic leaflets to 0.3-in. long. Small pink to purple
flowers are borne in rounded heads, from 0.6 to 0.8-in. wide, that are terminal on long stalks
from the leaf axils. Occasional. Dry, open areas. Scattered in TN, but generally absent in
the far western counties, the Central Basin and the northeastern counties. A more southern
species extending north to TN, KY, WV and IA. Jun-Sep. Leaves are quite sensitive and
fold up when touched. The genus name is in honor of Franz von Paula von Schrank, a 19th
century German botanist.

Jack Carman

Genus *Senna*
Four species are found in Tennessee.

Southern Wild Senna
Senna marilandica (L.) Link
Erect perennial from 3 to 7 ft tall. Leaves are
alternate and pinnately compound, and have
8 to 16 oblong leaflets from 0.8 to 2 in. long.
Flower clusters are terminal and long-stalked
from the upper leaf axils. The flowers have 5
unequal yellow petals from 0.4 to 0.6-in. long
that are open and expose the stamens.
Frequent. Open woods, fields, roadsides,
barrens. Found throughout TN and most of
the e U.S. Jul-Aug. *Cassia marilandica* L.

Sicklepod (*Senna obtusifolia* (L.) H.S.Irwin &
Barneby*) is somewhat similar, but an ill-
scented annual to 3 ft tall that has 4 to 6
obovate leaflets from 1 to 3 in. long. The
flowers are solitary or paired in the upper
leaf axils. Occasional. Moist open woods,
roadsides, waste places. Widespread in TN
and generally southern in distribution, but
extending north to VA, KY and MO. Jul-Sep.
Cassia obtusifolia L. Another common name
is Coffee Weed.

Pink Wild Bean
Strophostyles umbellata (Muhlenberg *ex* Willdenow) Britton

Trailing to twining perennial vine to 7 ft long. Leaves compound with 3 leaflets that are ovate to oblong, to 2 in. long, never lobed. Pink flowers about 0.5-in. wide occur in racemes of few to several flowers on naked stalks from 2 to 12 in. long. Frequent. Dry upland woods, open fields. Found throughout TN. A chiefly Coastal Plain species found from NY to FL and TX, but north in the interior to s IN. Jun-Sep.

Wild Bean (*Strophostyles helvola* (L.) Elliott) is similar, but annual. The leaflets usually have one or two lateral lobes. Rose to purple flowers often turn green with age. Occasional. Dry soil. Found throughout TN and the e U.S. Jun-Sep.

Small-Flowered Wild Bean (*Strophostyles leiosperma* (T. & G.) Piper) is an annual. Unlobed leaflets are densely covered with stiff hairs, and the pink flowers are about 0.33-in. wide. Infrequent. Dry or moist soil. Found in West TN, also Montgomery and Stewart counties. Jun-Sep.

Jack Carman

Three *Strophostyles* species are found in Tennessee. The genus name is from the Greek *strophe* (a turning) and *stylos* (a style).

Pencil Flower   *Stylosanthes biflora* (L.) BSP.

Prostrate, ascending, or erect perennial with few to many wiry stems, from 4 to 20 in. long, that are sometimes branched above. Leaves are alternate and trifoliate, and have narrow lance-shaped leaflets from 0.4 to 1.6 in. long. Short leafy spikes of 2 to 6 orange-yellow (sometimes white) flowers are borne at the summit of the stem and branches. The standard is from 0.25 to 0.4-in. long. Common. Dry rocky woods, barrens, roadsides, waste areas. Found throughout TN and most of the e U.S. Jun-Aug. The genus name is from the Greek *stylos* (a column) and *anthos* (a flower), alluding to the stalk-like calyx tube.

Jack Carman

Goat's Rue
Tephrosia virginiana (L.) Persoon
Erect perennial with one to several stems from 8 to 28 in. tall. The leaves are alternate and pinnately compound, and have 15 to 25 linear-oblong to elliptic leaflets from 0.4 to 1.2 in. long. A compact raceme of bi-colored flowers from 0.6 to 0.8-in. wide terminates the stem. Standards are pale yellow to cream, wings and keel are pink to pale purple. Common. Open woods, fields. Found throughout TN and most of the e U.S. Jun-Jul. Two *Tephrosia* species are found in TN. The genus name is from the Greek *tephros* (ash-colored or hoary).

Rusty Tephrosia (*Tephrosia spicata* (Walter) Torrey & Gray) is similar, but racemes are also opposite the leaves and flowers are reddish-purple. Occasional. Open fields and barrens. Found in Middle and East TN, and from s DE to FL west to s TN and LA. Jun-Jul.

Genus *Thermopsis*
Two species are found in Tennessee. The genus name is from the Greek *thermos* (the lupine) and *opsis* (appearance).

Jack Carman

Thermopsis ***Thermopsis mollis*** (Michaux) M.A. Curtis *ex* A. Gray
Erect perennial from 16 to 40 in. tall with appressed-hairy stems. The leaves are alternate, stalked and trifoliate with rhombic leaflets from 1.6 to 3.2 in. long that are hairy beneath. Lanceolate stipules are prominent, from 0.4 to 0.8-in. long. Loose racemes of 0.6-in. yellow flowers terminate the stem and branches. Infrequent. Open woods. Thinly scattered from the Cumberland Plateau east in TN (Franklin, Marion, Hamilton, Polk, Monroe, Blount, Sevier, Greene and Grainger counties). U.S. range from s VA to GA in the uplands. May.

Aaron's Rod (*Thermopsis villosa* (Walter) Fernald & Schubert) is similar, but has broad clasping stipules from 1.4 to 2.6 in. long. Infrequent. Open woods and clearings. Thinly scattered in Middle and East TN, occurring mainly in NC, TN and n GA. May-Jun.

George Hornal

Low Hop Trefoil
Trifolium campestre Schreber*

Widely-branched annual from 4 to 12 in. tall with a hairy stem and branches. The leaves are alternate, stalked and trifoliate with oblong-ovate leaflets from 0.3 to 0.6-in. long. The terminal leaflet is on a short stalk. Compact roundish heads, from 0.3 to 0.6-in. wide, have 20 to 30 yellow flowers, and are borne on long stalks from the leaf axils. Common. Lawns, fields, roadsides, waste places. Found throughout TN and much of North America. Apr-Oct. Introduced from Europe. *Trifolium procumbens* L.*

Least Hop Trefoil (*Trifolium dubium* Sibthorp*) is similar, but the heads are smaller and have only 5 to 15 flowers. Occasional. Found throughout TN and much of North America. Apr-Oct. Introduced from Europe.

Jack Carman

George Hornal

Genus *Trifolium*
Fourteen species are found in Tennessee but only 2 are native. Leaves are mostly palmately trifoliate and flowers are borne in heads or head-like racemes. The genus name is from *tres* (three) and *folium* (a leaf).

Crimson Clover
Trifolium incarnatum L.*

Annual from 8 to 16 in. (or more) tall with an appressed-hairy stem. The leaves are alternate and trifoliate, and have downy, broadly obovate leaflets from 0.4 to 1.6 in. long and nearly as wide. The somewhat egg-shaped flower heads, from 1 to 2 in. long, are borne on long stalks and have many crimson flowers from 0.4 to 0.6-in. long. Occasional. Roadsides, waste places, old fields. Found throughout TN and most of the e U.S. May-Aug. Introduced from Europe, and often planted as a cover crop or for hay.

George Hornal

Red Clover   *Trifolium pratense* L.*

Short-lived perennial from 8 to 20 in. (or more) tall with numerous appressed-hairy stems. Leaves are alternate and trifoliate, the lower long-stalked and the upper sessile or short-stalked. Elliptic to obovate leaflets are 0.4 to 2 in. long. The roundish flower heads, from 0.4 to 1.2 in. long, are sessile or short-stalked, and have many sessile, magenta to white flowers from 0.5 to 0.8-in. long. Frequent. Roadsides, fields, lawns, waste places. Found throughout TN and most of temperate North America. May-Aug. Introduced from Europe, likely as a hay and pasture crop. The flowers, leaves and young stems are edible. The flowers have been used in folk remedies for cancer, and the dried leaves have been used for tea.

Buffalo Clover (*Trifolium reflexum* L.) is similar, but the flowers in the head are stalked. The standard is brighter red, and the remaining flower parts are whitish pink. Rare. Upland woods, barrens. A native species that is found in Madison, Lewis, Montgomery and Davidson counties in TN, and in most of the e U.S. May-Jun.

Jack Carman

White Clover   *Trifolium repens* L.*

Perennial with creeping stems to 16 in. long, often rooting at the nodes, and bearing erect stalks with a single leaf or lone flower head at the summit. The leaves are alternate and trifoliate with elliptic to obovate leaflets from 0.4 to 0.8-in. long. The roundish heads, from 0.4 to 1.2 in. wide, have stalked, white (rarely pink-tinged) flowers less than 0.5-in. long. Occasional. Fields, roadsides, lawns, waste places. Found throughout TN and most of temperate North America. Apr-Sep. Introduced from Europe.

Alsike Clover (*Trifolium hybridum* L.*) flowers are similar, but stems are ascending and bear both flowers and leaves. Occasional. Found throughout TN and most of temperate North America. Apr-Sep.

Rabbit's-Foot Clover (*Trifolium arvense* L.*) is a freely-branched annual with long, fuzzy, grayish flower heads. Infrequent. Scattered throughout TN (Shelby, Fayette, Hardeman, Bedford, Montgomery, White, Grainger, Knox and Carter counties), and found in much of the U.S. and s CAN. May-Sep. Introduced from Eurasia.

Jack Carman

Wood Vetch   *Vicia caroliniana* Walter
Trailing or climbing perennial to 40 in. long. Pinnately compound leaves have 5 to 10 leaflet
pairs and a terminal tendril. The leaflets are elliptic to oblong-lanceolate, to 0.8-in. long.
Flowers, to 0.5-in. long, occur in loose racemes to 4 in. long and are white, the keel tipped
with blue. Frequent. Moist woods, woods borders, thickets. Found in Middle and East TN,
and in most of the e U.S. Apr-May.

Narrow-Leaf Vetch (*Vicia sativa* L. ssp. *nigra* (L.) Ehrend.*) is a slender, erect to climbing
annual to 3 ft tall. Leaves with 3 to 5 mostly linear, leaflet pairs. Flowers from 0.5 to 0.75-in.
wide are rose-purple and the fruit is black. Frequent. Roadsides, fields. Found throughout
TN and the e U.S. Mar-Jun. *Vicia angustifolia* L.*

Jack Carman

Genus *Vicia*
Six species and one additional subspecies
are found in Tennessee. The genus name is
the classical Latin name for vetch.

Smooth Vetch
Vicia villosa* Roth ssp. *varia* (Host) Corb.
Annual or biennial, the stems mostly smooth
to appressed hairy, to 3 ft long. Leaves are
pinnately compound with 5 to 10 leaflet
pairs, the leaflets narrowly oblong to lance-
linear, from 0.5 to 1 in. long. Racemes are
long-stalked, dense, one-sided, mostly with 5
to 15 blue flowers to 0.8-in. long. Frequent.
Native of Europe escaped to roadsides,
fields, waste places. Found throughout TN
and most of the U.S. May-Aug. *Vicia
dasycarpa* Tenore*.

Hairy Vetch (*Vicia villosa* Roth ssp. *villosa**)
is similar, but has hairy stems with flowers in
racemes of 10 to 40. Infrequent. Roadsides
and fields. Found scattered throughout TN,
and most of the U.S. and s CAN. Jun-Aug.

FABACEAE : BEAN FAMILY

Japanese Wisteria
Wisteria floribunda (Willd.) DC.*
High-climbing, twining, woody perennial vine. Leaves are alternate, pinnately compound with 13 to 19 lance-shaped leaflets to 3.2 in. long. Inflorescence a loose hanging raceme to 20 in. long. The 0.6 to 0.8-in. wide blue to lavender flowers open sequentially from the base of the raceme. The pods are velvety. Infrequent. An escape thinly scattered in TN and found in most of the se U.S. Apr-May.

American Wisteria (*Wisteria frutescens* (L.) Poiret) is quite similar, except racemes are compact (to 6 in. long) and pods are smooth. Frequent. Moist or wet woods, riverbanks. Found throughout TN, but more prevalent in West TN. U.S. range from VA to FL, west to AR and TX. Apr-May.

Chinese Wisteria (*Wisteria sinensis* (Sims) Sweet*) occasionally escapes from cultivation, and has 7 to 13 leaflets, racemes to 8 in. long, and flowers about 1 in. long that open simultaneously. Pods are velvety. Infrequent. An escape thinly scattered in TN and found in most of the se U.S. Apr-May.

Jack Carman

Jack Carman

LYTHRACEAE : LOOSESTRIFE FAMILY

Toothcup
Ammannia coccinea Rottboell
Smooth annual from 4 to 40 in. tall, the stems often freely branched. The leaves, to 6 in. long and 0.5-in. wide, are opposite, usually thick and fleshy, linear to narrowly oblong, often dilated at the base and somewhat clasping. The flowers are borne in the leaf axils on short stout stalks to 0.2-in. long. The calyx is from 0.12 to 0.16-in. long and the 4 petals are rose-purple, from 0.07 to 0.12-in. long. Occasional. Margins of ponds or other wet areas. Widely scattered in TN, but more prevalent west. The extended range is from NJ to ND south to tropical America. Jul-Sep. The genus name is in honor of Paul Ammann, a 17th century German botanist.

Sessile Toothcup (*Ammannia robusta* Heer & Regel) is similar, but the flowers are sessile and the petals are pale lavender. Rare. Margins of ponds or other wet areas. Found in Shelby, Tipton, Lauderdale and Lake counties in TN, and from NJ to WA south to Central America. Jul-Sep.

Jack Carman

Clammy Cuphea, Blue Waxweed   *Cuphea viscosissima* Jacquin
Sparingly-branched, upright, weedy annual or short-lived perennial to 2 ft tall that is sticky-hairy throughout. Leaves are long-stalked, opposite, lanceolate to ovate, from 0.8 to 2 in. long. Flowers are purple, solitary or paired in the upper leaf axils. Petals are clawed, the upper two the largest and about 0.3-in. long. Occasional. Woodlands, roadsides, barrens. Found in Middle and East TN, and in most of the e U.S., more prevalent south. Jul-Oct. *Cuphea petiolata* (L.) Koehne. The genus name is from the Greek *cyphos* (gibbous), alluding to the shape of the calyx.

Jack Carman

The Loosestrife Family members are herbs or shrubs usually with opposite entire leaves. Seven genera and 10 species are found in Tennessee.

Swamp Loosestrife
Decodon verticillatus (L.) Elliott
Perennial shrub that is woody below and has numerous slender and arching stems to 9 ft long that root at the tips. The leaves are opposite or more often in whorls of 3 or 4, lanceolate, from 4 to 6 in. long. Flowers, from 0.4 to 0.6-in. long, are pink-purple and occur in dense cymes in the upper leaf axils. Infrequent. Sloughs, pools, swamps, marshes. In TN, found in Lake, Obion, Rutherford, Coffee, Warren, White, Blount and Jefferson counties. A mostly Coastal Plain species found from ME to FL and LA, and inland in the Mississippi River valley to IN and MO. Jul-Aug. The genus name is from the Greek *deca* (ten) and *odous* (tooth), alluding to the summit of the calyx.

Jack Carman

Winged Loosestrife
Lythrum alatum Pursh
Erect smooth perennial from 16 to 32 in. tall with a 4-angled stem. Leaves are thick and firm, sessile, linear-oblong to lance-ovate, to 1.6 in. long but reduced in size upward. The flowers are lavender, from 0.2 to 0.5-in. wide, and are solitary in the upper leaf axils. Occasional. Moist or wet soil of open fields or barrens. Found throughout most of the eastern U.S., and in TN from the Eastern Highland Rim west, also in Hamilton and Bradley counties. Jul-Sep.

Jack Carman

Genus *Lythrum*
Two species are found in Tennessee. The genus name is derived from *lytron* and was early applied to Purple Loosestrife.

Purple Loosestrife
Lythrum salicaria L.*
Stout erect perennial to 5 ft tall. Leaves are opposite or in whorls of 3, sessile, lanceolate to linear, from 1 to 4 in. long. The inflorescence is a terminal cluster from 4 to 16 in. long. The flowers are red-purple, from 0.5 to 1 in. wide. Infrequent. Marshes, ditches, wet areas. Thinly scattered in TN (Decatur, Sumner, Clay, Warren, Marion, Scott and Unicoi counties). Extended range from Newfoundland to ND south to VA and KS. Jun-Sep. Native of Eurasia that is very invasive, particularly in northern wetlands. It will crowd out native aquatics that are valuable to waterfowl and other wildlife.

Jack Carman

Enchanter's Nightshade
Circaea lutetiana (L.) Asch. & Magnus
Perennial from 1 to 3 ft tall with opposite, long-stalked, oval leaves that are shallowly and irregularly toothed, from 2 to 4 in. long and half as wide. Many small white (pinkish) flowers less than 0.16-in. long are more or less well-spaced in terminal racemes to 8 in. long. Both petals of the tiny flowers are bi-lobed. One of few plants with 2-petaled flowers. The fruit is nutlike and does not split open at maturity. Frequent. Rich moist woods. Scattered throughout TN. Extended range from Nova Scotia to s Manitoba south to GA, LA and OK. Jun-Aug.

Small Enchanter's Nightshade (*Circaea alpina* L.) is similar, but only grows to 1 ft tall. The leaves are from 1 to 2.5 in. long and coarsely toothed. The open flowers are clustered at the top of the raceme. Infrequent. Moist rich woods. Found from the Cumberland Plateau east in TN. A northern species extending south in the uplands to NC and TN. Jun-Sep.

The names are from Circe, the mythological enchantress who supposedly used a poisonous genus member in her sorcery.

The Evening Primrose Family has 5 genera and 32 species that are found in Tennessee.

Genus *Epilobium*
Four species are found in Tennessee. The genus name is from the Greek *epi* (upon) and *lobon* (a capsule), alluding to the perianth surmounting the fruit.

Fireweed   ***Epilobium angustifolium*** L.
Usually single-stemmed perennial from 3 to 10 ft tall with numerous, crowded, alternate, lance-shaped, entire, sessile leaves to 6 in. long and 1.2 in. wide. Many magenta (to white) tubular flowers, from 0.75 to 1.6 in. wide, occur in a long raceme that is terminal or from the leaf axils. The four petals are obovate and short-clawed, and the stigma is shaped like a cross. Flower buds usually droop, but the reddish seedpods are ascending. Seed hairs are tawny. Rare. High elevation burned areas. Found in Carter and Unicoi counties in TN but widespread in North America. Jul-Sep.

Bob Hale

Purple-Leaf Willow Herb
Epilobium coloratum Biehler
Freely-branched perennial to 3 ft tall. Stem
and branches are often red-purple with hairs
occurring in lines. The leaves are usually
opposite, sharply toothed and narrowly
lance-shaped, from 1 to 5 in. long.
Numerous flowers are tubular, white or pink,
about 0.3-in. wide. Seeds are beakless with
brown hairs. Occasional. Marshes and wet
areas from the Western Highland Rim east in
TN. U.S. range from ME to MN south to NC,
AL and TX. Jul-Oct.

American Willow Herb (*Epilobium ciliatum*
Rafinesque) is quite similar, but the seeds
are broadly short-beaked with white hairs.
Rare. Wet areas, often in unstable habitats.
Found in Carter and Johnson counties in TN.
The extended range is from Newfoundland
to AK south to w NC, TX and CA. Jun-Aug.

Genus *Gaura*
Four species are found in Tennessee. The
genus name is from the Greek *gauros*
(superb) which may not seem appropriate for
some species. Look for the flowers early in
the day as they wilt rapidly in full sun.

Jack Carman

Jack Carman

Biennial Gaura   *Gaura biennis* L.
Coarse biennial or winter-annual to 80 in.
tall, branched above, usually hairy and
glandular in the inflorescence. Leaves are
lanceolate, toothed, to 4 in. long and 1 in.
wide. The inflorescence is a branched spike,
the branches from 1 to 8 in. long, and buds
are less than 0.8-in. long. White tubular
flowers, to 0.6-in. long with 4 narrow
spreading petals, turn pink with age, and
have sepals that are reflexed in pairs. The
protruding style has a cross-shaped stigma.
The stamens extend past the petals and
have large anthers. Occasional. Fields,
barrens, roadsides, disturbed areas. Thinly
scattered in TN. U.S. range from MA to NB
south to AL and TX. Jul-Oct.

Southern Gaura (*Gaura longiflora* Spach)
has narrow leaves (to 0.4-in. wide) and
flower buds over 0.8-in. long. White flowers
open near sunset, but turn pink and fade the
next day. Rare. Open woods, roadsides,
and fields, mostly in the Coastal Plain.
Found in Fayette, Hardeman, Madison and
Shelby counties in TN. May-Sep.

Slender Gaura *Gaura filipes* Spach

Clumped perennial to 7 ft tall with numerous linear to lance-shaped leaves (to 3 in. long) in the lower portion that are entire, or with a few coarse teeth. The inflorescence is long, almost naked, wand-like, branching, and finely hairy. The tubular flowers have 4 narrow, white, spreading petals about 0.4-in. long that turn pink with age. The protruding style has a cross-shaped stigma, the stamens are long and drooping, and the sepals are separately reflexed. Both flower and fruit have a distinct stalk (to 0.12-in. long). Occasional. Barrens, fields and open woods. Thinly spread across TN, mostly in the southern half. U.S. range from s IN to SC south to FL and LA. Aug-Sep.

Small-Flowered Gaura (*Gaura parviflora* Douglas*) is a coarse, erect, single-stemmed annual or biennial to 6 ft tall that is softly hairy all over. The small white flowers with 0.12-in. long petals are on one or more distinctive, very long, many-flowered spike(s). Rare. Fields, pastures, stream banks. A mostly western species known only from Knox County in TN. Jul-Oct.

Jack Carman

Seedbox *Ludwigia alternifolia* L.

Erect, usually freely-branched perennial to 4 ft tall. The leaves are alternate, lanceolate, entire, tapering to the base, 2 to 4 in. long. The bright yellow flowers with 4 petals are from 0.5 to 0.75-in. wide, short-stalked and arise from the upper leaf axils. The sepals are about the same size as the petals. The fruit ("Seedbox") is nearly cubic, about 0.25-in. wide, rounded on the base, slightly wing-angled, and opens by a terminal pore. Common. Marshes, ditches, wet soil. Found throughout TN and most of the e U.S. May-Oct.

Wingstem Water Primrose (*Ludwigia decurrens* Walter) is an annual with a 4-angled and commonly 4-winged stem. The flowers are about 1 in. wide, and the fruit shape is pyramidal. Frequent. Open wet areas. Found throughout TN, but chiefly in the Coastal Plain. Jun-Oct.

Jack Carman

Jack Carman

Eleven *Ludwigia* species are found in TN.

Spindleroot, Hairy Water Primrose
Ludwigia hirtella Rafinesque
Erect perennial to 3 ft tall that is densely hairy throughout. The leaves are alternate, erect or ascending, entire, lance-shaped, to 2 in. long, rounded at the base and sessile. The pale yellow flowers arise from the axils of the upper leaves. The flowers have 4 stamens and 4 rounded petals, about 0.6-in. long, that exceed the sepals. The root is shaped like a spindle. Infrequent. Open ditches and wet areas. A chiefly Coastal Plain species found in Fentress, Cumberland, Bledsoe, Van Buren, Warren, Cannon, Franklin, Coffee and Lewis counties in TN. Jun-Sep.

Narrow-Leaf Water Primrose (*Ludwigia linearis* Walter) is a perennial that has linear leaves about 0.2-in. wide and 2 in. long, bright yellow flowers to 0.5-in. wide, and a cylindric fruit that is somewhat widened above. Infrequent. Ditches, wet open areas. A chiefly Coastal Plain species found in Moore, Franklin, Coffee, Warren, Putnam, and Cumberland counties in TN. Jul-Sep.

Creeping Water Primrose
Ludwigia peploides (HBK.) Raven
Prostrate smooth perennial with creeping or floating stems that root at the nodes, often forming large dense mats. The leaves are alternate, lanceolate to obovate, about 3 in. long, and narrowed to a short stalk. The bright yellow flowers have 5 petals about 0.6-in. long and 10 stamens. The anthers are less than 0.07-in. long, and the fruit is cylindric. Occasional. Pools, mud flats and ditches. Mostly found in West TN, very thinly scattered elsewhere in the state. U.S. range from NC to s IN to KS south to LA and TX. May-Sep. The genus name is in honor of Christian Gottlieb Ludwig, a professor of botany at Leipsic in the 18th century.

Showy Water Primrose (*L. uruguayensis* (Cambessedes) H. Hara) is similar, but the stems and leaves are hairy. The flowers are larger (to 2 in. across), and the anthers are longer than 0.1-in. Rare. Sluggish streams, pools and marshes. Known from Stewart, Montgomery and Sumner counties in TN. A mostly southern species extending north to TN and NC. May-Sep.

Jack Carman

Jack Carman

Common Evening Primrose
Oenothera biennis L.

Biennial or short-lived leafy perennial to 6 ft tall, usually branched at the top. Leaves, to 8 in. long, are sessile, lanceolate, sometimes toothed, often wavy on the margin. The inflorescence is a stiff terminal spike with pale-yellow tubular flowers that have 4 roundish petals to 1 in. long and a cross-shaped stigma. The flowers open at twilight. The fruiting capsules to 1.6 in. long are thickest near the base. Frequent. Dry open places. Found throughout TN and most of the U.S. and s CAN. Jun-Oct. It is the source of a pain-relieving compound for headaches.

The Large-Flowered Evening Primrose (*Oenothera grandiflora* L'Her. *ex* Aiton) is similar, but has large, obovate flower petals from 1.2 to 2.4 in. long. Rare. Woods and meadows. A southern Coastal Plain species known from Marion County in TN. May-Oct.

Jack Carman

Sundrops   *Oenothera fruticosa* L.

Perennial to 3 ft tall, usually spreading-hairy above. Leaves are narrow, entire, seldom over 2.5 in. long. Several flowers are usually borne in a compact inflorescence, the bright yellow petals to 1 in. long and notched at the tip. The fruit pods are four-sided. Flowers open only during the day. Frequent. Meadows, fields, woods borders. Found mostly from the Western Highland Rim east in TN, and in most of the e U.S. Jun-Aug. *Oenothera tetragona* Roth.

Little Sundrops (*Oenothera perennis* L.) is a perennial to 2 ft tall with lance-like, petioled, stem leaves to 2.5 in. long. Inflorescence mostly nodding, the flowers opening singly, petals yellow to 0.4-in. wide and notched. Rare. Wet or dry fields, meadows, open woods. In TN, found in Johnson, Morgan and Scott counties. A mostly northeastern species extending south to TN and SC in the uplands. Jun-Aug.

Jack Carman

Cut-Leaf Evening Primrose   *Oenothera lacinata* Hill
Sprawling annual or biennial to 3 ft tall, usually branching from near the base. Leaves are lanceolate to oblanceolate, to 3 in. long and shallowly toothed to deeply lobed. The sessile flowers arise from the axils of the upper leaves, and have yellow (to reddish) petals to 0.8-in. long and reflexed sepals. The fruits are cylindric, straight or curved. Frequent. Dry fields, gardens, roadsides. Found throughout TN and the e U.S. May-Oct.

Thread-Leaf Sundrops (*Oenothera linifolia* Nutt.) is an annual to 2 ft tall with crowded, linear-filiform, stem leaves to 1.5 in. long. Flowers to 0.4-in. wide are borne in a long terminal raceme. Infrequent. Rocky ledges, sandy barrens. Thinly scattered in TN. The U.S. range is from KY to w FL west to e TX and e KS. Apr-Jun.

Jack Carman

Genus *Oenothera*
Ten species are found in Tennessee. The derivation of the genus name is somewhat obscure, but it was used in ancient times for a species of *Epilobium*, and subsequently adapted for use with this American genus.

Missouri Evening Primrose
***Oenothera macrocarpa* Nuttall**
Perennial that may have no above ground stem to a 2 ft trailing to erect stem. The leaves are entire, linear-lanceolate, narrowed to the base and tip, to 4 in. long. The large flowers have 4 obovate yellow petals to 3 in. long. The fruiting pod is 4-winged, the wings to 1 in. wide. The flowers open at evening twilight, and wilt rapidly in the morning sun. Rare. Dry rocky barrens in calcareous soil. A mostly western species found in Rutherford and Wilson counties in TN. May-Jul. *Oenothera missouriensis* Sims.

Jack Carman

Showy Evening Primrose   *Oenothera speciosa* Nuttall*
Perennial from creeping roots that is erect to ascending, to 2 ft tall. The leaves, to 3 in. long, are oblanceolate to linear, entire to pinnatifid, the lower usually more coarsely toothed or lobed. The flower buds nod and the flowers are pink to white, large (from 1.5 to 3 in. wide) and quite showy. Occasional. Fields, roadsides, waste areas. Found in Middle TN, also Shelby, Hardeman, McNairy and Madison counties west, and McMinn, Loudon, Blount and Knox counties east. U.S. range mostly MO to KS south to TX, and introduced eastward. May-Jun.

Three-Lobed Evening Primrose   *Oenothera triloba* Nuttall
Annual to short-lived perennial arising from a stout taproot and with almost no stem. Radially spreading leaves, to 8 in. long, are closely packed on the short stem, oblanceolate and pinnatifid to nearly the midvein. The flowers arise from the leaf axils. The four petals to 1 in. long are obovate, pale yellow turning white with age. Fruiting capsules are hard, woody, long-persistent, 4-winged, grouped into a "cone" at ground level. The flowers open at evening twilight. Occasional. Dry glades, barrens. Found in Middle TN (especially the Central Basin), also Knox, Blount and Hamilton counties. U.S. range from KY and TN west to KS and TX. May-Jun.

Jack Carman

The Meadow Beauty Family is represented by a single genus with 2 species (and an additional variety) in Tennessee.

Maryland Meadow Beauty
Rhexia mariana L.

Perennial from 8 to 40 in. tall with a glandular-hairy, obscurely square stem, often freely branched. Leaves are hairy, opposite, lanceolate, three-veined, and short-stalked, usually 1 to 2 in. long and a third as wide. Flowers have four pale pink (to white), slightly recurved petals from 0.5 to 0.7-in. long, and 8 stamens with prominent, curved, yellow anthers. The fruit is slightly hairy and urn-shaped with a neck that is as long or longer than the body. Common. Wet marshes and fields. Found throughout TN and most of the e U.S. May-Oct.

Jack Carman

Jack Carman

Genus *Rhexia*

The derivation of the genus name is somewhat obscure, but it was used in ancient times for some unknown plant, and subsequently adapted for use with this genus.

Virginia Meadow Beauty
Rhexia virginica L.

Perennial from 8 to 40 in. tall with a square, slightly hairy stem that has thin wings. Leaves are opposite, ovate or lanceolate, sparsely hairy, 3 to 5 veined, and usually 1 to 3 in. long and a third to half as wide. Flowers have four rose-lavender to purplish, recurved petals from 0.6 to 0.8-in. long, and 8 stamens with prominent, curved, yellow anthers. The fruit is urn-shaped with a neck that is shorter than the body. Frequent. Wet marshes and fields. Found throughout TN, the e U.S., and se CAN. Jul-Sep.

Jack Carman

SANTALACEAE : SANDALWOOD FAMILY

The Sandalwood Family is represented by 4 genera with one species each in Tennessee.

Bastard Toadflax
Comandra umbellata (L.) Nuttall

Smooth, simple or branched perennial from 4 to 16 in. tall that is colonial by rhizomes and parasitic on the roots of other plants. Leaves, from 0.8 to 2 in. long, are alternate, entire, sessile or short-stalked, lanceolate to elliptic or ovate, more or less veiny, green above but somewhat paler beneath. The inflorescences are 3 to 5-flowered clusters that are alternate in the axils of the upper leaves. The flowers have 5 petal-like sepals about 0.1-in. long and 5 stamens. The fruits are round and dry, about 0.2-in. wide. Frequent. Dry open woods, woods borders, roadsides, fields. Scattered across TN and widespread in North America. Apr-May. The genus name is from the Greek *come* (hair) and *aner* (man), alluding to the hairs of the calyx-lobes.

BUXACEAE : BOX FAMILY

Two genera with one species each are found in Tennessee.

Allegheny Spurge   ***Pachysandra procumbens*** Michaux

Sprawling perennial often forming large colonies. The stems, from 6 to 16 in. long, are often prostrate at the base. Evergreen leaves, from 1 to 3 in. long, are alternate, broadly ovate to rotund, coarsely toothed, abruptly narrowed to a long petiole, at first green but becoming mottled with age. The inflorescence is a dense erect spike from 2 to 4 in. tall, lateral from near the base of the stem. The flowers are unisexual, male flowers uppermost in the spike. Stamens, styles and pistils are white. Frequent. Rich woods. Found in Middle and East TN. Extended range from KY to NC south to w FL and s LA. Mar-Apr. The genus name is from the Greek *pachys* (thick) and *andros* (used for stamen), alluding to the large stamens.

Japanese Spurge (*P. terminalis* Siebold & Zuccarini*) is similar, but has narrow leaves and a terminal inflorescence. A cultivated species that sometimes escapes.

Jack Carman

Jack Carman

Woolly Croton   ***Croton capitatus*** Michaux
Erect, silvery to tawny annual from 0.5 to 3 ft tall, sparingly branched above and densely
covered with branching hairs. Leaves are stalked, alternate, mostly oblong, and 1.5 to 4 in.
long. The dense inflorescence (about 1 in. wide) is terminal, and has many small whitish
flowers, male above and female below. The fruits are normally 3-seeded and the seeds are
glossy brown. Occasional. Cedar glades, barrens, waste areas, roadsides, particularly on
shallow limestone soil. Found in the western half of TN, and from OH to NB south to FL and
TX. Jun-Oct. The genus name is the Greek *croton* (a tick) from the resemblance of the seed
to a tick.

The Spurge Family is represented by 7 genera and 34 species in Tennessee.

Prairie Tea   ***Croton monanthogynus*** Michaux
Somewhat weedy annual from 8 to 24 in. tall that is usually branched above. Leaves are
alternate, entire, ovate to ovate-oblong, 0.4 to 1.6 in. long, mostly blunt at the tip and broadly
rounded at the base, silvery-green, and covered with branched hairs. The male and female
flowers are tiny and grow in a dense inflorescence less than 0.4-in. wide. The fruit has only 1
seed. Frequent. Cedar glades, barrens, roadsides, waste areas, particularly on shallow
limestone soil. Found throughout most of TN, and from OH to CO south to FL, TX and
northern Mexico. Jun-Oct.

Jack Carman

Jack Carman

Wood Spurge
Euphorbia commutata Engelmann
Smooth, almost succulent perennial from 8 to 16 in. tall, often branched from the base. The young stems and leaves are commonly somewhat reddened.   Stem leaves, about 0.6-in. long, are usually pale yellowish-green, numerous, mostly sessile, obovate or oblanceolate below, ovate or oval above, all shallowly toothed. The involucres terminate umbel-like branches at the top of the stem. Leaves of the umbel are broadly triangular-reniform, tending to be fused together. The tiny flowers lack sepals and petals, and the yellow color in the inflorescence comes from crescent-shaped glands in the involucre. Frequent. Moist rich woods. Found from the Western Highland Rim east in TN. The U.S. range is from PA to MN south to FL and TX. Apr-Jun.

Jack Carman

Spurge   Genus *Euphorbia*
A total of 18 native and introduced species are found in TN.   Several male flowers surround a single female flower, forming a cup-like inflorescence called the cyathium that simulates a single flower, but mostly is not showy. The genus name is in honor of Euphorbus, physician of King Juba of Numidia.   The Christmas poinsettia is a *Euphorbia*.

Flowering Spurge
Euphorbia corollata L.
Erect perennial from 12 to 40 in. tall that arises from a deep root and has milky sap. The stem is smooth to coarsely hairy and multi-branched above (like an umbel or a panicle).   The stem leaves below the branching are alternate, linear to elliptic, from 1 to 2.5 in. long. Leaves just below the primary branches are similar but whorled. Small "flowers" terminate the many branches, forming a loose cyme that may be 12 in. across.   The "flower" cups have conspicuous white "petals" (appendages). Common. Fields, roadsides, barrens, open woods. Widespread in TN, and found from NH to MN south to FL and TX. Jul-Sep.

Wild Poinsettia
Euphorbia heterophylla L.
Smooth erect annual to 3 ft tall, usually branched. Leaves are mostly alternate, and quite variable even on the same plant, linear to broadly oblong to ovate, entire to serrate to lobed. Upper leaves mostly lobed, and blotched with red (sometimes white) at the base, which provides the showy color from this plant. The involucre has two-lipped, cup-shaped glands that are usually wider than high. Capsule smooth, about 0.25-in. wide. Rare. Moist soil in shade. Only recorded from Davidson and Shelby counties in TN, but certainly more prevalent. U.S. range from VA, WV and KY south to TN, NC and AL. Jun-Oct.

Jack Carman

Jack Carman

Cumberland Spurge
Euphorbia mercurialina Michaux
Perennial from 8 to 16 in. tall with milky sap, the stem branched above. Lower leaves are alternate, leaves just below branches are opposite or whorled, and leaves of branches are opposite. "Flowers" on long stalks terminate the central stem, or each branch at each fork. The "flowers" have a narrow ring of "petals" (appendages) with white margins. Frequent. Rich woods. Found in Middle and East TN, and in the Cumberland Plateau region from s KY to n AL and nw GA. Apr-Sep.

Snow-on-the-Mountain (*E. marginata* Pursh*) is an erect annual from 12 to 30 in. tall, densely softly hairy and freely branched above. Stem leaves alternate, sessile, and mostly broadly ovate to elliptic, 1.5 to 4 in. long. Leaves within the inflorescence smaller, margined with white or wholly white. Cymes crowded and involucres hairy, the 5 appendages white and the 5 lobes unevenly fringed. Rare. Waste places. Found in Stewart, Montgomery, Knox and Blount counties in TN. A mostly western species introduced eastward as a cultivar. Jul-Nov.

Jack Carman

EUPHORBIACEAE : SPURGE FAMILY

Eyebane   ***Euphorbia nutans*** Lagasca
Annual with stems to 32 in. tall that are usually ascending above and erect below. Older plant parts are usually smooth, but younger parts often have a single line of soft short hairs. Leaves, from 0.4 to 1.4 in. long, are opposite, oblong or oblong-ovate, conspicuously unequally toothed around the margin. Clusters of reddish "flowers" on short stalks terminate the branches or sometimes arise from the leaf axils. The "flowers" have a narrow ring of "petals" (appendages) which are white-margined. Common. Lawns, gardens, waste areas. Found throughout TN and from NH to ND south to FL and TX. Jun-Oct.

RHAMNACEAE : BUCKTHORN FAMILY

Three genera and 6 species of the Buckthorn Family are found in Tennessee.

New Jersey Tea   ***Ceanothus americanus*** L.
Freely-branched shrub to 40 in. tall. Leaves, from 1.2 to 3.2 in. long, are alternate, ovate, 3-nerved, sharply toothed, rounded to almost heart-shaped at the base. Flower clusters are terminal or arise from the leaf axils on stalks from 2 to 10 in. long. The clusters are cylindric to egg-shaped and flowers are small and white. The fleshy fruit is 3-lobed and capsule-like. Common. Open woods, roadsides, waste areas, barrens. Found throughout TN (less prevalent west) and from Quebec to MN south to FL and TX. May-Aug. Leaf tea was once a popular beverage, and root tea has been used to treat asthma, sore throat, bronchitis, whooping cough, colds, fevers and stomach aches.

Jack Carman

LINACEAE : FLAX FAMILY
Genus *Linum*
Tennessee's 5 native flaxes are yellow-flowered perennials. A blue-flowered annual, commercial flax, occasionally escapes.

Common Yellow Flax
Linum medium (Planchon) Britton
    var. ***texanum*** (Planchon) Fernald
Smooth, erect, leafy perennial to 3 ft tall with solitary stems and stiffly ascending to spreading upper branches. Leaves, from 0.5 to 1 in. long, are mostly opposite, entire, narrow, lanceolate to oblanceolate, reduced above. The inflorescence is corymb-like with 5-petaled flowers about 0.6-in. wide. Inner sepals have some prominent stalked glands. Frequent. Upland woods, fields, barrens. Widely scattered in TN and found in most of the e U.S. Jun-Sep.

Virginia Yellow Flax (*L. virginianum* L.) is similar, but has spreading inflorescence branches and inner sepals usually with a few small sessile glands. Occasional. Upland woods, fields, barrens. Widely scattered in TN and found in most of the e U.S. except the Coastal Plain. Jun-Sep.

Jack Carman

POLYGALACEAE : MILKWORT FAMILY

The Milkwort Family is represented by 12 species in Tennessee, all in the genus *Polygala*.

Drumheads, Cross-Leaf Milkwort   *Polygala cruciata* L.
Erect annual to 12 in. tall, sparingly branched. Leaves, from 0.4 to 1.6 in. long, are linear to oblanceolate or narrowly elliptic, occurring in whorls of 3 to 4. The small pinkish flowers are packed into a dense, cylindric raceme which is 0.4 to 2.4 in. long and 0.4 to 0.6-in. wide. Occasional. Marshes and meadows. In TN, found from the Eastern Highland Rim east, also in Lawrence and Lewis counties. U.S. range along the Coastal Plain from ME to FL and TX, and extending inland to OH and MN. Jul-Sep.

George Hornal

Curtiss' Milkwort
Polygala curtissii A. Gray
Erect annual to 16 in. tall, freely branched. Leaves are linear, linear-oblong or narrowly oblanceolate, to 0.8-in. long and 0.15-in. wide. The small pinkish to white flowers occur in a compact raceme, which is 0.4 to 0.8-in. long and 0.3 to 0.5-in. thick with the buds forming a small cone at the top. Bracts persist after the lower flowers fall. Frequent. Dry soils. Found from the Eastern Highland Rim east in TN, also in Lawrence, Lewis, Dickson, Henry, Carroll and Fayette counties. U.S. range from DE to OH south to SC and MS. Jun-Sep.

Nuttall's Milkwort (*Polygala nuttallii* T. & G.) is similar, but smaller and more slender. Stems to 12 in. tall and racemes less than 0.25-in. thick. Rare. Dry soils. Currently recorded only from Coffee and Hickman counties in TN. U.S. range from MA to GA. Jul-Sep.

Jack Carman

Jack Carman

Pink Milkwort   *Polygala incarnata* L.
Erect annual to 24 in. tall with sparingly-branched, slender, smooth, glaucous stems. The leaves are alternate, ascending, linear, to 0.5-in. long. The flowers, to 0.4-in. long, are rose-purple and occur in a dense raceme from 0.4 to 1.6 in. long with only a few flowers open at one time. The corolla is 3 times as long as the wings. Occasional. Dry fields and barrens. Thinly scattered in West and Middle TN, and found in most of the eastern U.S. Jun-Aug.

Jack Carman

Dwarf Milkwort, Bachelor's Button   *Polygala nana* (Michaux) DC.
Erect biennial to 6 in. tall. Leaves are mostly in a basal rosette, stem leaves few. The small lemon-yellow flowers occur in a dense, compact raceme from 0.4 to 1.4 in. long and 0.5 to 0.8-in. thick. The wings are about 0.3-in. long. Rare. Moist, open, areas. In TN, known from Rhea and Warren counties. A southern species extending north into TN. Mar-Oct. The genus name is from the Greek *polys* (much) and *gala* (milk). When fed to cattle, milkworts were believed to increase milk production.

Gaywings   *Polygala paucifolia* Willdenow
Colonial perennial from 3 to 6 in. tall with stems having scale-like leaves below, and alternate, oval leaves from 0.6 to 1.6 in. long near the summit. The showy rose-purple (to white) flowers have long stalks, obovate wings about 0.6-in. long, and corolla length about equal to the wings. Occasional. Moist rich woods. Found from the Cumberland Plateau east in TN, it is a northeastern species extending south to TN and GA in the mountains and uplands. Apr-May. The orchid-like flower somewhat resembles a bird in flight, accounting for another common name, Bird-on-the-Wing. Also thought to resemble a tiny tailless airplane.

Jack Carman

Jack Carman

Field Milkwort   *Polygala sanguinea* L.
Erect annual to 16 in. tall that is branched above. The leaves are alternate, linear or narrowly elliptic, to 1.6 in. long. The white to pinkish flowers occur in a dense, tight, cylindric raceme which is 0.4 to 0.8-in. long, 0.4-in. thick, and nearly flat-topped. The wings are about 0.2-in. long, twice as long as the corolla. The bracts persist as the lower flowers fall. Occasional. Fields, barrens, and meadows. Thinly scattered throughout most of TN. Extended range from Nova Scotia to MN south to SC and LA. Jul-Sep.

Maryland Milkwort (*Polygala mariana* Miller) is similar, except that the bracts fall with the flowers, and the corolla is nearly as long as the wings. Rare. Dry soil. In TN, known from Bradley, Hardin, Lawrence, McNairy and Montgomery counties. A chiefly Coastal Plain species found from NJ to FL and TX, and inland in TN and KY. Jun-Sep.

Seneca Snakeroot
***Polygala senega* L.**
Perennial to 20 in. tall with several stems from one base. Leaves, from 1.2 to 3.2 in. long, are alternate, the lower reduced and the upper linear-lanceolate. The small flowers occur in a dense raceme from 0.6 to 1.6 in. long and 0.3-in. thick, and are white with broad elliptic wings about 0.15-in. long, exceeding the corolla. Occasional. Dry or moist woods and barrens. Found from the Western Highland Rim east in TN, and throughout most of the e U.S. and s CAN. May-Jun. It has been used to treat respiratory maladies.

Boykin's Milkwort (*P. boykinii* Nuttall) is similar, but the racemes are longer and narrower, and most of the leaves are whorled. Rare. Barrens. In TN, known from Bedford and Rutherford counties. A southern species extending north into TN. Mar-Aug.

Jack Carman

POLYGALACEAE : MILKWORT FAMILY

Whorled Milkwort
Polygala verticillata L.
Erect annual from 4 to 16 in. tall, branched above. Leaves are linear to linear-oblong, from 0.4 to 0.8-in. long, the lower usually opposite or in whorls of 3 to 5. The inflorescence is a terminal, continuous, loose, conic raceme from 0.3 to 2 in. long which appears truncate at the base, and extends well above the leaves. The flowers are small, greenish-white or pinkish-white. Frequent. Moist to dry areas, grasslands and woods. Widely scattered in TN, and found in most of the eastern U.S. Jul-Oct.

Jack Carman

SAPINDACEAE : SOAPBERRY FAMILY
Two genera with one species each are found in Tennessee.

Balloon Vine   *Cardiospermum halicacabum* L.*
Somewhat woody, much-branched, climbing vine to 7 ft long with axillary tendrils. The leaves are alternate, ternately or twice ternately compound, the lance-shaped leaflets from 0.8 to 1.6 in. long, coarsely toothed or lobed, weakly hairy. The white flowers, about 0.2-in. wide, are borne in small clusters on long stalks from the leaf axils, and the petals are mostly unequal. The fruiting capsule is green, downy, inflated, papery, almost round to egg-shaped, from 1 to 1.4 in. wide. Infrequent. Fields, waste areas. An escape from cultivation found in Shelby, Henry, Stewart, Montgomery, Houston, Humphreys, Davidson, Wilson, Maury and Bedford counties in TN. U.S. range from NJ to IL and MO south. Aug-Sep. The genus name is from the Greek *cardia* (heart) and *spermum* (seed).

Jack Carman

Fragrant Sumac
Rhus aromatica Aiton
Straggly, upright, rounded shrub that is 1 to 7 ft tall, not poisonous. The leaves are long-stalked, ternately compound with the three leaflets sessile, thick, ovate to elliptic-ovate, roundly toothed, from 0.8 to 3 in. long. The small flowers are pale yellow and borne in spike-like lateral clusters from the leaf axils. The fruits, about 0.2-in. wide, are roundish, very hairy, bright red and quite conspicuous. Frequent. Open woods, cedar glades, barrens. Found in the eastern 2/3 of TN, also Hardin, Decatur and Carroll counties, and in most of the U.S. and s CAN. Feb-Apr.

Smooth Sumac (*Rhus glabra* L.) is similar to Winged Sumac, but the leaves are without wings, and twigs and leaf stalks are smooth. Frequent. Open dry areas, roadsides. Widespread in TN and the e U.S. Jun-Jul.

Staghorn Sumac (*Rhus typhina* L.) is similar to Smooth Sumac, but the twigs and leaf stalks are densely hairy. Occasional. Open dry areas, roadsides. Found in Middle and East TN, also Carroll County. A ne U.S. and se CAN species that irregularly extends south to n GA and n AL. Jun-Jul.

Jack Carman

The Cashew Family is represented by 3 genera and 8 species in Tennessee.

Winged Sumac   *Rhus copallina* L.
Sparingly-branched shrub to 20 ft tall with densely hairy stems. The leaves are pinnately compound with 7 to 21 leaflets that are firm, shining above, oblong to lanceolate, from 1.2 to 3 in. long, entire or with a few teeth. Leaf rachis are winged, the wings from 0.04 to 0.2-in. wide and interrupted at the base of each leaflet pair. The inflorescence, to 12 in. long, is a dense showy panicle of very small yellowish flowers that terminates the stem or branches, and extends well above the leaves. The fruits are red, densely hairy, roundish but somewhat flattened, about 0.2-in. wide. Frequent. Open dry areas, roadsides. Found throughout TN, and from ME to WI south to FL and TX. Jun-Jul.

Jack Carman

Jack Carman

ANACARDIACEAE : CASHEW FAMILY

Poison Ivy   ***Toxicodendron radicans*** (L.) Kuntze
Climbing or trailing perennial vine with abundant aerial roots. Leaves are alternate and have 3 leaflets that are mostly flat, ovate to elliptic, entire or often with a few irregular, more or less pointed teeth or shallow lobes, from 2 to 6 in. long. The inflorescence arises from the lower leaf axils and is loose, branched, panicle-like with numerous small whitish to cream-colored flowers. Frequent. Open woods, disturbed areas, lawns. Found throughout TN and likely more prevalent than officially recorded. Extended range from s Nova Scotia to se MN south to FL and TX. May-Jul. **Leaves and stems contain a severe contact poison** that may cause a rash, inflammation, swelling and itching in susceptible individuals.

Jack Carman

ZYGOPHYLLACEAE : CALTROP FAMILY
In Tennessee, the Caltrop Family is represented by the following species.

Puncture Weed   ***Tribulus terrestris*** L.*
Prostrate annual that has hairy stems, is diffusely branched from the base, and forms mats to 40 in. wide. The leaves are opposite, short-stalked, pinnately compound, from 0.8 to 2.5 in. long. Leaflets are usually in pairs of 6 to 8, oblong, from 0.2 to 0.6-in. long. Yellow flowers, about 0.4-in. wide, are solitary in the leaf axils and borne on stalks from 0.2 to 0.4-in. long. The fruit body is about 0.4-in. thick, each of the 5 segments with 2 stout divergent spines. Rare. Fields, roadsides, disturbed areas. Found in Shelby, Dyer and Lake counties in TN, and from s NY to SD south to FL and TX. A native of the Mediterranean region now well established in the U.S. Jun-Sep. The genus name is the Latin name for the caltrop, the form of which is suggested by the prickly fruit.

Jack Carman

Northern Wood Sorrel   *Oxalis acetosella* L.
Perennial arising from a slender scaly rhizome. The leaves are all basal and long-stalked, each blade with 3 heart-shaped leaflets. The flowers are solitary on stalks from 3 to 6 in. long, slightly surpassing the leaves. Petals are white, veined with pink, cleft at the tip, from 0.4 to 0.6-in. long. Infrequent. Rich mountain woods, especially spruce-fir forests. In TN, it is found in the Blue Ridge and northern Cumberland Plateau counties. Extended range from se CAN southward in the mountains to n GA. May-Aug. *Oxalis montana* Rafinesque.

Genus *Oxalis*
Leaves have long petioles and the blades are divided into three radial leaflets, each notched at the tip and heart-shaped, forming a "shamrock". Leaves have a sour taste and may be eaten in salads, but sparingly. Genus name from the Greek *oxys* (sour). Eight species are found in TN.

Large Yellow Wood Sorrel   *Oxalis grandis* Small
A very showy perennial from 1 to 3 ft tall. Stems erect, simple or sparingly branched. The leaves, with long stalks and 3 shamrock-like leaflets, are from 1 to 2 in. wide. The leaflets usually have a narrow purplish-black margin. The inflorescence is cyme-like, usually extending well above the leaves. The flowers are yellow with 5 petals from 0.5 to 0.75-in. long. Frequent. Found in rich woods from the Western Highland Rim east in TN, also in Shelby County. U.S. range from PA to s IL south to GA and TN. May-Jun.

Jack Carman

Jack Carman

Price's Wood Sorrel
Oxalis macrantha (Trelease) Small
A showy perennial from 4 to 12 in. tall, usually hairy below and much branched. The leaves have long stalks and 3 shamrock-like leaflets, each leaflet from 0.25 to 0.6-in. wide. The inflorescence is umbel-like, scarcely surpassing the leaves. The petals are yellow marked with red near the base, from 0.5 to 0.8-in. long. Infrequent. Open calcareous areas. In TN, found in the limestone barrens and cedar glades of the Central Basin (Giles, Marshall, Bedford, Rutherford, Wilson, Davidson and Sumner counties), and also Cocke County in East TN. U.S. range from KY south to FL and MS. Apr-May. *Oxalis priceae* Small.

Southern Yellow Wood Sorrel
Oxalis stricta L.
A variable weedy perennial to 16 in. tall. The stem leaves have long stalks, and the blades have 3 heart-shaped, shamrock-like leaflets from 0.4 to 0.8-in. wide. The inflorescence is umbel-like with 2 to several flowers from a single node. The 5 petals are yellow, from 0.15 to 0.4-in. long. The stalks of the seedpods are bent abruptly down, but the pods, from 0.6 to 1 in. long, are erect and appressed-hairy. Common. A nearly cosmopolitan weed found throughout TN and the e U.S. Mar-Oct. *Oxalis dillenii* Jacquin.

Common Yellow Wood Sorrel (*Oxalis fontana* Bunge) is similar, but the inflorescence is cyme-like with a single flower at each node. The cylindric, pointed fruit pods, to 0.6-in. long, have spreading hairs and are on more or less ascending stalks. Common. A nearly cosmopolitan weed found throughout TN and the eastern U.S. May-frost. *Oxalis europaea* Jordan. Also *Oxalis stricta* L. in some references.

Jack Carman

OXALIDACEAE : WOOD SORREL FAMILY

Violet Wood Sorrel   *Oxalis violacea* L.
Perennial arising from a scaly bulbous base. The leaves are all basal and long-stalked, each blade with 3 heart-shaped leaflets that are red-purple on the underside. The flowering stalk is erect, from 4 to 8 in. long, much surpassing the leaves, terminated by an umbel-like cluster of 2 to several flowers. The 5 petals are purple to pink or white, from 0.4 to 0.7-in. long. Common. Dry upland woods, barrens. Found throughout TN and most of the e U.S. Apr-Jun.

Jack Carman

GERANIACEAE : GERANIUM FAMILY

Carolina Cranesbill
Geranium carolinianum L.
Bushy hairy annual to 2 ft tall. Leaves are round to reniform, to 3 in. wide, and have 3 to 5 long, linear-oblong lobes that are deeply toothed at the tips. Flowers are borne mostly in pairs, and are pale pink to whitish, from 0.3 to 0.5-in. wide. Common. Weed of waste places, barrens, roadsides and fields. Found throughout TN, and most of the U.S. and s CAN. May-Aug.

The Geranium Family is numerically precise: 5 sepals, 5 petals, 10 stamens (in two circles of 5), and a pistil with 5 divisions united into one long slender style. The style forms a long beak on the fruit capsule. Seeds are dispersed when the outside of the capsule splits into 5 pieces that coil upward from the base and usually remain attached at the tip. Two genera and 9 species are listed in TN.

Jack Carman

Wild Geranium   *Geranium maculatum* L.
Erect perennial from 12 to 28 in. tall, arising from a stout rhizome. Leaves are opposite, long-stalked below but short-stalked upward. Leaf blades, from 2.5 to 6 in. wide, have 5 to 7 narrow lobes that are deeply toothed at the tips, and are hairy and purplish-green. The inflorescence is an open cyme with few to several flowers, from 1.0 to 1.4 in. wide, that are pink to purplish (rarely white). Common. Rich open woods. Found throughout TN and most of the e U.S. Apr-Jun. Tannin-rich roots are highly astringent, styptic.

GERANIACEAE : GERANIUM FAMILY

Eight *Geranium* species are found in TN. The genus name is from the Greek *geranos* (a crane), alluding to the resemblance of the fruit to the bill of that bird.

Dove's-Foot Cranesbill
Geranium molle L.*

A spreading or ascending annual from 8 to 20 in. tall, branched from the base. Basal leaves are almost round, from 1 to 2 in. wide, deeply 5 to 9-lobed, shallowly toothed at the tips, on long hairy stalks that appear attached to the leaf center. Stem leaves are mostly 3-lobed, reduced in size. Petals are about 0.25-in. long, deeply notched, bright pink. Occasional. Pastures and disturbed areas. Found in Middle and East TN, and sporadically throughout the e U.S. Apr-Sep.

Herb Robert (*G. robertianum* L.) has leaf segments that are pinnately lobed or cleft, and flowers that are bright pink to red-purple, about 0.75-in. wide, the petals not notched. Plants have a bitter-aromatic scent. Rare. A northern species known in TN only from a bluff along the Cumberland River in Smith County. May-Sep.

Jack Carman

Jack Carman

BALSAMINACEAE
TOUCH-ME-NOT FAMILY

One genus with 2 species is found in TN.

Spotted Touch-Me-Not, Jewelweed
Impatiens capensis Meerburgh

Smooth annual from 2 to 5 ft tall with almost succulent stems that are widely branched above. Leaves are soft, pale or glaucous beneath, toothed, long-stalked, elliptic to ovate, from 1 to 4 in. long. Reddish-orange flowers thickly spotted with reddish-brown are solitary on slender drooping stalks from the leaf axils, and have a cone-shaped, pouch-like sepal with a narrow spur curved forward beneath the pouch. Mature seed pods, about 0.8-in. long, instantly explode elastically when touched or jarred. Frequent. Wet woods, roadsides, stream banks, swamps, often in large colonies. Found throughout TN, and from s CAN south to SC, AL and OK. Jun-Sep. A poultice of crushed leaves may be used to relieve irritation from poison ivy and nettle rash – a well known folk remedy. Water droplets on the leaves sometimes produce jewel-like reflections, hence the common name Jewelweed.

BALSAMINACEAE : TOUCH-ME-NOT FAMILY

Pale Touch-Me-Not
Impatiens pallida Nuttall

Smooth annual from 2 to 6 ft tall with almost succulent stems that are widely branched above. Leaves are soft, pale or glaucous beneath, toothed, long-stalked, elliptic to ovate, from 1 to 4 in. long. Yellow flowers lightly spotted with reddish-brown are solitary on slender drooping stalks from the leaf axils, and have a cone-shaped, pouch-like sepal with a narrow spur curved down at a right angle. Mature seed pods, about 0.8-in. long, instantly explode elastically when touched or jarred. Occasional. Moist woods, roadsides, stream banks, often in large colonies. Widespread in the eastern 2/3 of TN, and found from s CAN south to NC, TN and OK. Jul-Sep. _Impatiens_ is Latin for impatient, alluding to the bursting fruit.

ARALIACEAE : GINSENG FAMILY

Woody plants or perennial herbs with alternate, simple or compound leaves. The inflorescence is usually an umbel with many small flowers. Three genera and 6 species are found in Tennessee.

Jack Carman

American Ginseng
Panax quinquefolius L.

Perennial from 8 to 24 in. tall. A whorl of 3 to 4 leaves and the flower stalk grow from the top of the solitary, naked stem. Leaves are palmately compound, usually with 5 stalked, elliptic, toothed leaflets. Small greenish-white flowers occur in a single, short, terminal umbel, normally below the leaves. Bright red berries develop in late summer. Frequent, but disappearing from over-collection of the roots. Cool, moist, upland woodlands. Found throughout most of the e U.S. and e CAN, scattered across TN. May-Jul. Research supports the belief that Ginseng may increase mental efficiency and physical performance, and aid in adapting to stress. It's effect is called "adaptogenic" – tending to return the body to normal. Large doses are said to raise blood pressure. The genus name is from the Greek _pas_ (all) and _akos_ (cure), alluding to the reputed healing power of the plants in China.

Jack Carman

Jack Carman

ARALIACEAE : GINSENG FAMILY

Dwarf Ginseng   *Panax trifolius* L.
Perennial from 4 to 8 in. tall. The 3 compound leaves have 3 to 5 leaflets, from 1.6 to 3.2 in. long, that are lance-shaped to elliptic or oblanceolate, finely toothed and sessile. The simple umbel of small white flowers extends above the leaves. Fruit yellow. Occasional. Rich upland woods. Found in TN from the Cumberland Plateau east, it is a northern species extending south to TN and GA in the uplands. Apr-Jun.

APIACEAE : PARSLEY FAMILY

Economically important members of the Parsley Family are: parsley, celery, carrot, parsnip, dill, caraway, and fennel. Other members are deadly poisonous. The typical inflorescence is an umbel. In an umbel, the flowers are on stalks (rays) that radiate from the tip of the stem as the ribs of an umbrella radiate from the axis. In a compound umbel, the rays bear smaller umbels instead of a single flower. There are 33 genera and 59 species found in TN.

Hairy Angelica   *Angelica venenosa* (Greenway) Fernald
Stout perennial to 6 ft tall. The leaves, from 4 to 8 in. long, have long petioles with broad bases that sheath the stem, and are pinnately divided (the lower leaves sometimes twice). Upper leaves are reduced. Leaflets are oblong to elliptic to lanceolate, finely toothed, from 0.8 to 1.6 in. long. Inflorescence and upper stem downy. Umbels are 2 to 6 in. wide and the flowers are white. The downy fruit has two lateral wings. Frequent. Woodland margins, roadsides, fields. Found in the eastern 2/3 of TN, and in most of the e U.S. Jun-Aug. The species name **venenosa means very poisonous**. Three *Angelica* species are found in TN.

Mountain Angelica (*Angelica triquinata* Michaux) is similar, but has smooth stems and inflorescences. Infrequent. Mountain woods. Blue Ridge from PA to NC and TN. Jul-Sep.

Jack Carman

Hare's Ear, Thoroughwax
Bupleurum rotundifolium* L.
Glabrous and glaucous annual from 1 to 2 ft tall with alternate roundish leaves, the lower sessile and the upper perfoliate. The umbels are yellow with tiny, almost sessile flowers. Pointed showy bractlets, to 0.5-in. long, surround the umbels, much surpassing the flowers. Infrequent. Cedar glades, barrens. Found in Davidson, Wilson, Rutherford, Maury, Marshall and Bedford counties in the Central Basin, in Knox, Washington, Cocke and Hawkins counties in East TN, and in most of the e U.S. from TN north. May-Jun. The genus name is from the Greek *bous* (an ox) and *pleuron* (a rib).

Genus *Chaerophyllum*
Three species are found in Tennessee. The genus name is from the Greek *chairo* (rejoice) and *phyllon* (a leaf), alluding to the agreeable odor of the foliage.

Jack Carman

Southern Chervil   *Chaerophyllum tainturieri* Hooker
Downy weedy annual to 30 in. tall, mostly branching above. The leaves are triple pinnate, to 5 in. long and nearly as wide, dissected into small leaflets, appearing fern-like. Leaflets elliptic to narrowly oblong, pointed, hairy beneath. The compound umbels usually have 3 branches with 3 to 10 small white flowers per umbellet, and are terminal or lateral. The bracts of the umbel are strongly reflexed in fruit. Common. Moist to dry soil. Widespread in TN and the se U.S. Mar-Apr.

Spreading Chervil (*Chaerophyllum procumbens* (L.) Crantz) is similar, but stems are smooth, more spreading, and usually branched from the base. Umbel bracts are spreading in fruit. Occasional. Moist woods and alluvial soil. Found mostly in Middle TN (thinly scattered in East TN), and from s IN south in the e U.S. Mar-Apr.

Jack Carman

Jack Carman

Spotted Cowbane, Water Hemlock   *Cicuta maculata* L.
Smooth, stout, much-branched perennial from 3 to 7 ft tall, the stems with hollow bases and purple streaked or spotted. Leaves are double or triple pinnate with thin serrate leaflets, from 1.2 to 4 in. long, that have the lateral veins of each leaflet directed to the valleys between the teeth at the leaflet margin. Compound umbels, from 2 to 5 in. wide, are numerous, both terminal and lateral, on stalks from 1 to 5 in. long. The flowers are white. Frequent. Swamps, ditches, marshes, wet fields. Widespread in TN and e North America. May-Aug. **Too lethal for medicinal use. Very poisonous and ingestion can cause death.** The genus name is the classical Latin name for the Old World poison hemlock.

Jack Carman

Poison Hemlock
Conium maculatum L.*
Taprooted freely-branched biennial to 10 ft tall, the stem hollow and purple-spotted. Leaves, from 8 to 16 in. long, are broadly triangular, 3 to 4 times pinnately compound with ovate-oblong leaflets to 0.4-in. long that are toothed and incised. Compound umbels, from 1.6 to 2.4 in. wide, are both terminal and lateral, on stalks from 1 to 4 in. long. The terminal umbels bloom first but are soon overtopped by others. Flowers are white. The leaves are ill-scented when bruised. Occasional. Roadsides, fence rows, waste places, along railroad tracks. Introduced from Eurasia and found throughout most of the U.S. The TN records are from Middle TN, also Carroll and Unicoi counties. May-Jun. **Deadly poisonous. Ingestion can be lethal. Contact can cause dermatitis. Juice highly toxic.** The genus name is from *coneion*, the Greek name of the Old World poison hemlock. It is the hemlock of classical antiquity used in the execution of Socrates.

Jack Carman

Honewort
Cryptotaenia canadensis (L.) DC.

Erect smooth perennial from 12 to 40 in. tall with fibrous roots and a single stem that is branched above. The leaves have 3 leaflets, from 1.6 to 6 in. long, that are lanceolate to rhombic or ovate, sharply and irregularly (often doubly) toothed or cleft to lobed. Lower leaves are long-stalked, and upper leaves are short-stalked. Numerous loose, irregular, compound umbels are terminal and from the upper leaf axils. The umbellets bear only a few small white flowers. Common. Rich woods. Found throughout TN and from New Brunswick to Manitoba south to GA and TX. Jun-Jul. The genus name is from the Greek *cryptos* (hidden) and *tainia* (a fillet), alluding to the concealed oil-tubes.

Genus *Daucus*

Two species are found in Tennessee. *Daucus* is the ancient Greek name for carrot.

Jack Carman

Queen Anne's Lace   *Daucus carota* L.*

Slender to coarse, freely-branched biennial to 5 ft tall with a stout taproot. Leaves, from 8 to 10 in. long, are repeatedly dissected, the final segments linear, lanceolate or oblong and less than 0.15-in. wide. The showy umbels, from 2 to 5 in. wide, have white flowers but the central flower is often purple. Bracts below the umbels are spreading or reflexed, pinnately divided into mostly filiform lobes that are rough below. The fruit is distinctive with the ribs bearing curved, sharp barbs. Frequent. Dry fields, roadsides, waste places. Introduced from Europe, now widespread in TN and most of North America. May-Sep. The root is thought by some to be sweet and tender, and the cultivated carrot was derived from this species.

American Wild Carrot (*Daucus pusillus* Michaux) is similar, but an annual. The umbel bracts are bipinnate, smooth below, and appressed to the umbel branches in fruit. Rare. Dry open places. Found in Wayne, Lewis, Marshall and Davidson counties in TN. A southern species extending north to NC and MO. May-Jun.

Harbinger-of-Spring
Erigenia bulbosa (Michaux) Nuttall

Delicate smooth perennial from 1 to 4 in. tall at flowering, larger later. The stem is simple and bears one or two leaves and a few-flowered, leafy-bracted umbel. Leaves, from 4 to 8 in. long (at maturity), are 2 to 3 times ternately divided and leaflets are linear or spatulate. The flower petals are white, to 0.16-in. long, and the anthers are red-brown. Frequent. Rich moist woods. Widespread in TN and the e U.S. Feb-Apr. One of the first wildflowers to bloom in the spring. Also called Pepper-and-Salt because of the red-brown anthers and white petals. *Erigenia* is a monotypic (single species) genus, and the name is from the Greek, meaning born in the spring.

Jack Carman

Genus *Eryngium*

Three species are found in Tennessee. The genus name is from *eryngion*, the classical name for some prickly plant.

Eryngo
Eryngium integrifolium Walter

Slender or occasionally robust, erect perennial from 1 to 3 ft tall with a solitary stem that is branched above. The basal leaves are thin, long-stalked, mostly ovate and toothed, from 1 to 4 in. long. The stem leaves are alternate, mostly sessile, narrow, toothed or lobed and reduced. The inflorescence is cyme-like with dense, roundish, flower heads to 0.4-in. wide that have pale to dark blue flowers. Rare. Wet meadows. Found in Benton, White, Coffee and Warren counties in TN, it is a southern Coastal Plain species. Aug-Oct.

Prostrate Eryngo (*Eryngium prostratum* Nuttall) is similar, but has weakly ascending or prostrate stems that often root at the nodes, and solitary flowers from the leaf axils. Occasional. Wet areas, moist ditches and roadsides. Found mostly in West TN and western Middle TN (rare east), and throughout the se U.S. Jul-Sep.

George Hornal

George Hornal

Rattlesnake Master
Eryngium yuccifolium Michaux
Coarse erect perennial to 4 ft tall. The lower leaves, from 6 to 32 in. long, are silvery green, narrow, sharp-tipped and have spine-like serrations. The upper leaves are similar, but reduced. The roundish flowering heads are 0.4 to 0.8-in. wide with white to green flowers. The flower bracts are lance-ovate, but rarely project from beneath the head. Occasional. Fields, open woods, barrens, and roadsides. Widespread in TN and found in the U.S. from MN to n VA south. Jun-Aug. American Indians use the root as poultice for snakebites.

Genus *Hydrocotyle*
Five species are found in Tennessee and all are rare. The genus name is from the Greek *hydor* (water) and *cotyle* (a flat cup), alluding to the peltate leaves of several species being cup-shaped.

Buttercup Water Pennywort   *Hydrocotyle ranunculoides* Linne
Aquatic perennial with floating or creeping stems rooting at the nodes and forming large colonies. The leaves, to 2.8 in. wide, are long-stalked, round-reniform with a basal cleft, and 5 to 6 lobed to about the middle of the leaf. The inflorescence is a simple umbel on a well-developed stalk occurring below the leaves. Each umbel has 5 to 10 white flowers on pedicels to 0.12-in. long. Rare. Lakes, ponds. Found in Lake and Obion counties in TN and across the southern U.S. May-Aug.

Marsh Water Pennywort (*Hydrocotyle americana* L.) is similar, but the leaves are shallowly lobed and the flower umbels are sessile or nearly so. Rare. Moist low ground. A northern species found in Van Buren, Scott, Greene and Washington counties in TN. Jun-Sep.

Jack Carman

Jack Carman

American Lovage   *Ligusticum canadense* (L.) Britton
Stout freely-branched perennial to 5 ft tall. The lower leaves are 3 to 4 times ternately compound, the upper less divided, and the uppermost sometimes simple. Leaflets are thin, lanceolate to ovate, to 2.5 in. long, sharply toothed and broadly rounded at the base. The terminal (sometimes lateral) umbels are often double compound, the primary stalks to 8 in. long, the secondary to 2 in. long. The umbellets are small, the flowers are white, and the fruit is elliptic with narrowly winged ribs. Occasional. Margins of rich woodlands, stream banks. Widespread in TN and the Southeast. Jun-Jul.

Sweet Cicely   *Osmorhiza claytonii* (Michaux) Clarke
Erect perennial to 3 ft tall with densely hairy stems and thick roots with a licorice-like odor. Leaves to 1 ft long, often hairy, twice triple-compound, the lower with long petioles and the upper mostly sessile. The leaflets are ovate to lanceolate, toothed or lobed, and from 0.4 to 1.6 in. wide. The umbels are compound with hairy stalks from 2 to 6 in. long. The umbellets have 5 to 20 flowers with white petals that are longer than the styles. Occasional. Rich moist woods. Found from the Western Highland Rim east in TN, a mostly northeastern species extending south to NC, AL and AR. Apr-Jun. The genus name is from the Greek *osme* (a scent) and *rhiza* (a root).

Sweet Anise (*O. longistylis* (Torrey) DC.) is similar, but plants are anise-scented and styles are much longer than the petals. Frequent. Moist woods. Widespread in TN. Extended range from s CAN south to GA, TX and CO, more prevalent south and west. Apr-Jun.

Jack Carman

Jack Carman

Cowbane
Oxypolis rigidior (L.) Rafinesque
Smooth perennial from 2 to 5 ft tall. Leaves and branches are few, roots are spindle-shaped. The pinnately-divided leaves have 5 to 9 sessile leaflets that are from 2 to 6 in. long, linear to oblanceolate to elliptic. Leaflets with few or no teeth, but any teeth are above the middle of the leaflet blade. The umbels are compound, loose, to 6 in. wide, and have white flowers. Frequent. Swamps, wet meadows, and stream banks. Widespread in the eastern 2/3 of TN and in most of the e U.S. Aug-Oct. The genus name is from the Greek *oxys* (sharp) and *polios* (white). **Considered to be poisonous**.

Genus *Ptilimnium*
Three species are found in Tennessee that are easily confused and difficult to differentiate. The genus name is from the Greek *ptilon* (feather or down) and *limne* (mud), alluding to the feather-like leaves and habitat.

Jack Carman

Big Mock Bishop's Weed
Ptilimnium costatum (Elliott) Rafinesque
Erect branching annual to 5 ft tall with pinnate leaves, from 2 to 6 in. long, that are dissected into many filiform leaflets. Leaflets are crowded on the leaf axis, appearing whorled. The umbel, from 1.6 to 3.2 in. wide, is compound with white flowers and with bracts that are usually filiform and undivided. Infrequent. Stream banks, wet meadows, swamp margins. Found in Middle TN, also Hamilton County, and from s IL and MO south to NC, GA and TX. Jul-Aug.

Atlantic Mock Bishop's Weed (*Ptilimnium capillaceum* (Michaux) Raf.) is similar, but has less-crowded leaflets not appearing whorled, and 3-parted umbellar bracts. Occasional. Found in the western 2/3 of TN, and chiefly near the coast from MA to FL to TX, interior to KY, MO and KS. Jun-Oct.

Ozark Mock Bishop's Weed (*Ptilimnium nuttallii* (DC.) Britton) has even fewer but longer leaflets, and the umbellar bracts are filiform and undivided. Infrequent. Wet soil. Found in the western 2/3 of TN, and from KS to TN south to LA and TX. Jun-Jul.

Water Parsnip   *Sium suave* Walter
Smooth perennial to 7 ft tall, usually with a rank odor. The stems are stout and angled, solitary, hollow, and the branches are stiffly ascending. The once-pinnate compound leaves, from 4 to 10 in. long, have 7 to 17 linear to lance-ovate leaflets, from 2 to 4 in. long, that have finely toothed margins. Submersed leaves, if present, are twice pinnately dissected. The umbels are compound, from 1 to 5 in. wide with small white flowers. The fruit is smooth and strongly ribbed. Infrequent. Meadows, swamps, creek margins, and wet barrens. Found in Lake, Obion, Stewart, Montgomery, Robertson, Humphreys, Coffee and Sullivan counties in TN, and widely scattered across North America. Jun-Aug. The genus name was adapted from the Greek *sion*, the ancient name of some marsh plant.

Jack Carman

Jack Carman

Yellow Pimpernel
Taenidia integerrima (L.) Drude
Smooth, often glaucous, branched perennial from 16 to 32 in. tall. Leaves, from 1 to 6 in. long, are alternate, 2 to 3 times ternately compound, the lower with long stalks, and the upper with wholly sheathing stalks. The leaflets are ovate to oblong or elliptic, 0.4 to 1.6 in. long with entire margins. The yellow-flowered compound umbels are loose and open. The umbellets have fertile flowers around the margin but the inner flowers are male only. The fruit is smooth and oblong with low ribs. Occasional. Rocky woods and outcrops, ledges along bluffs, roadsides, barrens, cedar glades. Found from the Western Highland Rim east in TN, and broadly distributed throughout eastern North America. Apr-May. The plants have a light, pleasant, celery-like odor. The genus name is from the Greek *tainidion* (a little band), in reference to the scarcely prominent ribs of the fruit.

Genus *Thaspium*
Three species and one additional variety are found in Tennessee. The genus name is adapted from *thapsia*, a related genus.

Hairy Meadow Parsnip
Thaspium barbinode (Michaux) Nuttall
Perennial to 3 ft tall, branched above, with small stiff hairs around the upper nodes. The basal and stem leaves are usually twice ternately-compound, the leaflets lanceolate to ovate, toothed and incised, 0.6 to 2.4 in. long.   Umbels are yellow flowered, and commonly from 1.2 to 2.5 in. wide, the stalks of the umbellets about equal. The central flower of each umbellet is distinctly stalked. The fruit is ribbed, winged and smooth. Frequent. Woods and barrens. Widespread in Middle and East TN, and most of the eastern U.S. May-Jun.

Mountain Meadow Parsnip (*Thaspium pinnatifidum* (Buckley) Gray) is similar, but the flowers are pale yellow to white and the fruit is hairy. Rare. Mountain woods. Found in DeKalb, Clay, Hamilton and Cocke counties in TN, and from VA and KY to NC and TN. May-Jun.

Jack Carman

Jack Carman

Smooth Meadow Parsnip
Thaspium trifoliatum (L.) Gray
Smooth sparingly-branched perennial to 3 ft tall. Basal leaves are simple (rarely ternate), long-stalked, finely toothed, cordate to reniform in shape. The upper leaves are compound with 3 (rarely 5) lanceolate to ovate, toothed leaflets from 1.6 to 3.2 in. long.   All leaves have a distinct hyaline (transparent) margin. The umbels are compound, long-stalked, to 3 in. wide, and the central flower of each umbellet is distinctly stalked. The fruit is winged and smooth. Moist woods, stream banks. East and central U.S. Apr-May. This species has two varieties.   The more western **var. *flavum*** Blake (as shown here) has yellow flowers. Common. Widespread in TN. The more eastern **var. *trifoliatum*** has maroon or dark purple flowers. Infrequent. Blue Ridge Mountains, also Davidson, Cheatham, Sumner, Stewart and Claiborne counties in TN.

Golden Alexanders (*Zizia*) are easily confused with Meadow Parsnip, but the central flower of each umbellet is not stalked. Three *Zizia* species occur in TN.

APIACEAE : PARSLEY FAMILY

Genus *Torilis*
Two species are found in TN. The derivation of the genus name is uncertain.

Field Hedge Parsley
Torilis arvensis (Hudson) Link*
Weedy, freely-branched, taprooted annual to 3 ft tall. The leaves are ovate to lance-ovate in outline, 1 to 3 times pinnate, the lower leaflets usually stalked. The leaflets are linear-lanceolate, coarsely toothed, the central one largest and to 2 in. long. Umbels are compound, terminal and lateral, on stalks to 8 in. long. Umbellet stalks usually 5 to 9, ascending or spreading, to about 1 in. long. The flowers are white. Occasional. Fields, roadsides. Widespread in TN. Introduced from Europe and established in much of the e U.S. Jun-Jul. *Torilis japonica* (Houtt.) DC.*

Knotted Hedge Parsley (*T. nodosa* (L.) Gaertner*) is similar, but the inflorescence has a very short stalk (under 0.8-in.), and is compact and head-like. Rare. Waste places. Found in Davidson and Knox counties in TN, and in GA, AL and MS. May.

Jack Carman

Jack Carman

LOGANIACEAE : LOGANIA FAMILY
In Tennessee, the Logania Family is represented by 5 genera with one species each.

Mitrewort
Mitreola petiolata (J. F. Gmelin) T. & G.
Mostly smooth annual from 8 to 24 in. tall with a solitary stem that is branched above. The leaves, from 1.2 to 2.4 in. long, are opposite, entire, lance-shaped to elliptic or ovate with the lower short-stalked and the upper sessile. The inflorescence is a secund (one-sided) cyme that terminates the stem and branches. The white flowers are about 0.1-in. long. Infrequent. Barrens, meadows, ditches, moist or wet soil. Found in Wilson, Rutherford, Bedford, Coffee, Warren, White, Sequatchie, Hamilton and Bradley counties in TN. Chiefly a Coastal Plain species found from se VA to FL to Mexico, and inland to AR and TN. · Jul-Sep. *Cynoctonum mitreola* (L.) Britton.

George Hornal

LOGANIACEAE : LOGANIA FAMILY

Indian Pink   *Spigelia marilandica* L.
Erect leafy perennial from 12 to 28 in. tall.
Leaves are opposite, mostly sessile, entire,
narrowly or broadly lance-shaped, from 2 to
5 in. long. The flowers are borne in a
secund (one-sided) cyme that terminates the
stem. The sepals are narrow and pointed.
The corolla, from 1.2 to 2.5 in. long, is scarlet
(red) outside and greenish-yellow inside, and
tubular with 5 conspicuous, spreading,
pointed lobes. The style usually extends
well outside the corolla tube. Common.
Rich moist woods, thickets. Widespread in
TN and found from NC to s IN to OK south to
FL and TX. May-Jun. The plant **contains a
poisonous alkaloid (Spigeline)**, and root
tea was once used as a vermifuge by
American Indians and physicians. Pinkroot
and Wormgrass are other common names.
The genus name is in honor of Adrian
Spiegel, who was the first to give directions
for preparing a herbarium.

GENTIANACEAE : GENTIAN FAMILY
Six genera and 16 species are found in TN.

Jack Carman

Two *Bartonia* species are found in TN. The
genus name is in honor of Benjamin Smith
Barton, a 19th century Philadelphia botanist.

Yellow Bartonia
Bartonia virginica (L.) BSP.
Perennial from 4 to 16 in. tall with an erect
wiry stem that is often spiraled. The stem is
leafless, but has mostly paired scales. The
4-lobed flowers, less than 0.15-in. long, are
greenish and borne on short stalks (or
branches) arising from the upper stem
scales. Fruit to 0.2-in. long. Occasional.
Moist meadows, marshes, swamps. Found
from the Eastern Highland Rim east in TN,
also in Lewis County, and throughout the
eastern U.S. and se CAN. Jul-Oct.

Screwstem or Branched Bartonia (*B.
paniculata* (Michaux) Muhlenberg) is similar,
but the scales are alternate on the stem, and
the inflorescence is usually paniculate.
Flowers greenish to white. Infrequent. Wet
meadows, swamps. Found in Weakley,
Henry, Stewart, Coffee, White, Fentress,
Morgan and Blount counties in TN. A chiefly
Coastal Plain species found from
Newfoundland to FL and MS, and inland to
KY and OK. Aug-Oct.

Jack Carman

American Columbo
Frasera caroliniensis Walter
A robust, smooth, short-lived perennial from 3 to 10 ft tall when in flower. The basal rosette has oblanceolate leaves to 16 in. long. Stem leaves are in whorls (usually 4), progressively reduced in size upward. The 4-lobed flowers are numerous in terminal clusters, and are greenish-white sprinkled with purple. Each petal-like lobe, from 0.4 to 0.7-in. long, has a large, round, green gland below the middle. The plant consists of only a basal rosette each year until the year it flowers; then it dies. Occasional. Rich woods and limestone glades. Thinly spread in TN, more prevalent in Middle TN. The U.S. range is from w NY to MI and IL south to n GA, e OK and LA. May-Jun. *Swertia caroliniensis* (Walter) Kuntze.

Genus *Gentiana*
Seven species are listed for TN, and two are endemic to the southern Appalachian Mountains. The genus was named in honor of Gentius, King of Illyria, who supposedly discovered the original species and its medicinal value.

Soapwort Gentian   *Gentiana saponaria* L.
Smooth erect perennial from 8 to 28 in. tall. The leaves are opposite, linear to elliptic to obovate, from 2 to 4 in. long. The flowers, from 1 to 2 in. long, are clustered, terminal and in the leaf axils. The blue to purple corolla is tubular with the lobes usually closed at the tips. Occasional. Wet meadows. Found in the eastern 2/3 of TN. U.S. range from s NY to FL, west irregularly to IL and e TX. Sep-Oct.

Appalachian Gentian (*G. decora* Pollard) is similar, but has downy stems. The flowers, from 1 to 1.8 in. long, are somewhat open with white tubes and blue lobes. Infrequent. Moist woods. Found at high elevation in East TN, and in the Blue Ridge from WV to GA Sep-Nov.

Jack Carman

Pale or Striped Gentian
Gentiana villosa L.
Erect smooth perennial from 8 to 20 in. tall. Leaves are opposite, usually widest above the middle, from 1.6 to 4 in. long. Flowers clustered, terminal and in the leaf axils. The corolla, from 1.2 to 2 in. long, has open lobes that are greenish-white and often striped with purple. Frequent. Open woods. Found throughout TN and most of the e U.S. from NJ south. Sep-Oct.

Blind Gentian (*G. clausa* Rafinesque) has smooth stems, mostly lanceolate leaves. Flowers, from 1.2 to 2 in. long, are blue to violet and corolla lobes are closed. Rare. Moist meadows, woods. Carter, Unicoi, Johnson and Washington counties in TN. A northern species extending south to TN in the mountains. Sep-Oct.

Blue Ridge Gentian (*G. austromontana* Pringle & A.Sharp) has pubescent stems and lanceolate to ovate leaves. Flowers, from 1.2 to 2 in. long, are tightly closed, whitish below, blue above. Rare. Upper elevation grassy balds of NC, VA and TN mountains (Washington, Carter, Unicoi and Johnson counties). Sep-Oct.

Jack Carman

Jack Carman

Stiff Gentian
Gentianella quinquefolia (L.) Small
Stiff annual from 8 to 32 in. tall, often freely branched above. Stem leaves are sessile, lanceolate to ovate, from 0.8 to 2.8 in. long. Tubular flowers in dense cymes terminate the stem and branches. The flowers, from 0.6 to 1 in. long, are blue to white, closed at the top and appearing pointed. Occasional. Woods, moist or wet open areas. Found from the Cumberland Plateau east in TN, also in Cannon and Smith counties, and in the Appalachian region from ME and w NY south to GA. Sep-Oct.

Prairie Gentian (*Gentiana puberulenta* J.Pringle), from 8 to 24 in. tall, has blue-purple striped flowers. Corolla lobes, from 1.4 to 2.4 in. long, have pointed tips that spread widely, but only in full sun. Rare. Meadows, prairies, barrens. Only known from Coffee County. A more northern and western species with a disjunct population in TN. Sep-Oct.

Pennywort   *Obolaria virginica* L.
Normally colonial perennial from 3 to 6 in. tall with a mostly unbranched stem and fleshy brittle roots. Lower leaves are scale-like and opposite, while upper leaves are rounded, mostly obovate, light green with a hint of purple, to 0.6-in. long. Tubular flowers are white (or purplish-white), almost sessile, from 0.4 to 0.5-in. long with 1 to 3 clustered in the upper leaf axils and the terminal flower solitary. Common. Rich moist woods. Found throughout TN, and from NJ to s IL south to FL and TX. Mar-Apr. The genus name is from *obolos* (a small Greek coin), alluding to the thick roundish leaves.

Genus *Sabatia*
Four species are found in Tennessee. The genus name is in honor of Liberato Sabbati, an 18th century Italian botanist.

Jack Carman

Jack Carman

Rose Pink   *Sabatia angularis* (L.) Pursh
Stout, erect, smooth biennial from 1 to 3 ft tall with many opposite branches and a 4-angled, winged stem. Leaves are mostly ovate, from 0.4 to 1.6 in. long. Inflorescence a loose, terminal cyme. Flowers, about 1 in. wide, have 5 spreading lobes, and are rose-pink (rarely white) with a prominent yellow-greenish center having a red line around the border. Common. Moist open areas, fields, roadsides. Found throughout TN and most of the e U.S. Jul-Aug. Another common name is Square-Stem Sabatia.

Small Rose Pink (*S. brachiata* Elliott) is similar, but smaller (to 20 in. tall) with a few opposite, erect branches, and basal leaves present at flowering. Stems not usually winged. Flowers pink with a greenish-yellow eye. Occasional. Found in Middle TN and much of the se U.S. Jun-Jul.

Slender Marsh Pink (*S. campanulata* (L.) Torr.) is similar, but perennial with the stem having alternate branches. Occasional. Eastern Highland Rim east in TN, also Dickson and Hickman counties. A Coastal Plain species found locally inland. July-Aug.

Plants of this family usually contain a milky sap. Leaves are simple and entire, the corolla has five lobes, and the fruit has two slender pods. The plants are **poisonous** Four genera and 8 species are found in TN.

Blue Star
Amsonia tabernaemontana Walter
A mostly smooth perennial from 16 to 40 in tall, sometimes weakly branched. Leaves are alternate, narrowly lanceolate to ovate o elliptic, from 3 to 6 in. long. Flowers are crowded in terminal panicles. The pale blue corolla is 5-lobed with the short hairy lobes opening to a star-shape about 0.5-in. wide The paired, erect, cylindric pods are from 2 to 5 in. long. Frequent. Moist or wet woods barrens. Found throughout TN, in the Coastal Plain from NJ south, and as far north in the interior as s IN and KS. Apr-May. The genus name is in honor of Dr. Amson, an 18th century physician of Gloucester Virginia, who was a friend of John Clayton.

Genus *Apocynum*
Three species are found in TN. *Apocynum* is the name for the Old World dogbane, from the Greek *apo* (far from) and *cyon* (a dog).

Jack Carman

Indian Hemp   *Apocynum cannabinum* L.
Erect branching perennial to 5 ft tall with a milky sap. Leaves are opposite, entire, ovate to lanceolate, from 2 to 5 in. long. The inflorescence is a loose axillary cluster of small white (to greenish-white) urn-shaped flowers overtopped by the foliage. Frequent. Roadsides, dry waste places, woodland margins. Found throughout TN and much of the e U.S. May-Jul American Indians used the berries and roots in weak teas for heart ailments and as a diuretic, but **this plant is considered poisonous**. Stems have been used for making rope.

Spreading Dogbane (*A. androsaemifolium* L.) is similar, but has bell-shaped, pink flowers marked with red inside. Rare. Upland woods. Found in Bledsoe, Blount, Cocke and Polk counties in TN, and in most of the U.S. Jun-Aug.

Jack Carman

Jack Carman

Climbing Dogbane
Trachelospermum difforme (Walter) A.Gray
Slender, woody, high-climbing vine that is smooth and reddish. Leaves are variable, lanceolate to broadly obovate, from 2 to 4 in. long on stalks to 0.6-in. long. Inflorescence a many-flowered cyme, arising from only one axil of the paired leaves. Flowers are pale yellow, the corolla tube funnelform, to 0.5-in. long with 5 spreading lobes at the end. Pods are 6 to 10 in. long. Occasional. Moist or wet woods, stream banks, swamp margins. Found in West TN, also Robertson and Hamilton counties, and in the Coastal Plain from DE to TX, and interior in the Mississippi River valley to sw IN and se MO. Jun-Aug. The genus name is from the Greek *trachelos* (a neck) and *sperma* (seed), based on the supposition that the seed was beaked.

Genus *Vinca*
Two species are found in Tennessee. The genus name is abbreviated from the ancient name *Vincapervinca*, reflected in the colloquial Italian *Pervinca*, the French *Pervenche* and the English *Periwinkle*.

Jack Carman

Periwinkle   ***Vinca minor*** L.*
Perennial, trailing, somewhat woody vine to 3 ft long that may form large mats. Leaves, from 1.2 to 2 in. long, are opposite, smooth, dark green and evergreen. Flowers, from 0.8 to 1.2 in. wide, arise from the leaf axils on erect stalks, and are 5-lobed, blue to lavender-blue with slender corolla tubes from 0.3 to 0.5-in. long. Occasional. Old home sites, cemeteries, waste ground, open woods. Widespread in TN and the eastern U.S. Apr-May. A native of Europe often escaped from cultivation.

Greater Periwinkle (*Vinca major* L.*) is similar, but more robust with flowering stems to 20 in. tall, and leaves that are deciduous or semi-evergreen. Flowers, from 1.4 to 2 in. wide, are lavender-blue with corolla tubes from 0.6 to 0.8-in. long. Infrequent. Thinly spread across TN and found in Hamilton, Bradley, Meigs, Roane, Knox, Davidson, Montgomery, Stewart and Fayette counties. A native of Europe, and an occasional garden escape in the se U.S., and as far north as VA and IL. Jun-Jul.

Milkweeds   **Genus** *Asclepias*

Thirteen species are listed for TN. Milkweeds are perennial and usually contain a milky sap. The flowers occur in dense to loose umbels. The corolla is deeply divided into 5 reflexed lobes that support a crown of 5 hoods and usually 5 horns. The fruit pods contain seeds that have long soft hairs and are wind dispersed. The genus name is after Aesculapius, Greek god of medicine, since some species have been used to treat a variety of ailments.

Blunt-Leaf or Curly Milkweed
Asclepias amplexicaulis J.E. Smith
Perennial with a simple, stout, erect stem from 1.5 to 3 ft tall with 2 to 5 pairs of leaves. Leaves are oval to broadly oblong, from 3 to 6 in. long, the margins wavy. The umbel is solitary, usually with many flowers, on a stalk from 4 to 12 in. long. The flowers are greenish-purple, hoods are pink, horns are longer than the hood. The pod is erect, from 4 to 5 in. long. Occasional. Dry soil, fields, thin woods, roadsides, barrens. Found throughout TN and most of the e U.S. May-Jul.

Jack Carman

The Milkweed Family is represented by 4 genera and 19 species in Tennessee.

Poke or Tall Milkweed   *Asclepias exaltata* L.
Erect perennial from 3 to 5 ft tall. Leaves are thin, broadly elliptic, tapered at both ends, mostly smooth, opposite, from 4 to 8 in. long. The 2 to 4 umbels arise from the upper leaf axils and are loosely flowered and drooping. The flowers are white to pale dull purple and the horns are longer than the hoods. Pods are erect, smooth, from 5 to 6 in. long. Occasional. Moist upland woods, forest margins. Found from the Cumberland Plateau east in TN, also in Sumner County. A more northern species extending south in the uplands to TN and GA. Jun-Aug.

Jack Carman

Prairie Milkweed
Asclepias hirtella (Pennell) Woodson
Erect or reclining perennial from 16 to 40 in. tall. Leaves are numerous, linear, rough, from 4 to 6 in. long. Two to 10, dense, nearly spherical umbels arise from the leaf axils. The individual flowers, on hairy stalks, are greenish-white or slightly purple, and are without horns. Infrequent. Prairies, barrens and glades. Found in Montgomery, Stewart, Lewis, Franklin, Coffee, Warren, Bledsoe and Bradley counties in TN. U.S. range from WV to WI south to AR and TN. Jun-Aug.

Jack Carman

Jack Carman

Swamp Milkweed
Asclepias incarnata L.
Erect, stout, mostly smooth perennial from 2 to 5 ft tall, branched above. Leaves are opposite, stalked, numerous, lanceolate to oblong, from 3 to 6 in. long, hairy beneath. Umbels are usually several to many. The flowers are pink to red (white), horns longer than the hoods. Pods are smooth and erect, from 2.4 to 4 in. long. Frequent. Moist meadows, ditches, and marshes. Found throughout TN, and in most of the east and central U.S. and s CAN. Jul-Sep.

Jack Carman

Aquatic Milkweed
Asclepias perennis Walter
Erect perennial from 16 to 32 in. tall with slender stems, often branched. Leaves, from 2 to 6 in. long, are thin, opposite, lanceolate to narrowly elliptic, acute at both ends, supported by a conspicuous stalk. Umbels are solitary or few. The flowers are white and the horns are longer than the hoods. The pods are somewhat drooping, from 1.6 to 2.4 in. long. Occasional. Swamps, wet woods, riverbanks. Found from the Western Highland Rim west in TN, along the Coastal Plain from SC to TX, and interior in the Mississippi River valley to s IN and s MO. Jul-Aug.

Jack Carman

Four-Leaf Milkweed
Asclepias quadrifolia Jacquin
Slender perennial from 8 to 20 in. tall, usually unbranched. Leaves are thin, lance-ovate to lanceolate, the larger from 2 to 5 in. long and stalked. Upper and lower leaves opposite and small, middle leaves usually a whorl of four and large. Umbels few (1 to 3), terminal or from the upper leaf axils. Flowers are pink to white, horns are shorter than the hoods. Pods are slender and erect, from 3 to 5 in. long. Frequent. Upland woods, woodland borders. Found from the Western Highland Rim east in TN. A more northern species extending south in the uplands to TN and n GA. Apr-Jun.

Common Milkweed   *Asclepias syriaca* L.
Colonial, stout, erect perennial from 3 to 7 ft tall, usually unbranched and hairy. Leaves are opposite, stalked, oblong to ovate to elliptic, hairy beneath, from 4 to 6 in. long. Umbels are dense, many-flowered, often numerous, terminal and lateral. Flowers are purple to greenish-white, horns same length as the hoods. Pods spiny, erect, several, from 4 to 5 in. long. Frequent. Fields, roadsides and waste places. Found from the Western Highland Rim east in TN, also in Shelby County. A more northern species that extends south in the uplands to TN and n GA. Jun-Aug. The plant contains cardiac glycosides that are absorbed by Monarch butterfly larvae, making the larvae and adults toxic to birds and other predators.

Purple Milkweed (*A. purpurascens* L.) has stout stems from 20 to 40 in. tall. The leaves are elliptic to ovate-oblong, stalked, from 4 to 6 in. long. Flowers purple, horns shorter than the hoods. Pods downy. Rare. Dry fields, roadsides. Found in Montgomery, Stewart and Greene counties. A northern species extending south to TN. Jun-Jul.

George Hornal

George Hornal

Butterflyweed   *Asclepias tuberosa* L.
Ascending or erect perennial sometimes branched above, from 12 to 28 in. tall, without milky sap. Leaves are numerous, alternate, oblanceolate or lanceolate to linear, from 2 to 4 in. long. Umbels are solitary and terminal, densely flowered. Flowers are orange or orange-red (rarely yellow), horns longer than the hoods. Pods are erect, from 3 to 5 in. long. Common. Roadsides, fields and waste places. Found throughout TN and in most of the eastern and central U.S. Jun-Aug. The root was chewed by Native Americans as a cure for pleurisy and other heart ailments.

Jack Carman

White Milkweed   *Asclepias variegata* L.
Erect, stout, usually unbranched perennial from 8 to 40 in. tall. The leaves are opposite, broadly oblong to ovate, stalked, from 3 to 5 in. long. Umbels 1 to 4, compact, terminal and from upper leaf nodes. Flowers are white with an external purple ring around the middle, horns are shorter than the hoods. Pods erect, from 4 to 6 in. long. Common. Upland woods, woodland margins, thickets. Found throughout TN and most of the e U.S. May-Jun. This showy species is also called Variegated Milkweed.

Whorled Milkweed
Asclepias verticillata L.
Slender erect perennial from 8 to 20 in. tall, sometimes branched at the top. Leaves are very numerous in whorls of 3 to 6, narrow, from 0.8 to 2 in. long and to 0.08-in. wide. Several umbels arise from the upper leaf nodes. Flowers are greenish-white, horns are much longer than the hoods. Pods are slender and erect, from 2.8 to 4 in. long. Occasional. Fields, roadsides, upland woods and barrens. Found from the Western Highland Rim east in TN, also in McNairy County. U.S. range from MA to FL west to ND and AZ. Jun-Aug.

Jack Carman

Jack Carman

Green Milkweed
Asclepias viridiflora Rafinesque
Erect to prostrate, thinly hairy perennial from 12 to 28 in. tall. Leaves are opposite, lanceolate to linear or broadly oblong, elliptic or ovate-oblong, rough on the margins, thinly hairy underneath, from 1.2 to 4 in. long. Umbels are densely flowered and arise from the upper leaf axils. Flowers are pale green and without horns. Pods slender and erect, about 4 in. long. Occasional. Dry upland woods, barrens. Thinly scattered in TN, and found in most of the eastern and central U.S., more common westward. Jul-Aug.

Jack Carman

Antelope-Horn Milkweed   *Asclepias viridis* Walter
Ascending or erect perennial from 8 to 24 in. tall. Leaves are alternate, oblong to lance-oblong or elliptic, rounded at the base, and short stalked, from 2.4 to 5 in. long. The umbels have greenish flowers with purple or violet hoods, horns are absent. Rare. Barrens, limestone glades, dry upland woods. Found in Davidson, Rutherford, Wilson, Hamilton and Rhea counties in TN. U.S. range from OH to NB south to FL and TX. May-Jun.

Three *Matelea* species are found in Tennessee.

Spinypod   *Matelea carolinensis* (Jacquin) Woodson
Downy perennial twining vine. Leaves are opposite, broadly heart-shaped, from 3 to 5 in. long (or larger). Clusters of 5 to 10 flowers arise from the leaf axils. Flower buds are ovoid and flowers are 5-lobed, brown-purple, flat, to almost 1 in. wide. Pods are sharply spiny, from 4 to 6 in. long. Occasional. Moist woods and thickets. Found mostly in Middle TN, and from DE to s MO south. Jun-Jul. Another common name is Climbing Milkweed.

Climbing Milkvine (*M. obliqua* (Jacquin) Woodson) is similar, but has rotund leaves and rose-brown to brownish-purple flowers with long lobes. Flower buds conical. Occasional. Found mostly in the eastern 2/3 of TN. U.S. range from PA to MO south to NC and TN. Jun-Jul.

Common Anglepod (*Matelea gonocarpa* (Walter) Shinners) has greenish-brown flowers and an angled smooth pod. Frequent. Found throughout TN, and from se VA to FL and TX, and in the Mississippi River valley to s MO and s IN. Jun-Jul.

Jack Carman

Notable family for the number of poisons provided by many of its species. Several species are familiar in gardens: ornamental tobaccos, petunia, potato, tomato, green and red peppers. Five genera and 21 species are listed for TN.

Jimsonweed   *Datura stramonium* L.*
Coarse, heavy-scented, weedy annual from 2 to 5 ft tall. The leaves are stalked, coarsely few-toothed, to 6 in. long. Flowers are funnelform with pleated lobes, white to lavender, 2.5 to 4 in. long and 1.2 to 2 in. wide, usually opening in the late afternoon. The fruit is an erect ovoid pod covered with short prickles. Occasional. Sunny disturbed ground, farmlots, barnyards, roadsides and fields. Introduced from Asia, now scattered throughout TN and most of temperate North America. Jun-Aug. The plant has been used as a folk cancer remedy, but it is **dangerously poisonous.** The genus name was adapted from either the Arabic *tatorah* or the Hindustani *dhatura*.

George Hornal

Apple-of-Peru   *Nicandra physalodes* (L.) Gaertner*
Smooth annual to 5 ft tall, the stem ridged, succulent, stout, highly-branched above. Leaves are ovate or lance-ovate, long-stalked, coarsely and unevenly toothed, from 4 to 8 in. long. Flowers are about 1 in. wide and long, light blue, broadly trumpet-shaped, solitary from the leaf axils, usually opening in the late afternoon. Fruit a many-seeded dry berry from 0.5 to 0.8-in. wide. Occasional. Disturbed ground and fields. Thinly scattered throughout TN and found in most of the e U.S. Jul-Sep. Introduced from Peru. The genus name is in honor of the poet Nicander of Colophon.

Jack Carman

Jack Carman

Ground Cherry   Genus *Physalis*

The ground cherries are quite variable and easily confused. The flowers are solitary and resemble a yellow hanging bell. The calyx is at first small but enlarges greatly to enclose the fruit (a berry) inside a papery-like bladder that is often indented at the top. Some berries are edible and have been used for making preserves, but others are **potentially toxic**. The genus name is the Greek word for bladder, alluding to the inflated calyx. Ten species are found in TN.

Angular Ground Cherry
Physalis angulata L.

Annual from 1 to 3 ft tall with a smooth, highly-branched stem. Leaves are mostly ovate to lanceolate-ovate, irregularly and coarsely toothed, 2 to 4 in. long. Flowers are small, yellowish, not dark in the center, about 0.4-in. wide. The fruiting calyx is smooth, sunken at the base, about as wide as long, usually 10-ribbed and purple veined. Occasional. Fields, roadsides, open woodlands. Thinly scattered across the western 2/3 of TN. A southern species extending north from se VA to MO. Aug-Oct.

Virginia Ground Cherry
Physalis virginiana Miller

Branched perennial from 1 to 2 ft tall with short hairs on the stem. The leaves are ovate to narrowly lanceolate, toothed or entire, from 1 to 4 in. long with stalks from 0.4 to 0.8-in. long. Flowers are yellow, the base of the lobes marked with brown, from 0.5 to 0.75-in. wide. The fruiting calyx is spreading-hairy, sunken at the base, 5-angled, notably longer than thick. The berry is orange. Frequent. Dry woods and fields. Found throughout TN. U.S. range from CT to MN south to AL and AZ. Jun-Aug.

Long-Leaf Ground Cherry (*P. longifolia* Nuttall) is similar, but the 10-ribbed calyx is merely pubescent. Frequent. Fields and open woods. Widespread across TN. U.S. range from VT to MT south to TN and AZ. Jul-Aug.

Clammy Ground Cherry (*P. heterophylla* Nees) has sticky hairs. Frequent. Upland woods and barrens. Found throughout TN, and most of the eastern and central U.S. and se CAN. Jun-Sep.

Jack Carman

Jack Carman

Horse Nettle *Solanum carolinense* L.

Coarse, erect, spiny, branched perennial from 8 to 32 in. tall. Leaves ovate, spiny and hairy with large teeth or shallow lobes, from 3 to 5 in. long. Flowers are 5-lobed, pale violet (to white), about 0.75-in. wide, and borne in lateral racemes. The yellow anthers are prominent, long and converging. The berries are yellow, from 0.4 to 0.6-in. wide, **deadly poisonous**. Common. Lawns, gardens, waste places. Found throughout TN and the e U.S. May-Sep.

Silverleaf Nightshade (*S. elaeagnifolium* Cav.) appears silvery and has lavender to violet flowers. Rare. Dry soil. Obion, Madison and Shelby counties in TN. Jun-Sep.

Buffalo Bur (*S. rostratum* Dunal*) is an annual and flowers are bright yellow. The spiny calyx wholly encloses the berry. Infrequent. Dry areas. Thinly scattered across TN. Jul-Sep.

Jack Carman

Eastern Black Nightshade
Solanum ptychanthum Dunal
Erect, branched, mostly smooth annual from 6 to 24 in. tall, without spines. Leaves are long petioled, ovate to deltoid, irregularly blunt-toothed or almost entire. Inflorescence lateral from the leaf nodes, short-stalked and umbel-like with 2 to 5 flowers. Flowers to 0.4-in. wide are white or pale violet with prominent yellow anthers. Berries are black and **poisonous**. Frequent. Cosmopolitan weed of disturbed habitats throughout TN and the e U.S. May-Oct. *Solanum americanum* Miller, *Solanum nigrum* L.

Bittersweet Nightshade (*S. dulcamara* L.*) is a scrambling or climbing perennial to 10 ft long. Leaves are simple or lobed at the base. Flowers, from 0.5 to 0.8-in. wide, are borne in clusters of 10 to 25, and are light blue to violet with 2 shiny green spots at the base of the lobes. Anthers are yellow and prominent. Berries bright red, **poisonous**. Rare. Moist disturbed ground, open woods, and cliffs. Found in Davidson, Hawkins and Carter counties in TN. A native of Eurasia found throughout most of the e U.S. Jun-Sep.

Jack Carman

Hedge Bindweed *Calystegia sepium* (L.) R. Brown
Perennial twining vine to 10 ft long. Leaves are from 2 to 4 in. long, long petioled, triangular (to oblong) in outline with sagittate or hastate bases. Flowers are solitary, white to rose-pink, funnelform, from 1.5 to 3 in. long. Involucral bracts to 0.8-in. long are mostly ovate, hiding the calyx. Frequent. Thickets, roadsides, disturbed areas. Found throughout TN and most of temperate North America. May-Aug. *Convolvulus sepium* L.

Low Bindweed (*C. spithamaea* (L.) Pursh) is similar, but more erect with less tendency to vine. Leaves feel velvety to the touch. Occasional. Thinly scattered in TN. A mostly northern species extending south in the uplands to TN and GA. May-Jul.

Field Bindweed (*Convolvulus arvensis* L.*) is similar, but the small involucral bracts do not hide the calyx. Flowers smaller. Occasional. Found throughout TN and the U.S. May-Sep.

The Morning Glory Family is represented by 8 genera and 22 species in Tennessee.

Genus *Cuscuta*
Cuscuta species are parasitic on many herbaceous plants. Because they are so different from other Morning Glory Family members, some botanical treatments place them in a distinct family. Five *Cuscuta* species are listed for TN, and identification is difficult.

Common Dodder, Love Vine
Cuscuta gronovii Willdenow
Slender parasitic herb with pinkish-yellow to orange or white, glabrous, twining stems. It is attached to the host plant with an intrusive specialized structure, through which the parasite extracts nourishment from the host. Tangles of the twining stems may eventually cover low-growing vegetation (the host). The stems have scale-like leaves and are without chlorophyll. The white bell-shaped flowers are small (0.10 to 0.16-in. wide), and occur in dense clusters. Frequent. Found throughout TN and most of the eastern and central U.S. Aug-Oct. This species was named in honor of Dutch botanist Jan Fredrik Gronovius, teacher of Linnaeus.

Jack Carman

Jack Carman

Small Red Morning Glory   *Ipomoea coccinea* L.*

Smooth, twining, annual vine from 3 to 10 ft long. Leaves, from 2 to 4 in. long, are mostly heart-shaped and entire, but sometimes coarsely toothed or angularly lobed. Scarlet (red) flowers are salverform, to 1.4 in. long and 0.8-in. wide, few to several in a raceme-like or cyme-like cluster at the end of a long axillary stalk. Occasional. Moist soil and waste places. Escaped and found in the eastern 2/3 of TN and most of the e U.S. Aug-Oct.

Morning Glory   **Genus *Ipomoea***

Seven species are listed for TN. All are twining vines with funnelform to campanulate or salverform flowers that have entire, angled, or shallowly lobed margins. The flowers are open in the morning, but wilt quickly in full sun.

George Hornal

Ivy-Leaf Morning Glory
Ipomoea hederacea* Jacquin

Twining annual vine from 3 to 6 ft long with pubescent stems. The leaves, from 2 to 5 in. long, are usually deeply three-lobed (rarely 5-lobed or entire), the lobes pointed. The pale blue or white funnelform flowers are from 1 to 2 in. long, and about as wide as long. Occasional. Waste areas, disturbed areas, roadsides, corn fields. Found throughout TN and much of the e U.S. Jun-Oct.

Scarlet Cypress Vine (*I. quamoclit* L.*) is a glabrous annual vine from 3 to 16 ft long. The scarlet flowers to 1.4 in. long and 0.8-in. wide are salverform, and the leaves are pinnately divided to the midvein into numerous, very narrow, linear lobes. Rare. Officially listed from Shelby and Blount counties in TN. Native of tropical America that is cultivated and has occasionally escaped into fields and waste places in TN and elsewhere. Jul-Oct.

Jack Carman

Small White Morning Glory   *Ipomoea lacunosa* L.

Twining annual vine from 3 to 10 ft long with smooth or sparsely hairy stems. The leaves, from 1.5 to 3 in. long, are ovate and the margins are usually maroon. The leaf base is deeply cordate, either unlobed or with two small lobes. The small, white (occasionally pink), funnelform flowers are 0.4 to 0.8-in. long and somewhat less wide. Frequent. Disturbed areas, moist fields, thickets. Widespread in TN. U.S. range from NJ to IL and KS south to FL and TX. Aug-Oct. The genus name is from the Greek *ips* (a worm) and *homoios* (resembling), alluding to the twining habit of the plants.

George Hornal

Wild Potato Vine
Ipomoea pandurata (L.) G.Meyer

Trailing or twining, smooth perennial vine to 15 ft long, arising from a large tuber-like root. The leaves, from 2 to 6 in. long, have a somewhat variable shape, usually ovate and entire with a cordate base and pointed tip. Large white funnelform flowers with purplish centers are from 2 to 3 in. long, and usually about as wide as long. Common. Dry woods, thickets, open areas. Widespread in TN and most of the e U.S. May-Jul.

The large tuber is edible and somewhat similar to that of the cultivated Sweet Potato (*Ipomoea batatas*). American Indians used a poultice from the root for rheumatism. Root tea has been used as a diuretic, laxative and expectorant.

Jack Carman

CONVOLVULACEAE
MORNING GLORY FAMILY

Common Morning Glory
Ipomoea purpurea (L.) Roth*
Twining annual vine to 15 ft long with pubescent stems. The leaves are broadly heart-shaped and from 2 to 5 in. long. The white, pink, purple or variegated funnelform flowers are from 1.4 to 2.5 in. long, and usually about as wide as long. Occasional. Disturbed areas, soybean and corn fields, roadsides, waste places. Widespread in TN, but few records from West TN. Native of tropic America that has escaped from cultivation, now widely established in most of the eastern U.S. Jul-Oct.

Jack Carman

MENYANTHACEAE : BUCKBEAN FAMILY
In Tennessee, the Buckbean Family is represented by the following species.

Yellow Floating Heart
Nymphoides peltata (Gmelin) Kuntze*
Aquatic perennial that arises from a rhizome. Leaves from the rhizome are long-stalked with broad cordate blades, usually floating but emersed if the water level recedes. Stems are stout and have a pair of opposite, short-stalked, usually unequal leaves. All leaves are almost round, 2 to 6 in. long and wide. Borne on long stalks that extend well above the water level, the yellow flowers have 5 spreading lobes from 0.8 to 1 in. long that are somewhat fringed below. The fruits are 0.5 to 1 in. long and strongly beaked. Rare. Ponds, quiet water. Found in Stewart and Montgomery counties in TN. A native of Europe introduced here and there in the eastern U.S. Jun-Sep.

The Phlox Family is represented by 3 genera and 13 species in Tennessee.

Genus *Phlox*

There are 11 species listed for the state. Species are often difficult to identify because of intergrading characteristics. *Phlox* is the Greek name for flame, and an ancient name of *Lychnis* that was transferred to this American (and Asiatic) genus.

Hairy Phlox   *Phlox amoena* Sims

Erect perennial to 12 in. tall, finely hairy. The leaves, from 0.6 to 2 in. long, are paired, narrowly oblong to lanceolate, ascending. The inflorescence is dense and compact, and the flower calyx is hairy. Flowers are tubular with 5 spreading lobes, usually red-purple (lavender to white), 0.6 to 0.8-in. wide. The shortest stamen is longer than the style, but the stamens are not visible at the opening of the corolla tube. Frequent. Dry woods and fields. Found in Middle and East TN. U.S. range from s KY to w NC south to n FL and e MS. Apr-Jun.

Jack Carman

Glade Phlox   *Phlox bifida* Beck **ssp. *stellaria*** (A. Gray) Wherry

Prostrate perennial with stiff, ascending, flowering branches to 12 in. long, with several plants having a carpet-like appearance. Leaves are paired, stiff, linear to narrowly lanceolate, 0.6 to 1.6 in. long. Cymes few flowered. The flowers, from 0.6 to 0.8-in. wide, are tubular with 5 spreading lobes that are deeply notched. Corolla pale blue-violet, style long, anthers/style visible at the corolla tube opening. Rare. Cedar glades. Found in Davidson, Rutherford and Wilson counties in TN. U.S. range from s MI to s WI south to TN, n AR and KS. Apr-May.

Moss Pink or Moss Phlox (*P. subulata* L.) is similar, but the leaves are hairy and shorter, and lobes are shallowly notched. Infrequent. Dry sandy or rocky areas. Thinly scattered in TN. A more northern species extending south in the uplands to TN and NC. Apr-May.

Jack Carman

Jack Carman

Blue Phlox　　　　　　*Phlox divaricata* L.

Erect perennial to 20 in. tall with spreading basal shoots. Leaves are well-separated pairs, ovate-lanceolate to oblong, from 1.2 to 2.0 in. long, broadest below the middle, and acute tipped. The inflorescence is a loose branched cyme with flowers on distinct pedicels. The flowers are tubular with 5 spreading lobes, and are from 0.8 to 1.2 in. wide, pale blue to red-purple (to white). The corolla tube is glabrous and the shortest stamen is longer than the style, but the stamens are not visible at the opening of the corolla tube. Common. Rich moist woods. Found throughout TN, and from VT to MN south to GA and TX. Apr-Jun. Another common name is Woodland Phlox.

Mountain Phlox (*P. ovata* L.) is similar, but has elliptic to obovate leaves, and the style is long. Anthers/style are visible at the end of the corolla tube. Infrequent. Open woods and thickets. Found in northeast TN (Knox, Grainger, Hancock, Sevier, Cocke and Greene counties), and chiefly in the mountains from PA and OH south to GA. May-Jun.

Jack Carman

Smooth Phlox　　　　　*Phlox glaberrima* L.

Erect perennial to 48 in. tall, usually completely glabrous. Leaves paired, firm, linear to narrowly lanceolate, tapering to a sharp tip, from 2 to 5 in. long. Inflorescences are dense cymes, terminal and from the upper leaf axils. Flowers are tubular with 5 spreading lobes, and are from 0.6 to 0.8-in. wide. Corolla red-purple, style long, anthers and style visible at the end of the corolla tube. Frequent. Wet woods and barrens. Found throughout TN. U.S. range from MD to s WI south to GA, AL and AR. Jun-Jul.

Fall or Garden Phlox (*P. paniculata* L.) is similar, but larger (to 80 in. tall) with the inflorescence, corolla tube and the leaf margins being finely hairy. Lateral leaf veins are conspicuous. Frequent. Rich moist areas. Found throughout TN, and from s NY to IL south to n GA and AR. Jul-Sep.

Broad-Leaf Phlox (*P. amplifolia* Britton) is similar to *P. paniculata* except smaller (to 5 ft tall), with the inflorescence glandular-hairy, and the corolla tube glabrous. Occasional. Dry or moist woods. Found in the eastern 2/3 of TN. U.S. range from s IN and MO south to w NC and AL. Jun-Sep.

Downy Phlox   *Phlox pilosa* L.
Erect perennial to 24 in. tall. Leaves paired, linear to ovate-lanceolate or ovate, from 1.5 to 3.2 in. long, narrowed to a sharp tip. The inflorescence is a loose, branched cyme with flowers on distinct stalks. Flowers are tubular, usually pale-purple (to white), 0.6 to 0.8-in. wide. The corolla tube is downy with 5 spreading lobes. The shortest stamen is longer than the style, but stamens are not visible at the corolla tube opening. Frequent. Upland woods, barrens. Found throughout TN and most of the e U.S. Apr-Jun.

Wild Sweet William (*Phlox maculata* L.) is an erect perennial to 32 in. tall, the stems usually spotted with red dots. Leaves are paired, mostly lance-shaped, from 2 to 5 in. long. The terminal and axillary cymes are densely and minutely hairy. Flowers, from 0.5 to 1 in. wide, are tubular with 5 spreading lobes. The corolla is red-purple, and the style and anthers are visible at the end of the corolla tube. Occasional. Wet woods and meadows. Found from the Eastern Highland Rim east in TN, also in Dickson and Wayne counties. A northern species extending south in the uplands to TN and GA. Jun-Jul.

Jack Carman

Jack Carman

Creeping Phlox   *Phlox stolonifera* Sims
Perennial with spreading stems to 16 in. long, and sterile basal shoots. Lower leaves are spatulate, narrowed to a petiole-like base; upper leaves, from 0.6 to 1.4 in. long, are lanceolate to oblong and nearly sessile. Cymes are loose and open, few flowered and glandular pubescent. Flowers are tubular with 5 spreading lobes, and from 1.0 to 1.2 in. wide. The corolla is pale bluish to red-purple, the style is long, and the anthers/style are visible at the end of corolla tube. Infrequent. Moist woods. In TN, distribution limited to the Blue Ridge (Polk, Blount, Sevier, Cocke, Unicoi, Carter and Johnson counties). U.S. range from PA and s OH south to GA, chiefly in the mountains but also in the Piedmont. Apr-May. Creeping Phlox is a showy roadside plant in the Great Smoky Mountains National Park in mid-to-late April.

Jack Carman

POLEMONIACEAE : PHLOX FAMILY

Greek Valerian, Jacob's Ladder
Polemonium reptans L.

Perennial to 20 in. tall with one to several erect or ascending slender stems. Leaves are alternate and pinnately compound with a terminal leaflet and 3 to 8 leaflet pairs. Leaflets are oblanceolate to oblong or elliptic, usually 0.8 to 1.6 in. long. The inflorescence is a loose, open, few-flowered panicle. Flowers, about 0.6-in. long, are cup-shaped, lavender (to white) with 5 lobes about half the length of the corolla, and stamens are cream-colored, shorter than the corolla. Frequent. Rich moist woods. Found throughout TN, and from NY to MN south to VA, AL and e OK, most abundant west of the Appalachians. Apr-May. The genus name is believed by some to be in honor of Polemon, an early Athenian philosopher.

Jacob's Ladder is also the common name for *Polemonium van-bruntiae* Britton, a northeastern Appalachian species that does not occur in TN.

HYDROPHYLLACEAE : WATERLEAF FAMILY

Appendaged Waterleaf   *Hydrophyllum appendiculatum* Michaux

Hairy biennial from 1 to 2 ft tall. Leaves shallowly and palmately 5-lobed. The inflorescence of 0.5-in. long lavender flowers rises above the leaves. Stamens extend 0.1-in. beyond the corolla. Occasional. Rich woods. A northern species extending south into Middle TN, it ranges from Ontario to MN south to PA, TN, MO and KS. May-Jun.

Broad-Leaf Waterleaf (*Hydrophyllum canadense* L.) is a perennial from 12 to 20 in. tall. Leaves have 5 to 9 palmate lobes, and overtop the flowers. The white to pink-purple flowers are from 0.3 to 0.5-in. long, and stamens extend 0.2-in. beyond the corolla. Occasional. Found in rich moist woods in Middle and East TN. The extended range is from VT to WI south to n GA and n AR. May-Jun.

Jack Carman

George Hornal

Large-Leaf Waterleaf   ***Hydrophyllum macrophyllum*** Nuttall
Densely hairy perennial from 12 to 28 in. tall. Leaves, 4 to 8 in. long, are mottled and
pinnately-divided with 7 or 9 lobes that have coarse teeth. Flowers are white or pinkish,
about 0.5-in. long. The stamens protrude well beyond the corolla. Occasional. Rich moist
woods. Found in Middle and East TN, and from OH to IL south to NC and AL. May-Jun.

Virginia Waterleaf (*Hydrophyllum virginianum* L.) is similar, but the mottled leaves have from
5 to 9 lobes and are mostly smooth. Flowers white to blue-purple. Rare. Rich moist woods.
Found in Knox, Sevier, Greene, Carter and Sullivan counties in TN, and from Quebec to ND
south to NC, AL and OK. May-Jun. The genus name is from the Greek *hydor* (water) and
phyllon (leaf), from the very watery stems and petioles of the original species.

Jack Carman

The Waterleaf Family has 4 genera and 14
native species listed for TN. The flowers are
bell-shaped or bowl-shaped. The corolla has
5 lobes and the 5 stamens usually extend
beyond the corolla.

Baby Blue Eyes
Nemophila aphylla (L.) Brummitt
Spreading branched annual from 4 to 16 in.
tall with weak stems. Leaves are alternate
and long-stalked with the blade deeply
divided into 3 to 5 lobes that are 0.4 to 1 in.
long. The flowers, about 0.12-in. long, are
white to pale blue and solitary on pedicels to
0.4-in. long opposite the leaves. Occasional.
Rich moist woods. Found in Middle TN, also
Shelby, Loudon, Polk, and Knox counties.
U.S. range from se MO to MD south to FL
and TX. Mar-May. The genus name is from
the Greek *nemos* (glade) and *philein* (to
love). *Nemophila microcalyx* (Nuttall)
Fischer & Meyer, *Nemophila triloba* (Raf.)
Thieret.

Jack Carman

Purple Phacelia   *Phacelia bipinnatifida* Michaux
Biennial from 8 to 20 in. tall with spreading-hairy stems and branched above. Leaves are 2 to 3 in. long, hairy, mottled and pinnately-divided twice, the lobes coarsely toothed. The inflorescence is a terminal cyme with blue-lavender, bowl-shaped flowers from 0.4 to 0.6-in. wide. Stamens hairy, extending beyond the corolla. Common. Moist woods, creek banks. Found in Middle and East TN, and from VA to OH to MO south to GA, AL and AR. Apr-May.

Blue Phacelia (*Phacelia ranunculacea* (Nuttall) Constance) is annual, from 2 to 8 in. tall. The blue flowers are almost funnelform, about 0.2-in. long. Stamens smooth, not extending past the corolla. Infrequent. Moist woods. Found in Stewart, Montgomery, Lake, Obion, Shelby and Lauderdale counties in TN, and from VA to s IL to se MO south to NC and TN. Apr-May.

Jack Carman

Five *Phacelia* species and one additional variety are found in TN. Genus name from the Greek *phacelos* (a fascicle), alluding to the coiled inflorescence when in bud.

Glade Phacelia
Phacelia dubia (L.) Trel. **var. *interior*** Fern.
Weak hairy annual from 4 to 16 in. tall that is branched from the base or unbranched. The leaves, to 2.5 in. long, are pinnately lobed with 1 to 5 toothed to entire segment pairs. The inflorescence is a terminal cyme, and flowers are bowl-shaped, lavender to white, 0.25 to 0.4-in. wide with unfringed lobes. The outer sepals are obovate-oblong. Infrequent. Found in the cedar glades and barrens of Middle TN (Montgomery, Sumner, Cheatham, Wilson, Davidson, Williamson, Rutherford and Marshall counties). Endemic to the Interior Low Plateau. Apr-Jun.

Appalachian Phacelia (*Phacelia dubia* (L.) Trel. var. *dubia*) is similar, but outer sepals are lance-shaped. Infrequent. Found in fields, woods, and barrens in East TN (Polk, Monroe, Blount, Roane, Knox, Grainger, Cocke, Unicoi and Carter counties). U.S. range from NY to PA south to GA, AL and TN. Apr-Jun.

Jack Carman

Fringed Phacelia   *Phacelia fimbriata* Michaux

Annual from 8 to 16 in. tall with weak stems and branches. Lower leaves are stalked and often pinnately compound. Upper leaves are sessile and clasping, pinnately lobed (3 to 11), to 1.5 in. long. The inflorescence is a one-sided cyme with 5 to 15 bowl-shaped white flowers that are 0.2 to 0.5-in. wide, the lobes deeply fringed. The stem and inflorescence are pubescent, the hairs spreading. Rare, but locally abundant. Rich mountain woods. Found in sw VA and w NC, and Blount, Sevier and Carter counties of East TN. This southern Appalachian endemic is found from mid to high elevation, and is abundant in the Chimneys picnic area of the Great Smoky Mountains National Park in mid-to-late April. Apr-May.

Miami Mist   *Phacelia purshii* Buckley

Annual from 8 to 16 in. tall with weak stems and branches. Lower leaves are stalked and often pinnately compound. Upper leaves are sessile and clasping, pinnately lobed (3 to 11), to 1.5 in. long. The inflorescence is a one-sided cyme with 10 to 30 bowl-shaped blue or pale lavender flowers with a white center that are 0.2 to 0.5-in. wide, the lobes deeply fringed. The stem and inflorescence are pubescent, the hairs appressed. Occasional. Rich moist woods, moist fields, roadsides. Found in Middle TN, also Claiborne, Monroe, Blount, Sevier and Johnson counties. U.S. range from PA to MO south to GA and AL. Apr-May. The species name is in honor of its discoverer, Frederick Traugott Pursh.

Jack Carman

Jack Carman

The Forget-Me-Not Family is represented by 12 genera and 24 species in Tennessee.

Two *Cynoglossum* species are found in TN. The genus name is from the Greek *cynos* (of a dog) and *glossa* (tongue), alluding to the shape of the leaves.

Wild Comfrey
Cynoglossum virginianum L.

Hairy perennial from 16 to 32 in. tall that is erect and unbranched. The basal leaves are long-stalked, elliptic-oblong, from 4 to 8 in. long. Upper leaves are sessile, often clasping, progressively smaller upward. The pale blue flowers are 0.3 to 0.6-in. wide in a raceme-like, forked inflorescence extending well above the leaves. Common. Upland woods. Found throughout TN and most of the e U.S. May-Jun.

Hound's Tongue (*C. officinale* L.*) is similar, but biennial. The stem is leafy to the inflorescence and the flowers are dull purplish-red. Infrequent. Open areas. Found in Cheatham, Davidson, Sumner, White, Bledsoe, Cumberland, Fentress and Knox counties in TN. A native of Eurasia, now widely established in the e U.S. and westward. May-Jul.

Genus *Echium*

Echium was a plant name attributed to Dioscorides and derived from *echis* (a viper), alluding to the fancied resemblance of the nutlet to a viper's head.

Viper's Bugloss
Echium vulgare L.*

Rough-hairy, erect, taprooted biennial from 1 to 3 ft tall. The basal leaves are whorled, oblanceolate, stalked, from 2.5 to 10 in. long. Stem leaves are alternate, reduced upward, becoming sessile. Flowers, in small clusters in the upper leaf axils, are showy, funnelform, blue (aging to pink), from 0.5 to 0.8-in. long. The stamens and style extend well past the corolla lobes. Infrequent. Roadsides, waste places, meadows. Found in Rutherford, Hickman, Cumberland, Roane, Sullivan, Scott, Carter, Washington, Hawkins and Unicoi counties in TN. Native of Europe widely established in the e U.S. Jun-Oct.

Wally Roberts

Jack Carman

Narrow-Leaf Vervain
Verbena simplex Lehmann
Smooth or slightly hairy perennial with branching stems from 6 to 24 in. high. The leaves, from 1 to 4 in. long and about 0.6-in. wide, are opposite, toothed and on short stalks. The inflorescence is a slender spike at the summit of each branch. Individual flowers are lavender (rarely white), about 0.3-in. wide. Common. Roadsides and dry fields. Found throughout TN and the eastern U.S. May-Sep.

White Vervain (*Verbena urticifolia* L.) is a weedy annual or short-lived perennial from 16 to 60 in. tall that is often branched near the base. The leaves, from 2 to 6 in. long, are stalked, broadly lanceolate to oblong-ovate, coarsely and somewhat doubly toothed. The minute white flowers grow in very slender spikes that terminate the stem and branches. Common. Fields and waste places. Found throughout TN and most of the eastern U.S. Jun-Sep.

Jack Carman

Hoary Vervain
Verbena stricta Ventenat
Perennial from 8 to 48 in. tall with a densely pale-hairy stem. Leaves, from 1.2 to 4 in. long, are opposite, elliptic to almost round, sessile, thick, sharply toothed, densely hairy, with prominent veins beneath. Flowers are 5-lobed, purplish to pink, from 0.3 to 0.4-in. wide, occurring on one or more long, thick, compact, terminal spikes. Infrequent. Fields, barrens, roadsides. Found in West TN (Shelby, Tipton, Dyer, Obion, Weakley, Henry and Carroll counties), also Pickett County in Middle TN. A mostly northern and western species introduced in the Southeast. Jun-Sep.

Blue Vervain (*Verbena hastata* L.) is similar, but less hairy. The leaves are more lance-shaped and have obvious stalks, and the flowers are usually bluish and smaller (to 0.2-in. wide). Occasional. Moist fields and wet areas. Thinly scattered in TN, but found throughout most of the U.S. and southern CAN. Jun-Sep.

PHRYMACEAE : LOPSEED FAMILY
Tennessee has only one species.

Lopseed   *Phryma leptostachya* L.
Erect leafy perennial from 20 to 40 in. tall, simple or with a few divergent branches. The leaves are opposite, sharply toothed, long-stalked below and sessile above, ovate, from 2 to 6 in. long. The pale-purple or white flowers are opposite and horizontal in long, interrupted, spike-like racemes at the end of the stem and branches. The corolla, about 0.3-in. long, is bilaterally symmetric with the upper lip straight and notched, and the lower lip 3-lobed. After flowering, the persistent calyx that encloses the fruit becomes closely reflexed against the main flowering stem, giving the appearance that the fruit has "lopped" down.   Common.   Rich moist woods. Found throughout TN, the eastern U.S. and se CAN. Jun-Aug.

LAMIACEAE : MINT FAMILY
General characteristics of the Mint Family include: aromatic odor, opposite and simple leaves, usually square stem, and irregular corolla (usually 2-lipped).   Represented by 31 genera and 88 species in TN.

Jack Carman

Jack Carman

Genus *Agastache*
Two species are found in TN.   The genus name is from the Greek *agan* (much) and *stachys* (a head of wheat), alluding to the numerous spikes.

Yellow Giant Hyssop
Agastache nepetoides (L.) Kuntze
Erect perennial to 60 in. tall with a smooth stem that is branched above.   Leaves are stalked, ovate to ovate-lanceolate, coarsely toothed, to 6 in. long but reduced above. Erect, densely-flowered spikes terminate the stem and branches.   Flowers, about 0.25-in. long, are yellowish-green with ovate calyx lobes and 4 long stamens that extend outside the corolla.   Occasional.   Open woods and woodland borders.   Widespread in TN. A mostly northern species extending south to TN and GA. Jul-Aug.

Purple Giant Hyssop (*A. scrophulariifolia* (Willd.) Kuntze) is similar, but has pubescent stems, triangular-shaped calyx lobes, and a purplish corolla.   Rare.   Upland woods. Recorded in Polk and Carter counties in TN. U.S. range from VT to se SD south to NC and e KS. Jul-Aug.

Genus *Blephilia*

Two species are found in TN. The genus name is from the Greek *blepharis* (the eyelash), alluding to the hairy fringe of the bracts and calyx-teeth.

Downy Wood Mint
Blephilia ciliata (L.) Bentham

Erect perennial from 16 to 32 in. tall with a finely downy stem. Leaves are lanceolate to ovate, to 2.5 in. long, entire or with a few low teeth, almost sessile. Dense flower whorls are terminal and in the upper leaf axils. The flowers, about 0.5-in. long, are lavender speckled with purple and two-lipped. The 2 stamens extend outside the corolla. Frequent. Meadows and woodlands. Found in the western 2/3 of TN, also Knox County. U.S. range from MA to WI south to GA and AR. May-Jul.

Hairy Wood Mint (*B. hirsuta* (Pursh) Benth.) is similar, but the leaves have petioles that are at least 0.4-in. long. Occasional. Moist woods. Found throughout TN. Extended range from Quebec to MN south to NC, AL and AR. May-Aug.

George Hornal

Jack Carman

Genus *Calamintha*

Three species are found in Tennessee.

Glade Savory
Calamintha glabella (Michaux) Bentham

Smooth, loosely-branched perennial to 2 ft tall with weak stems. Leaves are opposite, oblanceolate, 0.8 to 1.6 in. long and less than 0.4-in. wide, reduced above. From 2 to 8 flowers on short stalks arise from the upper leaf nodes. The lavender flowers, from 0.3 to 0.6-in. long, are two-lipped with a spreading lower lip. Infrequent. Found in open limestone glades and barrens of Middle TN (Dickson, Cheatham, Davidson, Wilson, Williamson and Rutherford counties), and also in KY, MO and AR. May-Aug. *Satureja glabella* (Michaux) Briquet.

Basil Thyme (*Calamintha nepeta* (L.) Savi*) is similar, but has hairy stems, commonly with tufts of small leaves at the leaf nodes. Occasional. Waste places and roadsides. An introduced species found in Middle and East TN, and from MD to KY south. Jun-Sep. *Satureja calamintha* (L.) Scheele*.

Jack Carman

Northern Horse Balm
Collinsonia canadensis L.
Erect perennial from 1.5 to 4 ft tall, branched above. Leaves are opposite, well spaced on the stem, ovate to obovate with a pointed tip, toothed, from 4 to 8 in. long. The stalks of the principal leaves are less than one-half as long as the blades. Clusters of flowers terminate the stem and branches. The corolla is pale yellow, about 0.5-in. long and two-lipped, the lower longer. The 2 stamens extend well beyond the corolla lip. Frequent. Rich woods. Found throughout TN, and from Quebec to s WI south to FL and AR. Jul-Sep. The foliage and flowers have a citronella-like odor. Tea can be brewed from the leaves, and the rhizome has been used as a diuretic, tonic and astringent.

Southern Horse Balm (*Collinsonia tuberosa* Michaux) is similar, but has white or cream-colored flowers about 0.4-in. long that are speckled with purple. The main stem leaf stalks are more than one-half as long as the blades. Rare. Rich woods. Found in Wayne, Hickman, Marion and Sequatchie counties in TN, and in GA, AL and MS. Jul-Aug.

Jack Carman

Genus *Collinsonia*
Three species are found in Tennessee. The genus name is in honor of Peter Collinson, an 18th century English botanist.

Whorled Horse Balm
Collinsonia verticillata Baldwin *ex* Elliott
Perennial to 20 in. tall with 2 or 3 leaf pairs that are usually near the base of the inflorescence and appear whorled. The leaves are ovate to oblong-obovate, hairy on the margins, on stalks from 0.6 to 1.6 in. long. The inflorescence is borne on a long axis that rises above the leaves, and has 3 to 6 flowers at each node. The pinkish flowers from 0.6 to 0.8-in. long have four stamens. Infrequent. Rich woods. Found from the Cumberland Plateau east in TN (Hamilton, Meigs, Rhea, Cumberland, McMinn, Roane, Knox, Blount and Sevier counties), and from s VA south to GA and AL. May-Jul.

Cumberland Rosemary
Conradina verticillata Jennison
Diffusely-branched perennial shrub to 20 in. tall. Leaves, from 0.4 to 0.8-in. long, are needle-like and appear whorled. From 1 to 3 flowers on short stalks arise from each upper leaf node. The flowers, about 0.7-in. long, are two-lipped, pinkish to lavender and spotted within. Rare. Restricted to the sandy banks of the larger Cumberland Plateau streams in KY and TN. Found in White, Cumberland, Morgan, Fentress and Scott counties. May-Jun. The genus name is in honor of Solomon White Conrad, a 19th century Philadelphia botanist.

Jack Carman

Jack Carman

Dittany   *Cunila origanoides* (L.) Britton
Smooth, freely-branched perennial from 8 to 16 in. tall with stems somewhat woody at the base. Leaves, from 0.8 to 1.6 in. long, are opposite, mostly sessile, ovate to deltoid-ovate, usually with a few teeth. The flowers are borne in clusters, terminal or from the upper leaf axils. The corolla, about 0.3-in. long, is rose-purple to white and 2-lipped with the upper lip erect and the lower lip spreading and 3-lobed. The 2 stamens are long and straight, surpassing the corolla. Occasional. Dry or rocky woods. Found in the Western Highland Rim and from the Cumberland Plateau east in TN. U.S. range from s NY to MO south to SC and OK. Aug-Oct. *Cunila* is an ancient Latin name for some fragrant plant that was transferred to this American genus.

Ground Ivy, Gill-over-the-Ground
Glechoma hederacea L.*

Perennial with creeping stems to 16 in. long, rooting at the nodes and often forming large mats. The leaves, from 0.4 to 1.2 in. long, are stalked, more or less round, bluntly toothed, evergreen, cordate at the base. The flowering stems, to 8 in. tall, are erect and blue-violet flowers, from 0.5 to 0.9-in. long, arise from the leaf axils with usually three at a node. Frequent. Moist woods, disturbed areas. Found throughout TN and the e U.S. Apr-Jun. "Gill" is from the French *guiller* (to ferment) as leaves were once used to help ferment or flavor beer. The genus name is from the ancient Greek *glechon* (pennyroyal).

Carpet Bugle (*Ajuga reptans* L.*) is similar, but the stem leaves are usually elliptic to ovate, and taper to a narrow, nearly sessile base. Rare. Only recorded from Knox and Montgomery counties, but certainly more prevalent. A native of Eurasia that has escaped into lawns and open areas throughout. May-Jun.

Jack Carman

Jack Carman

Genus *Lamium*

Two species are found in Tennessee. *Lamium* is an old Latin name of a nettle-like plant.

Henbit   *Lamium amplexicaule* L.*

Annual from 4 to 16 in. tall with weak stems that are usually branched at the base. The upper leaves are sessile, more or less round, clasping, and about 0.6-in. long. The lower leaves are similar, but have long petioles and coarse teeth. The flowers arise in whorls (verticils) from the leaf axils. The flowers, to 0.7-in. long, are two-lipped with the lips widely spreading, and pinkish-purple with the lower lip spotted. Frequent. A weed of open areas, lawns, fields, and waste places. Introduced from Eurasia, and found throughout TN and most of the e U.S. Mar-Nov.

Jack Carman

Purple Dead Nettle   *Lamium purpureum* L.*

Weak annual from 4 to 16 in. tall, usually branched at the base. The leaves, with blades from 0.3 to 1.2 in. long, are stalked, heart-shaped, progressively reduced in size upward. Upper leaves are crowded, overlapping, angled downward. Pinkish-purple flowers, from 0.4 to 0.6-in. long, arise in whorls from the upper leaf axils. Occasional. A weed of open areas, fields, lawns and waste places. Introduced from Eurasia, and found throughout TN and most of the e U.S. Apr-Oct.

Jack Carman

Genus *Lycopus*

Four species are found in Tennessee. The genus name is from the Greek *lycos* (a wolf) and *pous* (foot), from some imagined likeness in the leaves.

Cut-Leaf Water Horehound
Lycopus americanus Muhl. *ex* Barton
Perennial from 12 to 40 in. tall. Leaves, from 1 to 3 in. long, are usually stalked, mostly lanceolate and smooth, coarsely and irregularly toothed with lower leaves pinnately lobed near the base. The white flowers, less than 0.25-in. long, are crowded in whorls in the leaf axils. The calyx lobes are narrowly triangular and at maturity, surpass the nutlets. Occasional. Moist or wet areas. Found throughout TN, and most of the U.S. and s CAN. Jun-Sep.

Virginia Water Horehound (*Lycopus virginicus* L.) has hairy stems and leaves. The calyx lobes are broadly triangular and at maturity, do not surpass the nutlets. Common. Moist or wet areas. Found throughout TN and most of the e U.S. Jun-Sep.

Jack Carman

Bergamot, Bee Balm   Genus *Monarda*

Seven species are found in TN. The genus name is in honor of Nicolas Monardes, an author of many articles on medicinal and other useful plants, especially those of the New World, that were written in the latter half of the 16th century.

Eastern Bergamot, Eastern Bee Balm
Monarda bradburiana Beck

Perennial from 1 to 2 ft tall with a mostly smooth stem. Leaves, from 2 to 4 in. long, are usually sessile, mostly ovate, toothed. The flower heads, from 0.6 to 1 in. thick, are terminal and the floral bracts are usually tinged with pink or purple. The deep lavender (to white) corolla is dotted with purple, two-lipped, about 1 in. long. The stamens are longer than the upper lip. Occasional. Open woods and thickets. In TN, found in the Western Highland Rim, also Coffee County. U.S. range from s IN to IA south to AL and TX. May-Jun. *Monarda russeliana* Nuttall.

Basil Bee Balm   *Monarda clinopodia* L.

Simple to branched, smooth perennial to 3 ft tall. The leaves are stalked, mostly ovate, to 5 in. long. The flower heads are terminal and the floral bracts are green to whitish. The flowers are fragrant, white (to pale yellowish-white), two-lipped, the upper lip of each flower downy. Frequent. Woods and thickets. Found from the Western Highland Rim east in TN. U.S. range from CT to MO south to NC and AL. Jun-Jul.

Two *Monarda* species have both terminal and axillary flowering heads, and flowers with the upper lip strongly arched and longer than the stamens.

Lemon Mint (*M. citriodora* Cerv. *ex* Lag.) is an annual with a white (to pink), purple-dotted corolla, and long, pointed calyx lobes. Infrequent. Pastures. Meigs, Trousdale, Knox, Rutherford, Cannon and Marshall counties in TN. Jun-Aug.

Horse Mint (*M. punctata* L.) is a perennial with pale yellow, purple-dotted flowers. Calyx lobes are less than 0.06-in. long. Rare. Open areas. Unicoi and Washington counties in TN. Jul-Oct.

Jack Carman

Crimson Bee Balm, Oswego Tea
Monarda didyma L.

Perennial from 2 to 5 ft tall. Leaves are thin, ovate to lanceolate, from 3 to 6 in. long. The flower heads are terminal and the floral bracts are usually red-tinted. The scarlet to crimson flowers, from 1.2 to 1.8 in. long, are two-lipped and not fragrant. Stamens are longer than the upper corolla lip. Infrequent. Moist woods and thickets. Found in the Blue Ridge Province (Polk, Monroe, Blount, Sevier, Cocke, Greene, Unicoi, Carter and Johnson counties) and Cumberland County in TN. A mostly northeastern species extending south in the mountains to TN and GA. Jul-Sep. The leaves were used by the Oswego Indians of New York to brew tea, and early settlers learned to do the same.

Jack Carman

Wild Bergamot   *Monarda fistulosa* L.

Aromatic, often branched perennial from 2 to 4 ft tall with a hairy upper stem. Leaves are lanceolate to ovate, toothed, to 4 in. long on petioles to 0.6-in. long. The inflorescence is head-like (to 1.6 in. wide), terminating the stem and branches, and the floral bracts are often pink-tinged. The flowers are lavender, two-lipped with the upper lip of the corolla very hairy at the tip. Stamens are longer than the upper corolla lip. Common. Upland woods and borders, thickets. Found throughout TN, and most of the U.S. and s CAN. Jun-Sep.

Purple Bergamot (*Monarda x media* Willdenow) is similar, but flowers and floral bracts are deep red-purple. Rare. Moist woods and thickets. Recorded in Polk and Monroe counties in TN. Extended range from ME to s Ontario south to w NC and e TN. Jul-Aug. Likely a hybrid of *M. didyma* and *M. fistulosa*.

George Hornal

Obedient Plant, False Dragonhead
Physostegia virginiana (L.) Bentham
Perennial to 5 ft tall, often branched at the
top. The leaves are oblanceolate or elliptic,
sessile, sharply toothed, from 1 to 7 in. long.
The inflorescence has both showy terminal
and lateral racemes. The showy pink to
lavender flowers, from 0.7 to 1.4 in. long, are
two-lipped with the upper lip concave-
hooded, and the lower lip spreading and
three-lobed. Occasional. Moist open areas,
damp thickets. Found from the Western
Highland Rim east in TN, also in Shelby
County, and in most of the eastern U.S. and
southeastern CAN. Jul-Sep. The genus
name is from the Greek *physa* (a bladder)
and *stege* (a covering), alluding to the calyx,
which is somewhat inflated at maturity.
Dracocephalum virginianum L.

Jack Carman

Heal All   *Prunella vulgaris* L.*
Erect to reclining perennial from 4 to 20 in. tall. The leaves are lanceolate to elliptic to
broadly ovate, entire or obscurely toothed, from 1 to 3.5 in. long. The blue-violet flowers,
from 0.4 to 0.8-in. long, are borne in a crowded terminal spike from 0.8 to 2 in. long and are
two-lipped. The upper lip of the corolla is entire and helmet-like, and the lower lip is shorter
with 3 lobes. Common. Fields, meadows, pastures, roadsides. Found throughout TN and
the e U.S. May-Oct. Traditionally, leaf tea was used as a gargle for sore throats and mouth
sores, and to treat ulcers, wounds, bruises and sores. Research suggests the plant
possesses antibiotic qualities. The genus name is of uncertain and much disputed origin,
often written *Brunella*, which was a pre-Linnaean form.

Jack Carman

Jack Carman

Clustered Mountain Mint   *Pycnanthemum muticum* (Michaux) Persoon
Erect perennial from 16 to 48 in. tall with short-hairy stems that are branched above. The
leaves, from 1.6 to 3 in. long with stalks about 0.1-in. long, are smooth, lance-shaped, few-
toothed, with prominent veins. Upper leaves are velvety and whitish above. Flowers are in
dense, rounded, terminal or axillary heads to 0.6-in. wide. Corolla lobes white, spotted with
purple, about 0.2-in. long. Occasional. Moist meadows, barrens. Found in East and Middle
TN, and from MA to MI to MO south to FL and LA. Jun-Aug.
Hoary Mountain Mint (*P. incanum* (L.) Michaux) is similar, but leaves are toothed, leaf stalks
are 0.2 to 0.6-in. long, and heads are loose, from 0.6 to 1.4 in. wide. Common. Barrens,
woods edges. Found throughout TN and from VT to s IL south to NC and TN. Aug-Sep.
Thin-Leaf Mountain Mint (*P. montanum* Michaux) has broadly lance-shaped, toothed leaves
and smooth stems. Infrequent. Mountain woods. WV to GA in the Blue Ridge. Jun-Aug.

Narrow-Leaf Mountain Mint   *Pycnanthemum tenuifolium* Schrader
Smooth erect perennial to 3 ft tall that is branched above. Leaves, from 1 to 2 in. long, are
linear, entire, short-stalked. The flower heads are numerous, rounded, dense. Upper bracts
are sharp-pointed. Corolla lobes white, to 0.3-in. long, stamens 4. Common. Dry open
areas. Found throughout TN, and from ME to MN south to FL and TX. Jun-Jul.
Hairy Mountain Mint (*P. pilosum* Nuttall), to 5 ft tall, is branched above and softly hairy.
Leaves lanceolate, hairy beneath, from 1 to 2 in. long. Inflorescence dense, bracts velvety
with hairy margins. Occasional. Upland woods, thickets. Mostly West TN and Western
Highland Rim. Extended range from Ontario to KS south to TN and AR. Jul-Sep.

Jack Carman

Genus *Salvia*

Flowers are borne in a terminal, spike-like inflorescence or in a verticil (flowers whorled) with 1 to 3 or more flowers at a node. The calyx is 2-lipped and stamens are 2. *Salvia* is the old Latin name for Sage.

Blue Sage

Salvia azurea Michaux & Lamarck
var. *grandiflora* Bentham

Leafy erect perennial from 2 to 5 ft tall with stems that are simple or branched above and minutely hairy. Leaves are downy, linear to lanceolate or elliptic, from 1 to 4 in. long. Racemes are terminal, dense and spike-like with 6 to 20 flowers per node. The calyx is hairy, about 0.3-in. long, and the corolla is blue to white, about 0.8-in. long. Rare. Barrens. Found in the western prairies and plains from NB to MO south to TX, and extending east to TN in the western Tennessee River valley (Stewart, Henry, Decatur, Perry and Hardin counties). Aug-Oct. *Salvia pitcheri* Torrey.

Jack Carman

Jack Carman

Lyre-Leaf Sage   *Salvia lyrata* L.

Fibrous-rooted, erect perennial from 1 to 2 ft tall with a single stem. Principal leaves, from 4 to 8 in. long on stalks from 1 to 4 in. long, are in a basal rosette, oblong or obovate-oblong but pinnately lobed into rounded segments. Stem leaves are few, smaller, mostly sessile. The terminal raceme is from 4 to 12 in. long, and the flower clusters are few and widely separated, usually with 6 flowers per node. The corolla, about 1 in. long, is tubular and pale blue to lavender or white. Common. Upland woods, thickets, fields, lawns, roadsides and barrens. Found throughout TN, and from CT to MO south to FL and TX. May-Jun. Tea made from the whole plant has been used for colds and coughs, and American Indians used a root salve for sores.

Scarlet Sage (*Salvia splendens* Sellow) has a scarlet calyx and corolla, and is commonly cultivated.

Nettle-Leaf Sage   *Salvia urticifolia* L.
Perennial from 12 to 20 in. tall with one to a few hairy stems arising from a woody rhizome. Stem leaves, from 2 to 3 in. long, have winged stalks, and are toothed, rhombic-ovate to deltoid. The inflorescence is a terminal raceme, from 4 to 8 in. long, that has 6 to 10 flowers per node. The flowering calyx, about 0.2-in. long, is glandular-dotted, and the corolla, from 0.4 to 0.6-in. long, is tubular and deep lavender to blue. Occasional. Dry woods, barrens, thickets, usually on basic soil. Found from the Western Highland Rim east in TN, also in Decatur and McNairy counties. U.S. range from PA to w KY south to SC, AL and GA. Apr-Jun.

Lance-Leaf Sage (*S. reflexa* Hornemann) is an annual. The leaves are narrow, to 2 in. long and about one-fifth as wide. The lilac to blue corolla is less than 0.5-in. long, and the calyx is about equal to the corolla tube in length. Rare. A more northern and western species found in TN only in the cedar glades of Davidson County. Jun-Sep.

Doug Malone

Jack Carman

Skullcap   **Genus *Scutellaria***
Fourteen species and 2 additional varieties are found in Tennessee. All have a rounded, 2-lipped, tubular calyx with a prominent crest, the "skullcap," on the upper lip. In fact, the genus name is from *scutella* (a dish), alluding to the crest of the fruiting calyx.

Hairy Skullcap
***Scutellaria elliptica* Muhlenberg**
Erect perennial from 1 to 2 ft tall with a hairy stem that is sometimes branched above. In **var. *elliptica***, the hairs on the stem are fine, short, and ascending, and in **var. *hirsuta*** (Short & Peter) Fernald, the hairs are fine, spreading and glandular. The leaves to 3 in. long are short-stalked, mostly rhombic-ovate with the margin crenate from the widest part to the tip. Flowering racemes to 4 in. long arise from the upper 1 to 3 pairs of leaf axils. The calyx has spreading, glandular hairs, and the corolla is blue to violet, from 0.6 to 0.8-in. long. Common. Dry upland woods, barrens, fields. Found throughout TN (except the westernmost counties), and from NY to MI south to FL and TX. May-Jul.

Jack Carman

Downy Skullcap
Scutellaria incana Biehler

Erect perennial from 2 to 3 ft tall, the stem usually solitary and minutely hairy. The leaves, from 2 to 4 in. long on stalks from 0.8 to 1.2 in. long, are lance-ovate to rhombic-ovate, broadly rounded at the base, crenate, sparsely hairy above. Flowering racemes are usually several, terminal on the stem and also arising from upper leaf axils. Flowers are blue, from 0.75 to 1 in. long, and the calyx has appressed hairs without glands. In **var. *incana***, the leaves are soft-hairy across the entire surface beneath. In **var. *punctata*** (Chapman) Mohr, the leaves are smooth beneath except for sparsely-hairy veins. Frequent. Upland woods, fields. Found throughout TN, and from NY to WI south to GA, AL and KS. Jun-Aug.

Hyssop-Leaf Skullcap
Scutellaria integrifolia L.

Erect perennial from 12 to 28 in. tall, the stem finely hairy and sometimes branched above. Lower leaves are often toothed and stalked, but fall early. The middle and upper leaves, from 0.8 to 2.5 in. long, are entire, lanceolate to oblanceolate, tapering to a short-stalked or sessile base. The racemes terminate the stem and branches, and the inflorescence has both flowers and bracts, the latter progressively reduced upward. The corolla is blue or pink (or white), from 0.7 to 1.1 in. long. Occasional. Fields, barrens, open woods. Scattered throughout TN, but more prevalent from the Eastern Highland Rim east. A primarily Coastal Plain species found from MA to FL and TX, but extending inland to OH and KY. May-Jul.

Jack Carman

Jack Carman

Mad-Dog Skullcap
Scutellaria lateriflora L.
Erect perennial from 12 to 28 in. tall that arises from a slender rhizome. The solitary stem is freely branched above, smooth or sometimes with ascending hairs in lines. The leaves, from 1 to 3 in. long on stalks from 0.2 to 1 in. long, are thin, pinnately veined, toothed, broadly lance-shaped with a rounded base. The one-sided racemes, from 1 to 4 in. long, are numerous with the flowers often in pairs. The corolla, to 0.4-in. long, is blue to pink or white, the lower lip longer than the upper. Frequent. Moist to wet areas. Found throughout TN and from Newfoundland to British Columbia south to GA and CA. Jul-Sep.

Jack Carman

Large-Flowered Skullcap
Scutellaria montana Chapman
Erect perennial to 4 ft tall. Leaves, from 2 to 4 in. long on stalks from 0.2 to 0.8-in. long, are mostly ovate, crenate, rounded to a wedge-shaped base. Both stem and leaves are glandular-hairy. The terminal raceme, from 2 to 6 in. long, has blue flowers from 1 to 1.4 in. long with subtending bracts longer than the calyx. Rare. Deciduous open woods. Found in Marion, Sequatchie and Hamilton counties in TN, and across northern areas of GA, AL and MS. May-Jun.

Showy Skullcap (*S. serrata* Andrews) is similar, but the stem and leaves are mostly smooth. The flowers are slightly smaller, from 0.8 to 1.2 in. long. Rare. Rich woods. Found in Morgan, Greene, Unicoi and Sullivan counties in TN, and from PA to OH south to NC and East TN. May-Jun.

Jack Carman

Heart-Leaf Skullcap   *Scutellaria ovata* Hill

Erect stout perennial from 4 to 28 in. tall. Leaves, from 2 to 6 in. long on stalks from 1 to 3 in. long, are broad and heart-shaped with crenate margins. Racemes are 1 to few, about 4 in. long. The corolla, from 0.6 to 1 in. long, is blue to violet with a whitish lower lip, and the calyx is glandular. Occasional. Rich woods, woods edges. Found in the western 2/3 of TN, and from MD to MN south to SC, AL and Mexico. May-Aug.

Jack Carman

Small Skullcap
Scutellaria parvula Michaux

Small perennial from 4 to 8 in. tall. Stems have spreading glandular hairs, and several often arise from the end of a thin rhizome. The leaves are downy, sessile, ovate to nearly round, from 0.4 to 0.6-in. long, and have 3 to 5 veins on each side of the midvein. The flowers are borne in the leaf axils. The corolla is about 0.3-in. long and bluish, and the calyx is usually reddish. Occasional. Cedar glades, barrens. In TN, found in the Central Basin and Western Highland Rim, also Shelby, Meigs and Sullivan counties. Its range is Quebec to MN south to FL and TX. Apr-Jun.

Veined Skullcap (*S. nervosa* Pursh) is similar, but has downy stems to 2 ft tall. Leaves, from 0.8 to 1.8 in. long, are lance-ovate to round-ovate, rounded to nearly cordate at the base. Flowers are blue, to 0.4-in. long. Occasional. Moist woods. In TN, it is found in the Western Highland Rim, also Clay, Scott, Union and Knox counties. The U.S. range is NJ to IN south in the uplands to TN and NC. May-Jun.

Genus *Stachys*

Five species and 2 additional varieties are found in Tennessee. The genus name is from the Greek *stachys* (a head of wheat), alluding to a terminal raceme or spike.

Clingman's Hedge Nettle
Stachys clingmanii Small

Simple-stemmed perennial from 20 to 32 in. tall that is hairy on the stem angles. The leaves are elliptic-lanceolate to lance-ovate, from 2.4 to 5 in. long, pointed, sharply toothed, blunt at the base, usually hairy, the petioles from 0.4 to 1.2 in. long. Flowers occur in clusters of 6 in the axils of the upper leaves. The calyx tubes are hairy and have triangular-shaped lobes. Flowers, to 0.65-in. long, are two-lipped, white but lined and dotted with red-purple. Rare. Mountain woods at high altitude. Found in Monroe, Blount and Sevier counties in TN, and in the Appalachians from VA and WV to NC and TN. Jun-Aug.

Jack Carman

Jack Carman

Smooth Hedge Nettle
Stachys tenuifolia Willdenow

Perennial from 2 to 4 ft tall with a simple stem that is smooth or sometimes slightly hairy on the angles. Leaves, from 2 to 6 in. long on stalks from 0.3 to 1 in. long, are thin, usually smooth, toothed, oblanceolate to oblong but pointed at the tip. Flowers are borne in clusters of 6 in the axils of the upper leaves (verticils), and are white to pink to lavender, to 0.6-in. long. Frequent. Moist soil in the shade. Found throughout TN, and from NY to MN south to SC and TX. Jun-Aug.

Nuttall's Hedge Nettle (*Stachys nuttallii* Shuttleworth *ex* Bentham) is similar, but the stem is spreading hairy. Leaves are more or less lance-shaped and coarsely hairy, and petioles are less than 0.2-in. long. Occasional. Moist upland forests. Found in East and Middle TN, and from MD to IL south to KY and TN. Jun-Aug. *Stachys riddellii* House, *Stachys cordata* Riddell.

Gyandotte Beauty, Synandra
Synandra hispidula (Michaux) Baillon
Erect perennial from 8 to 24 in. tall, the stem covered with long, soft, curved hairs. Stem leaves, usually 2 or 3 pairs, are broadly heart-shaped, coarsely toothed, sparsely hairy, the blade from 1 to 3 in. long and the petiole often longer than the blade. The 4 to 12 flowers are solitary in the axils of small sessile leaves, forming a terminal spike. The flowers have 4 stamens, and are strongly 2-lipped with the tube much dilated, to 1.5 in. long, greenish yellow or greenish white with purple lines on the lower lip. The calyx is almost regular. Occasional. Rich woods. Thinly scattered from the Western Highland Rim east in TN, but more prevalent in northern Middle TN. Its range is from w VA to southern IL south to TN and n AL. Apr-May. *Synandra* is a monotypic genus, i.e., with only one species, and is from the Greek *syn* (together) and *andr* (man, but here used for anther), alluding to the paired anthers.

Jack Carman

Jack Carman

American Germander
Teucrium canadense L.
Erect perennial from 1 to 3 ft tall that arises from a rhizome, and has a solitary hairy stem. The leaves are toothed, lance-ovate to oblong, from 2 to 5 in. long on stalks from 0.2 to 0.6-in. long. The inflorescence is a terminal, crowded, spike-like raceme from 2 to 8 in. long. The flowers are rose-purple to pink to lavender, from 0.4 to 0.7-in. long. The upper lip is much shorter than the long and 3-lobed lower lip. Four long stamens extending from the 2-lipped calyx arch over the corolla lower lip. Common. Moist to wet soils, meadows, swamps, barrens. Found throughout TN, and in most of the U.S. and southern CAN. Jun-Aug. The genus name is adapted from *Teucrion*, an ancient name used for some related plant.

Jack Carman

Genus *Trichostema*

Three species are found in Tennessee. The genus name is from the Greek *thrix* (hair) and *stema* (stamen), in reference to the hair-like filaments.

False Pennyroyal
Trichostema brachiatum L.

Freely-branched annual from 8 to 16 in. tall, the stem finely hairy and also glandular above. The leaves, from 0.8 to 2 in. long and about ¼ as wide, are short-stalked, mostly elliptic to lanceolate, and usually 3-nerved. From 1 to 3 small flowers on stalks to 0.4-in. long are borne from the leaf axils. The corolla is blue with lobes about 0.08-in. long, and the calyx is regular with lobes about 0.12-in. long. The 4 stamens are almost straight and barely extend outside the corolla. Occasional. Dry soil of glades, barrens, roadsides, usually on limestone. Found in East and Middle TN, and from VT to MN south to FL and AZ. Jul-Sep. *Isanthus brachiatus* (L.) BSP.

Bluecurls
Trichostema dichotomum L.

Freely-branched annual from 4 to 28 in. tall, the stem minutely glandular-hairy. Leaves, from 0.6 to 2.5 in. long and not more than 5 times as long as wide, are oblong to elliptic or ovate with usually evident lateral veins. The flowers arise from the leaf axils on stalks to 0.2-in. long. The calyx is 2-lipped and the corolla is blue with lobes about 0.25-in. long. The prominent arching filaments of the 4 stamens are about 0.6-in. long. Frequent. Dry soil of roadsides, fields, glades, barrens. Absent from West TN (except Henry and Carroll counties) and the Central Basin, but found throughout the remainder of TN. U.S. range from ME to MI south to FL and TX. Aug-Sep.

Linear-Leaf Bluecurls (*T. setaceum* Houttuyn) is similar, but has one-nerved linear leaves to 0.2-in. wide that are at least 5 times as long as wide. Rare. Dry sites. Recorded in Fayette, Franklin, Rhea and Roane counties in TN, it is a mostly Coastal Plain species found from CT to FL and TX and irregularly inland to TN and OH. Jul-Oct.

Jack Carman

Jack Carman

Plaintain Family leaves are basal, more or less parallel veined, and flowers are crowded in spikes on scapes that are naked below. Each flower usually has 4 stamens and is mostly sessile in the axil of a bract. The corolla is long-persistent and fruit capsules open by means of a hinged lid. Nine species are found in TN, all members of the genus *Plantago*. The genus name is from the Latin *planta*, for footprint.

Bracted Plantain
Plantago aristata Michaux
Hairy winter annual that arises from a taproot. Basal leaves to 8 in. long are linear or very narrowly elliptic, smooth or covered with long hairs. Scapes to 10 in. tall have terminal spikes, from 1.2 to 4 in. long, that are densely flowered. Floral bracts to 1 in. long are reduced upward and linear, more or less hairy, extending well past the flowers. The small whitish flowers are about 0.15-in. wide. Frequent. Disturbed sites, fields, waste places, roadsides. Found throughout TN. Native from IL to LA and TX, but now naturalized over most of the e U.S. and adjacent CAN. May-Jul.

English Plantain   *Plantago lanceolata* L.*
Introduced weedy perennial with basal leaves that are mostly narrowly elliptic, from 4 to 16 in. long and less than 1/6th as wide. The scape, from 6 to 24 in. tall, has a dense terminal flower spike to 3 in. long at maturity. Flowers have spreading-to-reflexed lobes to 0.1-in. long, protruding stamens, and open first at the bottom of the spike. Buds on top give the spike a rounded cone appearance. Frequent. Lawns, waste places. Found throughout TN and the e U.S. May-Oct.

Pale Plantain (*Plantago rugelii* Decaisne) is perennial with scapes to 10 in. tall. The leaves are smooth, broadly elliptic to ovate, tapered to well-defined purplish stalks. Frequent. Lawns, waste places. Found throughout TN and the e U.S. May-Oct.

Dwarf Plantain (*Plantago virginica* L.) is a weedy, hairy, winter annual with a taproot and oblanceolate to obovate leaves. The scape, to 8 in. tall, has spikes to 4 in. long with hairy bracts. The corolla lobes, about 0.1-in. long, are erect and enclose the fruit. Common. Dry soil. Found throughout TN and the e U.S. Apr-Jun.

George Hornal

Genus *Agalinis*

Ten species are found in TN. The common name and former genus name (*Gerardia)* are in honor of John Gerarde, a celebrated herbalist of the late 16th and early 17th centuries.

Smooth Purple Gerardia
Agalinis purpurea (L.) Pennell

Annual to 4 ft tall with squarish smooth stems, often much branched. The primary leaves are narrow, to 0.16-in. wide, and noticeable clusters of small leaves in the leaf axils are lacking. The tubular flowers with spreading lobes are 0.8 to 1.6 in. long, pink to purplish, on stalks less than 0.2-in. long. The throat of the corolla is striped with yellow. Frequent. Moist open areas and barrens. Widely scattered in TN and the eastern U.S. Aug-Oct.

Fascicled Purple Gerardia (*Agalinis fasciculata* (Elliott) Rafinesque) is similar, but has a rough stem and many small leaves clustered in the primary leaf axils. Occasional. Dry soil. Found in West and Middle TN. U.S. range from s MD to FL and TX north to s MO in the interior. Aug-Oct.

Jack Carman

Jack Carman

Slender Gerardia
Agalinis tenuifolia (Vahl) Rafinesque

Smooth widely-branched annual to 2 ft tall with linear leaves to 0.25-in. wide. The pink to purplish tubular flowers, about 0.5-in. long, are on filiform, spreading pedicels to 0.8-in. long. The corolla is smooth within, the upper lip arches over the stamens, and the calyx is not veiny. The herbage is green to purplish, drying dark. Common. Dry to moist open areas. Found throughout TN and most of the e U.S. Aug-Oct.

Gattinger's Gerardia (*A. gattingeri* (Small) Small *ex* Britton) has a few small leaves and is abundantly branched, the slender greenish branches usually with a single terminal flower. The calyx tube is net-veined and the spreading corolla is pink, 0.5 to 0.7-in. long. Occasional. Open forests, barrens. Mostly found in Middle TN. Aug-Oct.

Ear-Leaf False Foxglove (*Tomanthera auriculata* (Michx.) Raf.) has lanceolate, entire leaves, the upper sometimes lobed at the base. Rare. Open woods, barrens. Found in Montgomery, Bledsoe, Carroll, Roane and Tipton counties in TN. Aug-Sep. *Agalinis auriculata* (Michaux) Blake.

The Snapdragon Family is represented by 29 genera and 75 species in Tennessee.

Genus *Aureolaria*

Five species are listed for TN, and all are presumably parasitic on the roots of oak trees. The genus name is from the Latin *aureolus* (golden), referring to the color of the flowers.

Yellow False Foxglove
Aureolaria flava (L.) Farwell

Smooth perennial from 3 to 7 ft tall that is branched above, usually with purplish and glaucous stems. The leaves are opposite, from 3 to 7 in. long and 0.6 to 3 in. wide, with the lower ones deeply pinnately lobed and the upper ones reduced and shallowly lobed or toothed. The flower stalks, from 0.15 to 0.4-in. long, are stout and abruptly curved upward. The flowers to 2 in. long are yellow with five lobes that are shorter than the tube. Frequent. Dry upland woods. Found throughout TN and the e U.S. Aug-Sep.

Jack Carman

Southern Fern-Leaf False Foxglove
Aureolaria pectinata (Nuttall) Pennell

Annual from 12 to 24 in. tall that is widely-branched and glandular-hairy. Principal leaves from 1.2 to 2.4 in. long, are mostly sessile, pinnately lobed into many fine divisions that are irregularly and sharply toothed. The calyx tube is hemispheric. Flowers to 1.6 in. long are yellow and tinged with brown, and have five lobes that are shorter than the tube. Frequent Dry upland woods and barrens. Scattered across TN, but mostly absent in westernmost counties of West TN and northern counties statewide. A southeastern species extending north into NC, KY, and MO. Jul-Oct.

Jack Carman

Downy False Foxglove
Aureolaria virginica (L.) Pennell
Perennial from 1.5 to 5 ft tall that is finely downy throughout. The leaves are opposite, from 2 to 5 in. long, with the lower ones lance-ovate, sometimes with lobes or teeth, and the upper ones reduced, lanceolate, entire or toothed. Flower stalks are less than 0.12-in. long. Flowers to 1.8 in. long are yellow with five lobes that are shorter than the tube. Frequent. Dry woods. Found from the Western Highland Rim east in TN, also in Carroll County, and in most of the e U.S. Jun-Sep.

Smooth False Foxglove (*Aureolaria laevigata* (Raf.) Raf.) is similar, but mostly smooth throughout. Occasional. Upland woods. Cumberland Plateau east in TN, and from PA to s OH south to GA. Jul-Sep.

Spreading False Foxglove (*Aureolaria patula* (Chapman) Pennell) is similar, but is sparsely hairy, the calyx lobes are longer than the calyx tube, and the flower stalks are to 1 in. long. Infrequent. Rocky river banks. Found in Stewart, Montgomery, Davidson, Pickett, Roane and Claiborne counties in TN, and from c KY to n GA. Jul-Sep.

Jack Carman

Jack Carman

Blue Hearts   *Buchnera americana* L.
Rough-hairy perennial from 16 to 36 in. tall that is usually not branched. Lower leaves, from 2 to 4 in. long, are sessile, opposite, lanceolate, coarsely few-toothed and rough. Upper leaves are progressively smaller and narrower. Flowers are borne in a terminal spike and the corolla, to 0.6-in. long, is red-purple, tubular with five widely-spreading lobes. Occasional. Open fields and barrens. Found in the Highland Rim and Cumberland Plateau, but generally absent from the remainder of TN. The extended range includes much of the e U.S. Jul-Sep. The only species of this genus found in TN. The genus name is in honor of Johann Gottfried Buchner, an 18th century German botanist.

Jack Carman

Indian Paintbrush, Painted Cups
Castilleja coccinea (L.) Sprengel
Annual or biennial from 8 to 24 in. tall with a usually solitary, more or less hairy stem that arises from a rosette of basal leaves. Stem leaves to 1.6 in. long are variable, entire to commonly 3 to 5-cleft with linear or oblong segments. The bracts are usually 3-lobed, occasionally 5-lobed, and reddish. The terminal spike, to 2.4 in. long, is dense, containing both reddish bracts and greenish-yellow flowers about 1 in. long. Infrequent. Moist fields, meadows and barrens. Found in Lewis, Coffee, Grundy, Van Buren, Bledsoe, Cumberland, Morgan, Roane, Sevier and Jefferson counties in TN. Widespread in the eastern and central U.S. May-Aug. The only species of this genus found in Tennessee. The genus name is in honor of Domingo Castillejo, a Spanish botanist.

Jack Carman

Genus *Chelone*
Three species are listed for TN. The flowers appear to be shaped like the head of a turtle, and the genus name is from the Greek *chelone* (a tortoise).

White Turtlehead   *Chelone glabra* L.
Erect perennial from 20 to 32 in. tall. The leaves are opposite, lance-shaped, toothed, short-stalked or sessile, and relatively narrow, to 6 in. long. The inflorescence is a showy terminal spike to 3 in. long. Flowers, to 1.4 in. long, are white and often purplish-tinged at the tip, two-lipped with the upper lip arched over the lower. Frequent. Moist ground, wet woods, stream banks. Widespread in TN, but infrequent in West TN and not reported from the Central Basin. Widespread in the e U.S. Jul-Sep. A leaf tea is said to stimulate the appetite, and also has been used as a folk remedy for fever and jaundice, and as a laxative.

George Hornal

Red Turtlehead   *Chelone lyonii* Pursh
Perennial from 16 to 40 in. tall. Leaves, to 6 in. long, are ovate to ovate-lanceolate, on stalks from 0.6 to 1.2 in. long. The terminal spike has rose to red-purple flowers, from 1 to 1.4 in. long, that are two-lipped with the upper lip arched over the lower. Infrequent. Rich coves, open stream banks. Found in Blount, Sevier, Cocke, Greene, Unicoi, Carter, Warren, Grundy and Marion counties in TN. Also known from NC and SC. Jul-Sep. Somewhat abundant at high elevation in the Smoky Mountains.

Narrow-Leaf Red Turtlehead (*Chelone obliqua* L.) is similar, but has elliptic leaves on stalks less than 0.6-in. long and a red-purple corolla. Rare. Wet woods and swamps in Lewis, Madison and Obion counties in TN. A primarily Coastal Plain species. Aug-Oct.

Blue-Eyed Mary   *Collinsia verna* Nuttall
Annual from 8 to 16 in. tall with prominent stem leaves below the inflorescence that are opposite, sessile, triangular-ovate, to 2 in. long. Flowers are mostly in 1 to 3 whorls of 4 to 6 flowers each. The showy corolla, about 0.5-in. wide, has two upper lobes that are white and two lower lobes that are bright blue. The central (third) lower lobe is folded between the lower lateral lobes into a pouch that encloses the four stamens. Rare. Rich moist woods, especially in alluvial soil. Found in Clay and Sumner counties in TN, but widespread north of TN. Apr-May. The only species of this genus found in TN. The genus name is in honor of Zaccheus Collins, an early 19th century Philadelphia botanist.

Jack Carman

Mullein Foxglove
Dasistoma macrophylla (Nutt.) Rafinesque
Somewhat hairy perennial from 3 to 6 ft tall
with opposite leaves. Lower leaves, from 8
to 16 in. long, are broadly ovate and deeply
lobed, and upper leaves are progressively
reduced to lanceolate and entire. The
inflorescence is a long, leafy, interrupted
spike. The yellow flowers are densely hairy
within, about 0.6-in. long, and last for one
day. The bell-shaped corolla tube is longer
than the spreading lobes. Occasional. Rich
moist open woods, limestone glades. Found
in Middle TN, also in Shelby, Lauderdale,
Tipton, Obion and Hardin counties, and
widespread in the eastern and central U.S.
Jun-Sep. *Dasystoma macrophylla* (Nuttall)
Raf. The genus *Dasistoma* is monotypic,
meaning it has only one known species.

Jack Carman

Genus *Gratiola*
Six species are found in Tennessee. The
genus name is a diminutive of *gratia* (grace
or favor), alluding to the supposed medicinal
properties of some species.

Sticky Hedge Hyssop
Gratiola brevifolia Rafinesque

Perennial to 16 in. tall that is somewhat glandular. Leaves are thick, linear, opposite with 1
to 3 prominent teeth on each margin. Flowers are solitary in the leaf axils on long stalks and
have 5 sepals and 2 sepal-like bracts. The corolla has a yellow tube with interior brown lines
and white lobes. Rare. Moist to wet places, ditches. Found in Coffee, Grundy, Montgomery,
Morgan, and White counties in TN, and in AL, GA and FL. Jul-Sep.

Clammy Hedge Hyssop (*Gratiola neglecta* Torrey) is annual, to 12 in. tall with stalked,
lanceolate to oblanceolate leaves. Frequent. Wet areas. Scattered in TN. May-Jul.

Hairy Hedge Hyssop (*Gratiola pilosa* Michaux) is a hairy perennial to 16 in. tall. Flowers
white-lobed, tube lavender-tinged. Occasional. Wet areas. Eastern Middle TN. Jul-Sep.

Jack Carman

Blue Toadflax
Linaria canadensis (L.) Dum.Cours.
Smooth, slender, biennial or winter annual with a rosette of prostrate stems that have opposite leaves. The erect flowering stems, from 4 to 20 in. tall, have linear leaves, from 0.4 to 1.4 in. long, that are alternate and basally disposed. Flowers are borne in loose racemes. Corolla light blue to purple, to 0.6-in. long including the slender spur. Upper lip erect and two-lobed; lower lip 3-lobed with a white palate. Occasional. Fields, roadsides, waste areas. Widespread in TN and eastern North America, also on the Pacific coast. Apr-May. *Nuttallanthus canadensis* (L.) D. A. Sutton.

Jack Carman

Two *Linaria* species are found in Tennessee. The genus name is adapted from *Linum* (flax), alluding to the similarity of the foliage.

Butter-and-Eggs, Yellow Toadflax
Linaria vulgaris P. Miller*
Erect, downy perennial from 12 to 32 in. tall, arising from a rhizome. Leaves, from 0.8 to 2 in. long, are many, narrow, alternate, pale blue-green, evenly distributed on the stem. Flowers, to 1.4 in. long including the spur, are borne in a dense terminal spike and are two-lipped, bright yellow with an orange palate on the lower lip. Occasional. Fields, roadsides, waste places. Thinly scattered in TN from the Western Highland Rim east. A European escape found throughout temperate North America. May-Oct.

Mazus   *Mazus pumilus* (Burm. f.) Steenis*
Low creeping annual to 6 in. long. Basal leaves are spatulate, opposite, to 0.6-in. long, and uppermost leaves are alternate, smaller. Flowers to 0.4-in. long have a 2-lobed upper lip and a 3-lobed, larger, projecting lower lip. The corolla is blue-violet and marked with yellow and white. Rare. Lawns, wet bottomlands. Listed in Obion, Davidson, Sevier, and Shelby counties in TN, but likely more prevalent. Introduced from Asia and widely but thinly spread in the e U.S. Apr-Nov. *Mazus japonicus* (Thunberg) Kuntze*. Found in the lawn of the Sugarlands Visitor Center at the Great Smoky Mountains National Park. Genus name from the Greek *mazos* (papilla), from the swellings at the throat of the corolla.

Jack Carman

Genus *Mecardonia*

Only one species of this genus is found in Tennessee. The genus name is in honor of Antonio de Meca et Carona, patron of the Botanical Garden at Barcelona in the 18th century.

Axilflower, Mecardonia

Mecardonia acuminata (Walter) Small
Smooth, sparingly-branched perennial with an erect or ascending stem from 8 to 20 in. tall. Leaves, from 0.8 to 1.6 in. long, are opposite, oblanceolate and sharply toothed above the middle. Solitary flowers, about 0.4-in. long, are borne on ascending stalks from 0.4 to 1.2 in. long that arise from the leaf axils. The corolla is tubular to narrowly bell-shaped, two-lipped, white with purple lines on the lower lip, and hairy within on the upper side. Frequent. Moist woods, open wet areas. Scattered in the western 2/3 of TN. A southeastern U.S. species that extends north to DE and MO. Jun-Sep.

Jack Carman

Cow Wheat   *Melampyrum lineare* Desrousseaux

Slender, erect, downy annual from 4 to 16 in. tall that is commonly branched above. Leaves are opposite, mostly short-stalked, narrowly linear to lance-ovate, from 0.8 to 2.5 in. long. Solitary flowers are borne in the upper leaf axils on stalks from 0.04 to 0.2-in. long. The corolla, from 0.25 to 0.5-in. long, is white and 2-lipped, the upper lip hooded and the lower lip with a yellow palate. The fruiting capsule is asymmetrical. Occasional. Open upland woods, balds, roadsides, wet areas. Found in the Blue Ridge in TN, also Fentress, Grundy and Wayne counties. A northern U.S. and s CAN species extending south in the uplands to GA. May-Jul. The genus name is from the Greek *melas* (black) and *pyros* (wheat), in reference to the color of the seeds of some species.

John MacGregor

Jack Carman

Sharp-Winged Monkeyflower   *Mimulus alatus* Aiton

Smooth perennial from 1 to 4 ft tall with square stems that are winged along the edges. Leaves, from 2 to 4 in. long, are opposite, sharply and coarsely toothed, lanceolate to ovate, and taper to stalks to 0.8-in. long (the upper almost sessile). Flowers, from 0.8 to 1.2 in. long, are solitary in the leaf axils on stalks shorter than the calyx. The corolla is lavender (rarely white), strongly two-lipped with the upper lip erect and 2-lobed, and the lower lip spreading downward, 3-lobed with an elevated palate. Common. Wet open woods, stream banks, ditches. Widespread in TN and the eastern U.S. Jul-Aug.

Jack Carman

Genus *Mimulus*

Two species are found in Tennessee. The genus name is a diminutive of *mimus* (a buffoon), alluding to the grinning corolla.

Square-Stem Monkeyflower
***Mimulus ringens* L.**

Perennial from 1 to 4 ft tall with square stems that are obscurely or not at all winged along the edges. Leaves are opposite, sessile, lanceolate to oblanceolate, from 2 to 4 in. long and progressively reduced upward. Flowers, from 0.8 to 1.2 in. long, are solitary in the leaf axils on stalks, from 0.8 to 1.8 in. long, that are longer than the calyx. The corolla is lavender (rarely white) and the throat tinged with yellow, strongly two-lipped with the upper lip erect and 2-lobed, and the lower lip spreading downward, 3-lobed with an elevated palate. Occasional. Wet open woods, stream banks, ditches. Found from the Eastern Highland Rim east in TN, also in Benton, Carroll, Dickson, Hardin and Henry counties. Widespread in the eastern U.S. Jun-Sep.

Wood Betony, Forest Lousewort
Pedicularis canadensis L.
Erect hairy perennial from 6 to 16 in. tall that is usually colonial by short rhizomes. Basal leaves, from 2 to 5 in. long, are lanceolate to elliptic or oblanceolate, deeply lobed and appearing fern-like. Stalks of the lower leaves are often longer than the blades. Stem leaves are alternate and reduced in size upward with the upper almost sessile. The terminal spike, from 1.2 to 2 in. long, has small leaf-like bracts and the tube-like flowers, from 0.7 to 1 in. long, appear whorled. The corolla is pale yellow to maroon, and two-lipped with an arched, hood-like upper lobe. Common. Upland woods and barrens. Found throughout TN and from Quebec and ME to Manitoba to CO south to FL, TX and northern Mexico. Apr-Jun.

Jack Carman

Jack Carman

Lousewort   Genus *Pedicularis*
Two species are found in TN. The genus name is from the Latin *pediculus* (a louse). Lousewort refers to the misconception once held by European farmers that sheep and cattle became infested with lice when grazing on, or even near an abundance of the European species. Semi-parasitic on the roots of other plants.

Swamp Lousewort
Pedicularis lanceolata Michaux
Short-lived, erect, smooth perennial from 1 to 2.5 ft tall. Leaves are mostly opposite, sessile or short-stalked, pinnately lobed, from 2 to 4 in. long. Inflorescence spikes are terminal and from the leaf axils. The creamy-white corolla, about 1 in. long, is two-lipped with an arched, helmet-like upper lobe. Infrequent. Marshes, open wetlands. Found in Bledsoe, Bradley, Coffee, Crockett, Cumberland, Stewart, Union and Warren counties in TN. A mostly northern species extending south into NC and TN. Aug-Sep.

Beardtongue   Genus *Penstemon*
The beardtongues are named from a long, sterile, 5th stamen (staminode) which often has a yellow beard (tuft of hairs) at its tip. *Penstemon* is the combination of *pente* (five) and *stemon* (in this sense stamen). Nine species are found in Tennessee.

Smooth Beardtongue
Penstemon calycosus Small
Perennial arising from a rosette of basal leaves. The flowering stem, from 2 to 4 ft tall, is mostly smooth with opposite, sessile, finely toothed, lanceolate to lance-ovate leaves from 0.8 to 2 in. wide. Flowers are borne in a terminal inflorescence that has stalked glands. The corolla, from 1 to 1.4 in. long, abruptly expands from the narrow base into an open throat and has 5 spreading lobes. It is usually bright violet-purple outside and much paler to white inside. Frequent. Roadsides, meadows, woodland margins. Found from the Eastern Highland Rim west in TN, also in Cumberland and Marion counties, and throughout most of the e U.S. May-Jun.

Jack Carman

Jack Carman

Foxglove Beardtongue
Penstemon digitalis Nuttall *ex* Sims
Perennial arising from a rosette of basal leaves. The flowering stem, from 2 to 5 ft tall, is shining and smooth below, often glaucous with paired, sessile, lance-oblong leaves from 4 to 6 in. long. Flowers are borne in a terminal inflorescence that has stalked glands. The corolla, to 1.2 in. long, abruptly expands from the narrow base into an open throat and has 5 spreading lobes. It is usually white outside and the inside is white marked with purple lines. Occasional. Moist open woods and meadows. Thinly scattered in TN and widespread in the eastern U.S. May-Jul.

Gray Beardtongue (*Penstemon canescens* (Britton) Britton), to 2.5 ft tall, has stem and leaves both finely-hairy. The corolla, from 0.8 to 1.2 in. long, is two-lipped and gradually expands from the base into an open, ridged throat. It is pale purple outside, white with purple lines inside. Frequent. Upland woods. Found from the Eastern Highland Rim east in TN, and from s IN to PA south to TN and n AL, chiefly in the uplands. May-Jun.

Eastern White Beardtongue
Penstemon pallidus Small

Perennial arising from a rosette of basal leaves. Stem erect to 2 ft tall, coarsely hairy below. Leaves are hairy, coarsely dentate to almost entire. Inflorescence not leafy, moderately spreading, glandular. Corolla from 0.6 to 0.9-in. long, white with spreading lobes, marked with conspicuous purple lines inside, the throat only gradually inflated. Infrequent. Dry woods and fields. A mostly ne U.S. species found in Hardeman, Hardin, Montgomery, White, Overton, Fentress, Roane and Union counties in TN. Apr-Jun.

Small's Beardtongue (_Penstemon smallii_ Heller), to 2.5 ft tall, has a finely downy stem and sharply toothed leaves. Lower bracts of the inflorescence are leafy, scarcely smaller than the stem leaves. The corolla, from 1 to 1.4 in. long, is purple outside, pale inside, the throat lined with purple and open, but the lower lip has two ridges. Infrequent. Mountain banks and cliffs. Found in the southern Appalachians of NC, SC, GA and TN, and west to Jackson, Hamilton, Loudon and Knox Counties in TN. May-Jun.

Jack Carman

Jack Carman

Slender-Flowered Beardtongue
Penstemon tenuiflorus Pennell

Perennial arising from a rosette of basal leaves. The flowering stem, from 16 to 32 in. tall, is hairy and leaves are opposite, sessile, toothed to entire, hairy, lanceolate to oblong, from 2 to 5 in. long. The corolla, from 0.8 to 1.2 in. long, is distinctly 2-lipped, white throughout, and the throat is usually closed by the palate on the lower lip. Occasional. Dry woods, barrens, glade margins, often found in the limestone cedar glades of Middle TN, and west to Hardeman, Chester, Carroll, and Henry counties. Also reported in s KY, n MS and n AL. May-Jun.

Hairy Beardtongue (_Penstemon hirsutus_ (L.) Willdenow) is similar, but the flowers are pale violet outside and whitish inside. The stem is finely hairy throughout and glandular above. Infrequent. Dry woods, fields. Found in Hickman, Montgomery, Cheatham, Davidson, Sumner, Trousdale, Smith and Pickett counties of Middle TN, and widespread in the e U.S. May-Jul.

Jack Carman

Carpenter's Square
Scrophularia marilandica L.
Erect branched perennial from 2 to 10 ft tall with angled and grooved stems. The leaves are opposite and have stalks from 0.6 to 2 in. long, the main ones about one third to one half as long as the blade. The leaf blades, to 10 in. long, are ovate to lance-ovate, sharply toothed. The inflorescence is terminal, loosely and irregularly branched, pyramid-shaped, often 4 to 6 in. wide. Flowers, about 0.3-in. long, are dull reddish-brown to greenish, two-lipped with the upper lip directed forward. Frequent. Open woods and woods borders. Found throughout TN, and from Quebec to MN south to SC and LA. Jul-Aug. American Indians used root tea for fever and as a diuretic and tonic. The genus name is so called because the fleshy knobs on the rhizomes of some species, by the Doctrine of Signatures, were supposed to cure scrofula.

Genus *Verbascum*
Mulleins are biennial. Only a rosette of basal leaves is produced the 1st year, but a tall flowering stalk is produced the 2nd year. Three species are listed for TN. The origin of the genus name is unknown.

Moth Mullein **Verbascum blattaria** L.*
Slender biennial with a rosette of basal leaves, the flowering stalk to 5 ft tall and glandular above. Basal leaves are large and oblanceolate, and stem leaves are smooth, alternate, sessile, coarsely toothed, narrowly triangular to lanceolate, from 3 to 6 in. long. The terminal flower raceme is long and loose with a single flower at each node on a stalk from 0.3 to 0.6-in. long. Flowers, from 0.8 to 1.2 in. wide, have 5 spreading lobes and are yellow or white, but only of one color on an individual plant. Seedpods are almost round. Frequent. Disturbed sites. Found throughout TN and the e U.S. May-Jun.

Jack Carman

Common Mullein
Verbascum thapsus L.*
Densely hairy biennial with a stem, from 3 to 6 ft tall, that is stout, erect, and mostly unbranched. The basal rosette has pale green, broadly oblong or oblanceolate leaves, to 1 ft long, that feel very soft to the touch, almost flannel-like. Stem leaves are alternate and upper leaves are reduced in size with the bases extending down the stem. The dense terminal spike, to 20 in. long and 1.2 in. thick, bears 5-lobed yellow flowers from 0.4 to 1 in. wide. Frequent. Roadsides, disturbed areas. Widespread across TN and temperate North America. Jun-Sep. Traditionally, leaf and flower tea has been used for chest colds, asthma, bronchitis and coughs, and flowers soaked in mineral or olive oil have been used as earache drops.

Clasping-Leaf Mullein (*V. phlomoides* L.*) is similar, but leaves are dark green, mostly wider near the middle, and somewhat clasping. The flowers are 1 to 1.4 in. wide. Rare. Known from Knox County in TN and found here and there in the e U.S. May-Jun.

George Hornal

Ivy-Leaf Speedwell   ***Veronica hederaefolia*** L.*
Low branched annual to 16 in. tall with reclining or ascending stems. Leaves, to 0.8-in. wide, are hairy, mostly 3-lobed and wider than long. Small flowers with 4 lobes are solitary in the leaf axils, pale blue, about 0.2-in. wide. Occasional. Lawns, waste areas. Widely scattered in TN and found from NY to OH south to SC and KY. Apr-May.

Common Speedwell or Gypsyweed (*Veronica officinalis* L.*) is a creeping, spreading-hairy perennial, the stems rooting at the nodes. Leaves are opposite, mostly elliptic, finely toothed, 0.6 to 2 in. long. Flowers are borne in terminal racemes that ascend from the leaf axils. Corolla light blue, sometimes with dark lines, about 0.25-in. wide. Occasional. Lawns, disturbed areas. Scattered in the eastern half of TN and throughout the e U.S. May-Jul.

Jack Carman

Jack Carman

Genus *Veronica*

Twelve species are found in Tennessee. The genus name is in honor of St. Veronica, popularly thought to be from *vera* (true) and the Greek *eicon* (image). An early Christian legend pictures St. Veronica, pitying Christ on the way to Calvary, wiping His face with a handkerchief which received a miraculous true image of His features.

Birdseye Speedwell
Veronica persica Poiret*

Somewhat hairy annual, the stems from 4 to 16 in. tall, loosely ascending, usually branched below. The leaves are mostly opposite, short-stalked, broadly elliptic or ovate, toothed, from 0.4 to 0.8-in. long and nearly as wide. The flowering portion of the stem has alternate leaf-like bracts, each with a single long-stalked flower. The corolla is 4-lobed, to 0.5-in. wide, bright blue with dark lines and a pale center. Infrequent. Lawns, roadsides, waste places. Introduced from sw Asia, now thinly scattered across TN and found throughout much of North America. Apr-Aug. Usually found in the lawn around the Sugarlands Visitor Center in the Great Smoky Mountains National Park.

Jack Carman

Culver's Root
Veronicastrum virginicum (L.) Farwell

A distinctive perennial from 2 to 7 ft tall, usually with a few erect branches. Leaves, from 1.6 to 6 in. long, are elliptic-lanceolate, finely toothed, in whorls of 3 to 6. The erect inflorescences are 3 to 8 in. long showy spikes that extend well above the leaves and have numerous, spreading, white flowers. The corolla is tubular, about 0.3-in. long, the two stamens protruding. Occasional. Barrens, roadsides, moist or dry upland woods. Found in the Western Highland Rim and Cumberland Plateau in TN, also in McNairy and Henderson counties west, Hamilton and Roane counties east and Rutherford County in the Central Basin. Extended range from VT to Manitoba south to GA and LA. Jun-Sep. American Indians used a tea made from dried roots as a strong laxative and for other medicinal purposes, but it is **potentially toxic**. *Leptandra virginica* (L.) Nuttall, *Veronica virginica* L.

George Hornal

Squawroot *Conopholis americana* (L.) Wallroth
Pale brown or yellowish-brown, oak-root parasite with an erect, stout, unbranched stem from 2 to 8 in. tall and about 1 in. thick. Stems are usually clumped and covered with numerous brown, overlapping, fleshy, leaf scales. Whitish flowers with leaf-like bracts are borne in a dense terminal spike that usually constitutes half (or more) of the shoot. Frequent. Rich woods under oak trees. Found from the Western Highland Rim east in TN, chiefly in the uplands, and from Nova Scotia to WI south to FL and AL. May-Jun. A favorite food of bears. The genus name is from the Greek *conos* (cone) and *pholis* (scale).

All members of this family contain no chlorophyll and are root parasites with scale-like leaves. Three genera and four species are listed for TN.

Jack Carman

Beechdrops
Epifagus virginiana (L.) Barton
Beech-root parasite from 4 to 20 in. tall with wiry stems having several long ascending branches that are pale brown with brown-purple lines. Leaf scales are alternate and triangular-ovate, about 0.1-in. long. Flowers, from 0.2 to 0.4-in. long, are borne singly in the axils of the leaves, and are 2-lipped, white with brown-purple stripes. The upper flowers are male (produce pollen) and the lower are female (produce fruit). Common. Rich woods under beech trees. Found throughout TN, the e U.S. and se CAN. Sep-Nov. Because they blend so well with the woodland background, Beechdrops can be easily overlooked. The genus name is from the Greek *epi* (upon) and *phagos* (the beech).

OROBANCHACEAE : BROOMRAPE FAMILY

Genus *Orobanche*

Two species are found in TN. The genus name is from the Greek *orobos* (vetch) and *anchein* (to strangle).

One-Flowered Cancer Root
Orobanche uniflora L.

Perennial that is parasitic on the roots of several hosts. The proper stems are all or mostly underground. From 1 to 3 slender, erect, leafless, finely-hairy, flower stalks from 2 to 8 in. tall arise from the stem, and have a solitary, somewhat nodding flower at the summit. The curved corolla tube, about 0.75-in. long, is creamy-white to lilac, and has 5 short spreading lobes. Occasional. Rich moist woods and stream banks. Found from the Western Highland Rim east in TN, and throughout most of the U.S. and s CAN. Apr-May.

Prairie Broomrape (*O. ludoviciana* Nuttall) is similar, but has many flowers in a spike or spike-like raceme. Rare in TN, found in Lauderdale County. Sandy to silty soil. A more western species found from IN to TX west. Jun-Aug.

George Hornal

ACANTHACEAE : ACANTHUS FAMILY

Three genera and 7 species of this family occur in TN. All are perennial.

American Water Willow   *Justicia americana* (L.) Vahl

Smooth colonial perennial from 20 to 40 in. tall. The leaves are opposite, lance-shaped, sessile or short-stalked, from 3 to 7 in. long. The flowers are borne in crowded spikes that are terminal on long stalks arising from the upper leaf axils. The spikes have opposite 2-lipped flowers about 0.5-in. long that are white to pale violet and marked with purple on the lower lip. Frequent. Mud and shallow water. Found throughout TN and the e U.S., but less prevalent in West TN. Jun-Sep. The genus name is in honor of James Justice, an 18th century Scotch horticulturist and botanist.

Jack Carman

Jack Carman

Coastal Plain Water Willow   *Justicia ovata* (Walter) Lindau

Smooth colonial perennial from 8 to 24 in. tall. The leaves are opposite, lance-shaped to elliptic or oblanceolate, sessile or short-stalked, from 1 to 4 in. long. The flowers are borne in loose (not head-like) spikes that are terminal on long stalks arising from the upper leaf axils. The spikes have 2-lipped flowers about 0.4-in. long that are white to pale violet and marked with purple on the lower lip. Infrequent. Shallow water and mud. Found in Lake, Obion, Gibson, Crockett, Lauderdale, Tipton, Shelby, Hardeman and Hardin counties in TN. A Coastal Plain species found from se VA to FL to TX, and inland in the Mississippi River valley to se MO and sw KY. Jun-Sep.

Four *Ruellia* species are found in TN. Genus name in honor of Jean Ruelle, a 16th century French herbalist.

Jack Carman

Glade Wild Petunia   *Ruellia humilis* Nutt. Branched perennial from 8 to 24 in. tall with hairy stems. Leaves are opposite, sessile, ovate, to 2.5 in. long. Flowers, to 2 in. long, are borne in the leaf axils, and are light purple, funnelform, and have very narrow, linear, hairy, calyx lobes. Occasional. Glades, barrens, open woods. Found from the Highland Rim to the Ridge and Valley in TN, and from PA to se MN south to w NC AL and TX. May-Jul.

Carolina Wild Petunia (*R. caroliniensis* (Gmelin) Steudel) is similar, but leaves are on stalks to 0.4-in. long. Common. Moist o dry woods. Found throughout TN, and from NJ to s IN south to FL and TX. May-Sep.

Limestone Wild Petunia (*R. strepens* L.) has wide, lance-shaped calyx lobes. Frequent Moist woods. Found throughout TN, and from NJ to IA south to SC, AL and TX. May Jul.

Pursh's Wild Petunia (*R. purshiana* Fern has single flowers in the middle to lower axils on stalks to 1.6 in. Rare. Dry woods Found in Hawkins County in TN, also VA GA and AL. May-Sep.

Jack Carman

Three genera and 4 species of this family are found in TN.

Cross Vine
Bignonia capreolata L.

Perennial, woody, climbing vine to 50 ft long. The leaves are opposite and pinnately compound, but reduced to only 2 basal leaflets with a terminal tendril between. The leaflets are smooth and firm, semi-evergreen, lanceolate, from 2 to 6 in. long. The inflorescences are axillary clusters of 2 to 5 tubular flowers with flaring lobes. The flowers are about 2 in. long, dull red outside and yellow inside. The fruit is a flat seedpod about 6 to 8 in. long and 1 in. wide. Common. Moist woods and barrens. Found throughout TN and most of the e U.S. Apr-Jun. *Anisostichus capreolata* (L.) Bureau. A cross-section of the stem shows a cross, thus the common name. The genus name is in honor of Jean-Paul Bignon, an 18th century court-librarian in Paris.

Trumpet Creeper, Trumpet Vine   *Campsis radicans* (L.) Seemann *ex* Bureau

Perennial woody vine to 30 ft or more long, sprawling or climbing by aerial roots. Pinnately compound leaves have 5 to 13 lanceolate to ovate, sharply and coarsely toothed leaflets from 1.6 to 3.2 in. long. The inflorescences are terminal and crowded, and the flowers are narrowly funnelform, red-orange, about 3 in. long. The seedpod is 4 to 7 in. long, narrow with pointed ends. Frequent. Woodlands, roadsides, fence rows. Found throughout TN and most of the e U.S. Jun-Sep. Cow-Itch Vine is another common name. The genus name is from the Greek *campsis* (curvature), alluding to the curved stamens.

George Hornal

Two-Flowered Bladderwort
Utricularia biflora Lamarck

Aquatic, stems creeping and forming tangled mats that radiate from the base of the scape. Leaves are very delicate, mostly less than 0.2-in. long, twice-forked with numerous bladders. Flower scapes from 2 to 5 in. tall with 1 to 4 (usually 2) yellow flowers. Lower lip to 0.4-in. long, spur equaling or exceeding the lip. Infrequent. Shallow water of ponds, marshes. Thinly scattered in TN. A Coastal Plain species found from MA to FL to TX, and occasionally inland. Jul-Aug.

Cone-Spur Bladderwort (*U. gibba* L.) is similar, but has 0.25-in. flowers. Occasional. Wet flats and ponds. Thinly scattered in TN and found throughout the e U.S. Jun-Sep.

Inflated Bladderwort (*U. inflata* Walter) has flower scapes with radial, inflated, floating leaves (floats) about 2 in. long. Rare. Acid ponds, ditches, streams. Found in Pickett County in TN, and in the Coastal Plain from DE to FL to TX. May-Oct.

Horned Bladderwort (*U. cornuta* Michaux) is a showy terrestrial species with lower lip and spur about 0.5-in. long. Rare. A Coastal Plain species found in Coffee County. Jul.

Jack Carman

Jack Carman

Genus *Utricularia*

Bladderworts are carnivorous, trapping and assimilating tiny aquatic organisms using very small bulbous traps, the bladders. Only annual flowering signals the presence of terrestrial species. Aquatic species mostly have feathery strands of stems and bladder-bearing leaves, forming mats on wet mud flats or floating mats in shallow water. Seven species are found in TN.

Zigzag Bladderwort
Utricularia subulata L.

Mostly terrestrial. Underground parts very delicate with tiny bladders to 0.02-in. The erect, slender and wiry, zigzag scape from to 8 in. tall bears 1 to 10 yellow flowers. Lower lip to 0.3-in. with prominent palate and spur about equaling the lip. Rare. Wet soil very shallow water. Found in Cumberland Coffee, Fentress, Rhea and Morgan counties in TN. A Coastal Plain species extending inland to TN and AR. May-Nov.

Lavender Bladderwort (*Utricularia resupinata* Greene *ex* Bigelow) is an aquatic species with violet flowers. Rare. Ponds, shallow water. A Coastal Plain species found in Cumberland County in TN. Jul-Aug.

Tall Bellflower
Campanula americana L.

Coarse, erect, often freely-branched winter-annual or biennial from 2 to 6 ft tall. Leaves are thin, alternate, lance-shaped, sharply toothed, from 3 to 6 in. long. Flowers, about 1 in. wide, are borne in a loose terminal spike, and have 5 blue lobes and a long down-curved style with an up-curved tip. Common. Moist open woods, stream banks. Found throughout TN, and from Ontario to MN south to FL and OK. Jul-Sep.

Marsh Bellflower (*Campanula aparinoides* Pursh) is a reclining perennial with 3-angled stems from 4 to 24 in. long. Leaves, to 3 in. long, are narrowly lanceolate or linear and progressively reduced upward. Solitary, pale blue to white, 5-lobed, bell-shaped flowers to 0.35-in. long arise on long pedicels. Infrequent. Wet meadows. Scattered from the Eastern Highland Rim east in TN (Cumberland, Fentress, Coffee, Blount, Unicoi, Carter and Johnson counties). Extended range from Nova Scotia to Saskatchewan south to GA and NB. Jun-Aug.

George Hornal

Jack Carman

In Tennessee, the Bluebell Family is represented by 3 genera and 14 species with one additional variety.

Genus *Campanula*
Four species are found in Tennessee. The genus name is a diminutive of the Latin *campana* (a bell), alluding to the shape of the corolla.

Southern Harebell
Campanula divaricata Michaux
Smooth perennial from 1 to 3 ft tall with few to many, spreading to erect branches. Stem leaves are alternate, sharply and coarsely toothed, lance-shaped, from 1 to 3 in. long. The inflorescence is a loose panicle with numerous bell-shaped flowers hanging on slender stalks. The corolla, about 0.3-in. long, is pale blue with 5 lobes that have curled tips. The style extends outside the corolla about 0.2-in. Occasional. Rocky woods, cliffs, slopes at low elevation. Found from the Cumberland Plateau east in TN. U.S. range from w MD to e KY south to GA and AL. Jul-Sep.

George Hornal

Genus *Lobelia*

Lobelias have bilaterally-symmetric flowers with a 2-lipped corolla. The upper lip has 2 erect lobes and the lower lip has 3 spreading lobes. Nine species are found in TN. The genus and common names are in honor of Matthias de l'Obel, a late 16th and early 17th century Flemish herbalist.

Gattinger's Lobelia
Lobelia appendiculata A. DC.
var. *gattingeri* (Gray) McVaugh

Annual from 6 to 12 in. tall with an erect, smooth, unbranched stem. The leaves are alternate, oval, usually finely toothed, about 1 in. long. Light violet flowers about 0.4-in. long are borne in a loose, mostly one-sided, terminal raceme. Infrequent. Endemic to the cedar glades and barrens of Middle TN, where it is often seen. Found in Wilson, Montgomery, Davidson, Williamson, Maury, Rutherford, Marshall and Bedford counties. May-Jun.

Jack Carman

Canby's Lobelia   *Lobelia canbyi* Gray

Erect perennial from 16 to 40 in. tall that is usually branched above and somewhat hairy below. Leaves are alternate, linear, to 2 in. long and 0.2-in. wide. Loose slender racemes with short-stalked, lavender to blue flowers, to 0.4-in. long, terminate the stem and branches. The lower lip of the corolla is bearded within. Rare. Swamps, wet fields, barrens. Found in Franklin, Coffee, Warren, Van Buren and Cumberland counties in TN. An Atlantic Coastal Plain species found inland in w NC and TN. Jul-Aug.

Nuttall's Lobelia (*Lobelia nuttallii* Roemer & Schultes) is similar, but the corolla lower lip is smooth and has 2 green dots. Infrequent. Moist low woods. Found in the Cumberland Plateau in TN (Cumberland, Fentress, Van Buren, Morgan, Marion, Grundy and White counties), also in Roane County. A Coastal Plain species found from NY to FL and TX, and inland in the uplands from s KY south. Jul-Sep.

Jack Carman

Cardinal Flower   *Lobelia cardinalis* L.
Erect, usually unbranched perennial from 2 to 6 ft tall.   Leaves are thin, alternate, coarsely toothed, lanceolate to oblong, from 2 to 6 in. long, the lower ones short-stalked and the upper ones mostly sessile.   A spectacular raceme of showy flowers is terminal on the stem.   The corolla, from 1.2 to 1.8 in. long, is intensely red or scarlet (rarely pink or white).   Common.   Wet soil, stream banks, roadside ditches.   Found throughout TN, the e U.S. and se CAN.   Jul-Sep.   The bright red flowers are usually pollinated by hummingbirds.   The common name refers to the bright red robes worn by Roman Catholic cardinals.

Jack Carman

Indian Tobacco   *Lobelia inflata* L.
Erect annual from 4 to 40 in. tall, freely-branched and usually hairy throughout. The leaves are alternate, mostly sessile, usually toothed, lance-shaped, from 2 to 3 in. long. Loose racemes from 4 to 8 in. long terminate the stem and branches. The light blue to white flowers are about 0.3-in. long and short-stalked. The inflated seed pods, from 0.25 to 0.45-in. long, are egg-shaped to almost round, and usually present while the plant is still in flower.   Common.   Fields, roadsides, open woods.   Found throughout TN and most of the e U.S.   Jul-Oct.   Indian Tobacco has had many traditional folk medicine uses.   However, it is considered **toxic** because of its strong expectorant, emetic and sedative effects, and rightly or wrongly, has been implicated in deaths from improper use as a home remedy.   **Do not ingest or smoke.**

Jack Carman

Downy Lobelia
Lobelia puberula Michaux

Erect, usually unbranched perennial from 1 to 4 ft tall with a hairy stem. The leaves are alternate, coarsely toothed, oblong to lance-shaped, from 2 to 4 in. long. A dense, mostly one-sided raceme from 4 to 12 in. long terminates the stem. The violet to blue flowers are nearly sessile, from 0.6 to 0.8-in. long. Common. Moist open woods, barrens, meadows, fields. Found throughout TN, and from s NJ to s IL south to FL and TX. Aug-Oct.

Southern Lobelia (*Lobelia amoena* Michaux) is similar, but the stems are smooth. The leaves are elliptic to lance-shaped, from 2 to 6 in. long. Rare. Marshes, stream banks, wet cliffs. Found in Polk and Monroe counties in TN, and in the mountains of the western Carolinas and north GA. Aug-Oct.

Jack Carman

Great Blue Lobelia
Lobelia siphilitica L.

Stout erect perennial from 2 to 5 ft tall that is sometimes branched above. The leaves are alternate, thin, sessile, irregularly toothed, lance-shaped, from 3 to 5 in. long. A crowded raceme terminates the stem and branches. The flowers, from 0.8 to 1.2 in. long, are blue (rarely white) with the corolla tube striped beneath and inflated. Frequent. Wet ground, swamps, stream banks, roadside ditches. Found throughout TN. Extended range from ME to Manitoba and CO south to NC and TX. Aug-Sep. American Indians used root tea to treat syphilis and a leaf tea for colds, fevers, stomach ailments, nosebleeds and croup. However, the plant is **potentially poisonous.**

Pale-Spiked Lobelia
Lobelia spicata Lamarck
Erect unbranched perennial from 1 to 4 ft tall that is often hairy, especially below. The leaves are alternate, ascending, toothed, lanceolate to obovate, from 2 to 4 in. long, progressively reduced upward. A crowded slender raceme terminates the stem. The flowers are nearly sessile, blue to white, about 0.4-in. long. Frequent. Meadows, glades, barrens, thickets. Found from the Western Highland Rim east in TN, also in McNairy County. Extended range from Nova Scotia to MN south to GA and AR. May-Aug. American Indians used leaf and root teas for several medicinal purposes including treatment of sores and trembling. However, the toxicity of the plant is unknown and it may have **poisonous** attributes.

Jack Carman

Jack Carman

Venus' Looking Glass
Triodanis perfoliata (L.) Nieuwland
Erect winter annual from 4 to 40 in. tall, sometimes with a few long branches. The leaves are alternate, clasping, toothed, almost round, from 0.2 to 1.2 in. long. The flowers, from 0.4 to 0.6-in. wide, are solitary in the leaf axils, and have 5 spreading lobes that are deep purple to pale lavender. The seed capsules, to 0.4-in. long, are mostly egg-shaped, opening by pores in the side to disperse the small shiny seeds. Common. Open woods, roadsides, barrens, gardens. Found throughout TN, the U.S. and s CAN. May-Aug. *Specularia perfoliata* (L.) A.DC.

The common name is from the European species *Specularia speculum-veneris* (mirror of Venus), alluding to the polished seeds believed to resemble tiny mirrors.

Jack Carman

Buttonbush   *Cephalanthus occidentalis* L.
Shrub from 3 to 10 ft tall. The leaves, from 3 to 6 in. long, are ovate-oblong or lance-oblong,
opposite or occasionally in whorls of 3. Dense spherical heads, from 0.8 to 1.2 in. wide, are
borne on long stalks that are terminal or from the upper leaf axils, and have numerous white
flowers from 0.25 to 0.33-in. long. The corolla is 4-lobed and tubular with a style that
protrudes well beyond the outside edge. The stigmas are often covered with masses of
pollen. Common. Low wet areas, swamps, stream banks, along edges of ponds, lakes and
marshes. Found throughout TN, the e U.S. and se CAN. Jun-Aug. The genus name is from
the Greek *cephale* (a head) and *anthos* (a flower).

Jack Carman

The Madder Family is represented by 9
genera and 34 species in Tennessee.

Genus *Diodia*
The genus name is from the Greek *diodos* (a
thoroughfare) with the likely reference being
that these plants are often found growing by
the wayside. Two species are found in TN.

Rough Buttonweed   *Diodia teres* Walter
Weedy, often branched annual with prostrate
to spreading or ascending stems from 8 to
32 in. long. The leaves, from 0.8 to 1.6 in.
long, are opposite, stiff, sessile, rough, linear
to narrowly lance-shaped and tipped with a
bristle. Stipules to 0.4-in. long have a short
sheath and 5 to 8 bristles.   Pinkish
funnelform flowers, about 0.25-in. long, are
4-lobed, sessile, borne in the leaf axils. The
fruit capsule is somewhat roundish, hairy
and topped by the 4 persistent sepals.
Common.   Dry fields, roadsides, woods,
waste places. Found throughout TN and
most of the e U.S. Jun-Sep. Also called
Poor Joe because it is often found in poor
soil.

Jack Carman

Virginia Buttonweed
Diodia virginiana L.
Weedy, branched and spreading annual with hairy stems from 8 to 32 in. long. The leaves, from 1 to 4 in. long, are opposite, thin, sessile, narrowly elliptic to lance-oblong with linear stipules to 0.2-in. long. White salverform flowers, about 0.4-in. long, are 4-lobed, sessile, borne in the leaf axils. The capsule is hairy, egg-shaped, ribbed, and topped by the 2 persistent sepals. Common. Wet ground, ditches. Found throughout TN, and from s NJ to s IL and MO south to FL and TX. Jun-Aug.

Genus *Galium*
Weak, often scrambling, slender herbs with square stems and whorled leaves. The tiny whitish flowers usually have 4 lobes and are borne in cyme-like clusters that are terminal or from the leaf axils. The fruit is composed of two small 1-seeded pods that are dry and often bristly. The genus name is from the Greek *gala* (milk), as milk is curdled by an ingredient contained in some species. There are 14 species found in TN.

George Hornal

Cleavers, Bedstraw   *Galium aparine* L.
Annual with stems from 4 to 40 in. long, the angles with rough, hooked, down-turned bristles. Narrow leaves from 0.4 to 3 in. long occur mostly in whorls of 8. Common. Shady damp woodlands, roadsides, waste places. Found throughout TN and most of temperate North America. Apr-May. Named Cleavers because the bristles "cleave" to animals, birds or clothing, aiding in dispersal of the seeds, and Bedstraw because in olden times, it was much used as bedding, as the stems remain soft and pliable when dried.

Fragrant Bedstraw (*Galium triflorum* Michaux) has a vanilla-like scent, weakly bristly stems, elliptic leaves in whorls of 6, flowers grouped in 3's. Common. Jun-Aug.

Wild Licorice or Forest Bedstraw (*Galium circaezans* Michaux) has stems hairy at the nodes, elliptic leaves in whorls of 4, yellow-green sessile flowers in loose clusters from the upper leaf axils only. Common. Jun-Jul.

Hairy Bedstraw (*Galium pilosum* Aiton) has elliptic leaves in whorls of 4, whitish stalked flowers borne in loose clusters from leaf axils all along the stem. Common. Jun-Aug.

Jack Carman

Quaker Ladies   *Hedyotis caerulea* (L.) Hooker
Delicate perennial that arises from a fragile rhizome, and has a slender erect stem from 2 to
7 in. tall, often occurring in small clumps. Leaves are opposite with the lower stalked,
spatulate to oblanceolate, from 0.2 to 0.5-in. long. Upper leaves are almost sessile and
much smaller. Salverform flowers, from 0.4 to 0.6-in. wide, are solitary on long stalks,
terminal or from the upper leaf axils, and have a smooth, 4-lobed, pale blue (rarely white)
corolla with a yellow eye. Common. Open woods, meadows, clearings. Found throughout
TN, and from Nova Scotia to WI south to GA and AR. Apr-May. The species name *caerulea*
is Latin for blue. *Houstonia caerulea* L.

Jack Carman

Genus *Hedyotis*
Eight species are found in TN. The genus
name is from the Greek *hedys* (sweet) and
otos (ear), but the significance of the
combination is unexplained.

Small Bluet
***Hedyotis crassifolia* Rafinesque**
Delicate annual with a slender, branched,
smooth, erect stem from 2 to 6 in. tall.
Leaves are opposite, short-stalked, mostly
basal, ovate to elliptic, from 0.2 to 0.4-in.
long. Solitary salverform flowers, from 0.15
to 0.3-in. wide, are borne on long stalks that
are terminal or from the upper leaf axils. The
corolla is 4-lobed, blue or purple with a
reddish eye. Occasional. Dry fields, open
woods, meadows, roadsides, lawns. Found
throughout TN, except in the mountains. A
Coastal Plain species found from VA to TX,
and inland from IL to NB south to TN and
TX. Mar-Apr. *Houstonia pusilla* Schoepf,
Houstonia patens Elliott.

Creeping Bluet, Mountain Bluet
Hedyotis michauxii Fosberg
Smooth perennial from 4 to 8 in. tall with creeping stems that often root at the nodes and have numerous erect branches. The leaves are opposite, short-stalked, rounded to ovate, from 0.1 to 0.3-in. long. Salverform flowers, from 0.4 to 0.6-in. wide, are solitary on long stalks, terminal or from the upper leaf axils. The corolla is 4-lobed, blue-violet with a light yellow eye, and the corolla tube is downy within. Infrequent. Stream banks, rich open woods, wet slopes and roadsides. In TN, found in the Blue Ridge (Monroe, Blount, Sevier, Unicoi, Carter and Johnson counties), also in Van Buren County. U.S. range from PA to GA in the mountains. Apr-Jun. *Houstonia serpyllifolia* Michaux.

Jack Carman

Jack Carman

Glade Bluet
Hedyotis nigricans (Lamarck) Fosberg
Taprooted perennial with branched erect stems from 8 to 24 in. tall, often hairy below. Leaves, to 1.2 in. long and 0.12-in. wide, are opposite, sessile, linear, rough, 1-nerved. Flowers are numerous and short-stalked, forming a crowded cyme-like panicle. The corolla is funnelform, about 0.3-in. long, 4-lobed, white to lavender in color. The fruit is egg-shaped to cylindric, longer than thick. Occasional. Dry soils and barrens. Thinly scattered from western Middle TN to western East TN. Extended range from OH to s MI to NB south to FL and Mexico. Jun-Aug. *Houstonia nigricans* (Lamarck) Fernald.

Long-Leaf Bluet (*Hedyotis longifolia* (Gaertner) Hooker) is similar, but fibrous-rooted. Leaves to 1.2 in. long are linear to oblong, narrowed to the base and 1-nerved. Fruit more or less spherical. Occasional. Dry open rocky areas. Thinly scattered in the eastern half of TN, also found in Williamson County, and from Saskatchewan to ME south to AR, MS and SC. Jun-Aug. *Houstonia longifolia* Gaertner.

Jack Carman

Roan Mountain Bluet   *Hedyotis purpurea* (L.) T. & G. **var.** *montana* (Small) Fosberg
Erect perennial with one to several stems from 4 to 12 in. tall that are often branched above
and have smooth internodes. Leaves, from 0.4 to 1.2 in. long, are opposite, ovate to lance-
oblong, rounded to almost cordate at the base with 3 to 5 main veins. Flowers are numerous
in terminal clusters. The deep-purple funnelform corolla is 4-lobed, about 0.3-in. long. Rare.
Found on rock outcrops at high elevation in the Blue Ridge mountains. In TN, known from
Carter County. Apr-Jun. *Houstonia montana* Small.

Large Bluet, Summer Bluet   *Hedyotis purpurea* (L.) T. & G. **var.** *purpurea*
Erect perennial with one to several stems from 6 to 20 in. tall that are often branched above
and have somewhat hairy internodes. The leaves, from 1.0 to 2.5 in. long, are opposite,
ovate to lance-oblong, rounded to almost cordate at the base with 3 to 5 main veins. Flowers
are many in terminal clusters. The white to lavender funnelform corolla is 4-lobed and about
0.3-in. long. Frequent. Dry open woods, barrens, rocky places. Found from the Western
Highland Rim east in TN, also in Hardeman County. U.S. range from NJ to IA south to GA
and TX. Apr-Jul. *Houstonia purpurea* L.

Jack Carman

Jack Carman

Partridgeberry   *Mitchella repens* L.

Prostrate and creeping, branched, evergreen perennial with stems from 4 to 12 in. long that usually root at the nodes and form large mats. The leaves are opposite, stalked, smooth, round-ovate, dark green, leathery, from 0.4 to 0.8-in. long. Fragrant flowers are borne in pairs on terminal stalks. The 2 corollas, about 0.5-in. long, are white, tubular, quite hairy inside, usually with 4 lobes, and have their ovaries united. A single scarlet to red berry is produced that has a scar where the 2 ovaries were attached. Berries are about 0.25-in. wide, and sometimes last until the next spring. Common. Rich or low woods, stream banks, preferring acid soil. Found throughout TN, the e U.S. and se CAN. May-Jun. The species name *repens* is Latin for creeping. This attractive woodland creeper can be used as a groundcover under acid-loving shrubs. The common name implies that the red fruits are relished by partridges, but they are not very important as a food source for other wildlife. The genus name is in honor of Dr. John Mitchell, an 18th century Virginia botanist.

Field Madder   *Sherardia arvensis* L.*

Annual from 4 to 16 in. tall with rough-hairy, erect or reclining, diffusely-branched, square stems. Leaves, from 0.2 to 0.8-in. long, occur mostly in whorls of 6, and are linear to narrowly elliptic, sharply-pointed, hairy. Pinkish to lavender tubular flowers, about 0.2-in. long, are borne in heads that are subtended by a large whorl of leaves with fused bases. Occasional. A Eurasian native often found in dense masses, and now naturalized in fields, lawns, roadsides and waste places throughout TN and the e U.S. Apr-Aug. The genus name is in honor of Dr. William Sherard, an 18th century patron of Dillenius.

Jack Carman

Mountain Bush Honeysuckle
Diervilla sessilifolia Buckley

Shrub from 2 to 6 ft tall. The leaves are glabrous, sessile, lanceolate to narrowly ovate, from 3 to 6 in. long, the margin toothed but not hairy. The flowers are tubular, 5-lobed, greenish-yellow, from 0.5 to 0.8-in. long. Infrequent. Woodlands, bluffs, roadsides. Found in Unicoi, Cocke, Sevier, Blount, Monroe, Polk, Hamilton and Marion counties in TN. A southern Appalachian species extending north from GA and AL to WV. Jul-Sep.

Northern Bush Honeysuckle (*Diervilla lonicera* Miller) is similar, but the leaves are short-stalked, the margins toothed and hairy. Infrequent. Dry, rocky soil. A northern species extending south to TN, and found in Cheatham, Marion, Polk, Roane, Anderson and Johnson counties. Jun-Jul.

American Fly Honeysuckle (*Lonicera canadensis* Bartram) has pale yellow flowers that grow in pairs. Rare. Woods at high elevation. Carter and Sevier counties in TN. A northern species extending south to TN in the mountains. May-Jun.

Jack Carman

Jack Carman

Mountain Honeysuckle
Lonicera dioica L.

Woody climber with smooth stems to 17 ft long. Leaves, from 2 to 6 in. long, are entire, opposite, glaucous beneath, sessile to short-stalked, elliptic to oblong to broadly ovate with the last three pairs usually united at the base. The flowers are borne in compact clusters at the end of the stem and branches. The pale yellow to purplish corolla, about 0.6-in. long, is tubular with spreading lobes. The stamens and style extend well outside the corolla tube. Berries are red. Infrequent. Moist woods and thickets. Found in Putnam, Jackson, Hamilton, Polk, Roane, Loudon, Claiborne, Hancock, Washington and Johnson counties in TN. A northern species extending south in the uplands to TN. May-Jun.

Yellow Honeysuckle (*Lonicera flava* Sims) is similar, but leaves are not glaucous and flowers are golden to orange. Rare. Rocky woods. Found in Hamilton, Marion, Franklin and Lewis counties in TN. The U.S. range is from s MO to KY and NC south to GA and AR. Apr-May.

Jack Carman

Japanese Honeysuckle   *Lonicera japonica* Thunberg*
High-climbing or trailing woody vine. The leaves are opposite, ovate to oblong, rounded or broadly wedge-shaped at the base, from 1.5 to 3 in. long. Flowers are borne in the leaf axils, and are white or pink fading to yellow, very fragrant, strongly two-lipped, to 2 in. long. The color of the outside of the corolla tube is variable, from white to cream or red. The berries are almost round, glossy, black. Frequent. Woods and fields. Found throughout TN and the eastern U.S. Apr-Jun. Native of east Asia. A very serious competitor with native flora that can engulf woodlands and strangle trees.

The Honeysuckle Family is represented by 8 genera and 30 species in Tennessee.

Jack Carman

Genus *Lonicera*
Nine species are found in Tennessee. The genus name is in honor of Adam Lonitzer (latinized Lonicerus), a German herbalist of the 16th century.

Trumpet Honeysuckle
***Lonicera sempervirens* L.**
Climbing or trailing vine to 16 ft long with smooth stems. The leaves, from 1 to 3 in. long, are entire, partially evergreen, smooth, glaucous beneath, mostly oval with the last 1 or 2 pairs below the flowers united and surrounding the stem. Flowers are borne in clusters at the end of the stem and branches. The corolla, from 1 to 2 in. long, is yellow or red outside, yellow inside, tubular with 5 short lobes. The stamens and style barely extend outside the corolla tube. The berries are red. Frequent. Woods and thickets. Widespread in TN and the e U.S. May-Jul. A favorite of hummingbirds.

Jack Carman

Common Elderberry　　　　　　　　　　　　　　　*Sambucus canadensis* L.

Shrub to 10 ft tall. Leaves are opposite, pinnately compound, usually with 7 lanceolate to ovate, sharply serrate leaflets. The inflorescence, to 6 in. or more across, is a flat-topped or convex cluster of numerous small white flowers. The fruit is a purple-black berry, edible, and makes tasty jelly and wine. Common. Moist woods, fields, and roadsides. Found throughout TN, the e U.S. and se CAN. Jul-Aug. An important food source for songbirds.

Red Elderberry (*Sambucus racemosa* L. ssp. *pubens* (Michaux) House) is similar, but has a long, pyramidal, panicle-like inflorescence and red fruit. Infrequent. A northeastern species extending south to TN in the Blue Ridge, also found in Grundy and Van Buren counties. May-Jun.

Yellow Horse Gentian　　　　　　　　　　　　　*Triosteum angustifolium* L.

Perennial from 4 to 32 in. tall. Leaves sessile, opposite, oblanceolate or obovate, to 7 in. long and 2.4 in. wide. Pale greenish-yellow flowers are solitary in the leaf axils. The showy orange-red fruits are crowned with 5 persistent sepals. Occasional. Moist woods and low ground. Widespread in TN and the e U.S. Apr-May.

Orange-Fruit Horse Gentian (*T. aurantiacum* Bicknell) has leaves widest near the base, red-purple flowers and orange-red fruit. Occasional. Rich woods. Eastern 2/3 of TN. May-Jul.

Feverwort (*T. perfoliatum* L.) has coarse crisp-hairy stems and main leaves broadly connate-perfoliate (united). Flowers purplish to dull greenish-yellow, fruits orange-yellow. Infrequent. Woods and thickets. Scattered in the eastern half of TN, not known from West TN. May-Jul.

Jack Carman　　　　　　　　　　　　　　　　　　Jack Carman

Jack Carman

Maple-Leaf Viburnum
Viburnum acerifolium L.
Shrub from 3 to 7 ft tall with stalked, opposite, shallowly 3-lobed, maple-like leaves. The inflorescence is a stalked terminal cyme (about 2 in. wide) with numerous small white flowers. The fruit is purple-black, egg-shaped to spherical. Frequent. Moist or dry woods. Found in the eastern half of TN, also Hardin County, and in most of the e U.S. May-Jun.

Swamp Haw (*V. nudum* L.) has shiny narrowly-revolute leaves with tiny red-brown scales beneath. Fruit blue-black, glaucous. Occasional. Wet woods and swamps. Found in West TN, the Eastern Highland Rim and the Cumberland Plateau, and from Newfoundland to Manitoba south to FL and TX. May-Jul.

Southern Black Haw (*V. rufidulum* Raf.) has nearly sessile cymes; petioles and young leaves are rusty-brown. Common. Woods and thickets. Found throughout TN and the se U.S. Apr-May.

Jack Carman

Genus *Viburnum*
en species are found in Tennessee. The enus name is the classical Latin name.

Witch Hobble
Viburnum lantanoides Michaux
Shrub 3 to 9 ft tall. Leaves are stalked, pposite, broadly ovate, finely toothed, from to 7 in. long. The inflorescence is a sessile yme about 4 in. wide with numerous small whitish flowers and large sterile showy owers around the margin. Fruit red, turning ark, egg-shaped. Infrequent. Moist woods. mostly northeastern species extending outh to TN in the mountains. Apr-Jun. *iburnum alnifolium* Marshall.

outhern Arrowwood (*V. dentatum* L.) has ince-ovate to rotund, sharply-toothed eaves and blue-black fruit. Occasional. arious habitats. Found in the eastern half f TN, and most of the e U.S. May-Jul.

Wild Raisin (*V. cassinoides* L.) has dull, vate to lanceolate, usually revolute leaves ith rounded teeth. Occasional. Wet or dry tes. Widely scattered in eastern half of TN. more northern species extending south in e mountains to GA and AL. May-Jun.

The Valerian Family is represented by 2 genera and 5 species in Tennessee.

Valerian *Valeriana pauciflora* Michaux
Erect perennial from 12 to 32 in. tall that arises from a slender rhizome. Basal leaves, from 2 to 3 in. long, are stalked, simple, broadly heart-shaped with a wavy margin. Stem leaves are pinnately divided into 3 to 7 leaflets. The terminal leaflet is broadly ovate or deltoid, much larger than the lateral ones. The inflorescence is compact with short branches that lengthen with age. The corolla, to 0.6-in. long, is pink, the tube very slender with short lobes. The calyx is small at flowering, but expands into 10 long feathery plumes in fruit. Occasional. Rich moist woods. Found in the Western and Eastern Highland Rims in TN, and from PA to s IL south to VA and TN. Apr-May. The genus and common names were said by Linnaeus to be in honor of Publius Aurelius Licinius Valerianus, Roman emperor from 253 to 260 A.D.

Jack Carman

Jack Carman

Genus *Valerianella*
The genus name is a diminutive of *Valeriana*. The four Tennessee species are succulent annuals from 8 to 24 in. tall with forked stems and branches. Stem leaves are opposite, entire or obscurely toothed, sessile, lance-shaped to spatulate. The inflorescence is cyme-like with bracts and tiny 5-lobed white flowers.

Beaked Corn Salad
Valerianella radiata (L.) Dufresne
Bracts are sparsely hairy on the margin. Flowers are tiny (less than 0.08-in. long). The fruit is egg-shaped, about 0.1-in. long. Common. Open disturbed sites, fields, waste places. Found throughout most of TN, and from VA to OH to KS south to FL and TX. Apr-May.

Navel Corn Salad (*Valerianella umbilicata* (Sullivant) A. W. Wood) has mostly smooth bracts, a loosely flowered inflorescence with long branches, and flowers from 0.12 to 0.20-in. long. Occasional. Open disturbed sites, fields, waste areas. Found in Middle TN, and from s NY to IL south to NC and TN Apr-May.

DIPSACACEAE : TEASEL FAMILY

Teasel   *Dipsacus fullonum* L.*
Stout coarse biennial from 2 to 7 ft tall with prickly stems and few branches. Basal leaves are oblanceolate with rounded teeth, and stem leaves to 12 in. long are lance-shaped, entire, opposite, sessile or often united at the base. All leaves are prickly on the midvein beneath. Heads are borne on long naked stalks, and are egg-shaped to cylindric, from 1.25 to 4.0 in. long. The bracts surrounding the head are upcurved and prickly. The calyx is densely hairy and the flowers, from 0.4 to 0.6-in. long, are slender and tubular, white with short pale-purple lobes. Occasional. Roadsides, waste ground. Found in East and Middle TN but mostly absent in the Cumberland Plateau. A European native now naturalized throughout most of North America. Jul-Sep. *Dipsacus sylvestris* Hudson*. Wool manufacturers once used the dried seed head, fastened to a spindle, to "tease" the cloth to raise the nap. The genus name is the Greek name for teasel. Thought by some to be adapted from *dipsa* (thirst) because the cup-shaped leaf bases of some species hold water.

George Hornal

ASTERACEAE : ASTER FAMILY
The Aster Family has 82 genera and 322 species found in TN.

Yarrow, Milfoil   *Achillea millefolium* L.
Aromatic rhizomatous perennial from 8 to 40 in. tall that is sparsely to densely hairy. Leaves, from 1 to 6 in. long and 1 in. wide, are very finely dissected and occur in a basal rosette and alternate along the stem. Dense, flat-topped or rounded flower clusters are terminal on the stem and upper branches. Each head, about 0.2-in. high, has 10 to 30 tiny white disk flowers and about 5 white (occasionally pink) rays from 0.08 to 0.12-in. long. Frequent. Fields, roadsides, waste places. Found throughout TN, the e U.S. and se CAN. Jun-Nov. Folk remedy used for fevers, stomach disorders, hemorrhaging, and as a poultice for rashes.

Jack Carman

George Hornal

Creeping Spotflower   ***Acmella oppositifolia*** (Lamarck) Jansen
Smooth to hairy perennial with weak stems to 2 ft long, often rooting at the lower nodes. Leaves paired, toothed, lanceolate or ovate, from 1 to 3 in. long and 0.2 to 1.2 in. wide on petioles to 0.8-in. long. Heads few on naked stalks, the disk domed, to 0.4-in. wide, and elongating with age. Rays several, yellow, 3-toothed, from 0.12 to 0.4-in. long. Rare. Low moist woods and swamps. A Coastal Plain species found from NC to TX and north in the Mississippi River valley to MO, s IL and TN (Shelby, Haywood, Lauderdale, Tipton and Rutherford counties). Jun-Oct. *Spilanthes americana* (Mutis) Hieron.

White Snakeroot   ***Ageratina altissima*** (L.) King & H. Robinson
Smooth or short-hairy perennial from 1 to 5 ft tall. Leaves are opposite, sharply toothed, mostly ovate, to 7 in. long and 5 in. wide on well-developed stalks over 1 in. long. The inflorescence may be flat-topped or rounded. Each flower head has 12 to 25 disk flowers with a bright white corolla, its lobes often short-hairy. Common. Open woods, woods borders. Found throughout TN and the e U.S. Jul-Oct. *Eupatorium rugosum* Houttuyn. "Milk sickness" may result from drinking the milk of cows that have grazed on this plant.

Aromatic Snakeroot (*A. aromatica* (L.) King & Rob.) is similar, but leaves have more rounded teeth and stalks less than 1 in. long. Occasional. Mostly eastern 2/3 of TN. Aug-Oct.

Braun's Throroughwort (*A. luciae-brauniae* (Fernald) King & Robinson) is similar, but leaf stalks are about as long as the blade. Rare. Endemic to the rock house habitats of the Cumberland Plateau in n TN and s KY. Sep.

Jack Carman

Jack Carman

Common Ragweed   *Ambrosia artemisiifolia* L.
Annual from 1 to 7 ft tall, branched above. Leaves, from 1 to 4 in. long, are opposite and stalked below, alternate and sessile above, once or twice pinnately dissected. The greenish flowers are tiny with female flowers borne in clusters from the upper leaf axils, and male flowers borne in spike-like clusters that terminate the stem and upper branches. Frequent. Fields, roadsides, waste areas. Found throughout TN and the U.S. Aug-Oct.

Genus *Ambrosia*
Three species are found in TN. Wind-carried ragweed pollen is responsible for about 90% of pollen-induced allergies in the U.S. *Ambrosia* is the Greek and later Latin name of several plants as well as food for the gods. Perhaps somewhat inappropriately applied to this genus.

Jack Carman

Great Ragweed (*A. trifida* L.) is similar to Common Ragweed, but has opposite leaves with 3 to 5 large, pointed, palmate lobes. Frequent. Waste areas, roadsides. Found throughout TN and the e U.S. Aug-Oct.

Lance-Leaf Ragweed (*A. bidentata* Michaux) is similar to Common Ragweed, but has a spreading-hairy stem and lance-shaped leaves. Occasional. Waste areas. Thinly scattered in TN, and found from OH to NB south to LA and TX. Jul-Oct.

Plantain-Leaf Pussytoes
Antennaria plantaginifolia (L.) Richardson
Colonial perennial from 4 to 16 in. tall with creeping runners (stolons). Basal leaves, to 2.4 in. long, are woolly beneath, stalked, ovate to elliptic or obovate, and mostly 3-veined. Stem leaves are narrow and smaller. From 3 to 21 flower heads are clustered at the top of the flowering stalk. The heads, from 0.2 to 0.4-in. long, have numerous whitish pappus bristles that are quite noticeable. Common. Open dry woods, roadsides. Found throughout TN and most of the e U.S. Apr-Jun.

Genus *Antennaria*

Two species are found in TN. Species of this genus are dioecious, meaning male and female flowers are found on separate plants. The genus name is from the resemblance of the pappus of the male flowers to the *antennae* of certain insects. Flower heads were believed to resemble a cat's paw, hence the common name "pussytoes."

Solitary Pussytoes
Antennaria solitaria Rydberg

Colonial perennial from 4 to 10 in. tall with creeping runners (stolons). Basal leaves, to 3 in. long, are woolly beneath, sessile or stalked, oblong to obovate, and mostly 3-veined. The flowering stalk is mostly without leaves and has a solitary, terminal, flower head. The head, from 0.3 to 0.4-in. long, has numerous whitish pappus bristles. Frequent. Dry open woods. Found from the Western Highland Rim east in TN, and throughout most of the southeastern U.S. Apr-May.

Genus *Anthemis*

Two species are found in Tennessee. The genus name is the ancient name of chamomile.

Jack Carman

Mayweed, Dog Fennel   *Anthemis cotula* L.*

Ill-smelling, bushy annual from 4 to 36 in. tall. Leaves, from 0.8 to 2.5 in. long, are alternate, 2 to 3 times finely-divided into narrow linear lobes. Solitary flowers are borne on long stalks from the upper leaf axils, and have a yellow disk from 0.2 to 0.4-in. wide and 10 to 16 white rays from 0.2 to 0.45-in. long. The ray flowers are sterile. Occasional. Fields, waste places, disturbed areas. Found throughout TN and the e U.S. May-Aug. Introduced from Europe.

Corn Chamomile (*A. arvensis* L.*) is similar, but not ill-smelling. The ray flowers are pistillate (female) and fertile (produce seed). Occasional. Fields, waste places. Widespread in TN and the e U.S. May-Aug. Introduced from Europe.

Jack Carman

Genus *Aster*
There are 36 species listed for TN. The genus and common names are from the Greek *aster* (a star), alluding to the radiate heads of flowers.

Eastern Silvery Aster
Aster concolor L.
Slender, sparingly-branched perennial from 12 to 40 in. tall that is usually silky-hairy above, smooth below. The leaves are entire, mostly silky-hairy, lanceolate or oblong to broadly elliptic, to 2 in. long and 0.6-in. wide, sessile and broad-based but not strongly clasping. The flowers are borne in long narrow clusters at the top of the stem or branches. The flower heads have 8 to 16 blue to pinkish rays from 0.4 to 0.8-in. long and yellow disk flowers. The achenes are densely silky-hairy. Occasional. Dry open areas, fields, barrens. Found in the eastern half of TN, also Hardeman, McNairy, Hardin and Dickson counties. A Coastal Plain species found from MA to FL to LA, up the Mississippi embayment to sw TN, and less commonly inland in the uplands of KY and TN. Sep-Oct.

Jack Carman

George Hornal

Stiff-Leaf Aster   *Aster linariifolius* L.
Colonial stiff perennial from 4 to 28 in. tall that is usually unbranched. Leaves are numerous, stiff, linear, entire, to 1.4 in. long, without veins except for the midvein. The flower heads are clustered at the top of the stem. Each head has from 10 to 20 blue to violet rays to 0.5-in. long that are broad and showy. The disk flowers are yellow. Occasional. Open dry woods and woods borders. In TN, found from the Western Highland Rim east, also in McNairy County, and throughout the e U. S. Sep-Oct.

Bushy Aster (*A. dumosus* L.) has one to many branched stems with leaves that are stiff and linear, to 4.5 in. long. Branch leaves are much reduced in size. Flowers are numerous and have 13 to 30 lavender to bluish rays to 0.4-in. long. Frequent. Dry or moist areas. Found throughout TN and the eastern U.S. Aug-Oct.

Wavy-Leaf Aster (*A. undulatus* L.) is mostly hairy. The leaves are entire, sessile and clasping, or with winged petioles that are clasping. Rays bluish. Frequent. Dry open woods. Middle and East TN. Aug-Nov.

New England Aster
Aster novae-angliae L.

Perennial from 1 to 7 ft tall with clustered stems that are hairy and glandular upward. Leaves are alternate, lanceolate, clasping at the base, from 1 to 5 in. long. The flower heads have bracts that are glandular-sticky and more than 50 showy, violet or pink rays to 0.8-in. long. Occasional. Moist open areas and thickets. Widespread in TN and the e U.S. Aug-Oct.

Large-Leaf Aster (*A. macrophyllus* L.), to 4 ft tall, has toothed, heart-shaped, basal leaves from 1 to 8 in. wide. The 9 to 20 rays are bluish, to 0.6-in. long. Infrequent. Woods. East TN. Northern species extending south to TN and GA in the uplands. Aug-Sep.

Heart-Leaf Aster (*A. cordifolius* L.), to 4 ft tall, has toothed leaves from 1 to 3 in. wide that are deeply cordate at the base. Rays bluish. Frequent. Statewide. Aug-Oct.

Short's Aster (*A. shortii* Lindley) has smooth stems to 4 ft tall, and leaves are entire, narrowly heart-shaped, to 6 in. long. Rays bluish. Occasional. Woods, clearings. East and Middle TN. Aug-Oct.

Jack Carman

George Hornal

Southern Aster
Aster paludosus Aiton
ssp. *hemisphericus* (Alex.) Cronquist

Smooth perennial from 8 to 32 in. tall with alternate, grass-like leaves to 8 in. long. The inflorescence is long and raceme-like with flower heads borne in the leaf axils. The heads, from 1 to 2 in. wide, have 15 to 35 showy blue or violet rays. Frequent. Barrens, roadsides, open woods, less often in moist to wet sites. Found in West and Middle TN, also Hamilton and Rhea counties. A more southern species that extends north into TN. Aug-Oct. *Aster hemisphericus* Alexander.

The Western Silvery Aster (*Aster sericeus* Ventenat) is similar to the Eastern Silvery Aster, but the inflorescence is more loose and open, and the achenes are smooth. Rare. Dry open areas. Observed in Decatur County in TN, and found from MI to SD south to MO and TX, and irregularly east into TN. Sep-Oct.

Jack Carman

Late Purple Aster   ***Aster patens*** Aiton
Hairy perennial from 8 to 60 in. tall. Leaves are entire, ovate to oblong, cordate-clasping, from 1 to 6 in. long. Flower heads are terminal and solitary on the side branches. The 15 to 35 rays are blue, from 0.3 to 0.6-in. long. Common. Woods, dry open places. Widespread in the eastern 2/3 of TN and most of the e U.S., but few records from West TN. Aug-Oct.

Smooth Aster (*A. laevis* L.) stems are smooth, green, usually glaucous. Leaves are smooth, mostly entire, clasping. Rays bluish. Frequent. Middle and East TN. Aug-Oct.

Purple-Stemmed Aster (*A. puniceus* L.) stems are purplish, mostly spreading-hairy. Leaves are toothed, rough, clasping. Rays bluish. Occasional. Found in the East TN highlands, it is a northern species extending south to AL and GA in the mountains. Aug-Oct.

Jack Carman

White Heath Aster, Awl Aster
Aster pilosus Willdenow
Widely-branched perennial from 1 to 10 ft tall. Stem leaves are mostly sessile, linear to lance-shaped, usually less than 4 in. long and 0.4-in. wide. Branch leaves are much reduced. Flower heads are numerous, often only on one side of the branches. The 16 to 35 ray flowers are white, from 0.2 to 0.4-in. long. Common. Open dry areas. Found throughout TN and the e U.S. Sep-Oct.

Lowrie's Aster (*Aster lowrieanus* Porter) has smooth, toothed, heart-shaped leaves with winged stalks. Rays whitish. Occasional. Open woods. Found in the eastern half of TN. A northern species extending south to TN and GA in the uplands. Jul-Sep.

Whorled Wood Aster (*Aster acuminatus* Michaux) has alternate, thin, sharply few-toothed, elliptic or obovate leaves that appear whorled on the stem. Rays whitish. Infrequent. Mountain woods. Blue Ridge. A northern species extending south to TN and GA in the uplands. Jul-Oct.

Jack Carman

Western Daisy
Astranthium integrifolium (Michx.) Nuttall
Hairy annual from 2 to 18 in. tall, sparingly to freely branched, often from near the base. The leaves, to 3 in. long and 0.8-in. wide, are alternate, mostly spatulate below, linear to elliptic above. The flower heads, from 0.7 to 1.4 in. wide, have yellow disk flowers and 8 to 30 white rays that are tinged with lavender. Occasional. Roadsides, borders of barrens. Found in Middle TN, also Hamilton County. The U.S. range is from TX to se KS east to KY and nw GA. Apr-Jul. The genus name is from the Greek *astron* (star) and *anthos* (flower).

Genus *Bidens*
Nine species are found in Tennessee that are annual or perennial herbs with opposite leaves and usually yellow rays. The Latin word *bidens* means two-toothed.

Spanish Needles   *Bidens bipinnata* L.
Erect, mostly smooth annual from 1 to 6 ft tall that arises from a taproot. Fern-like leaves, from 1.5 to 8 in. long, are stalked and 2 or 3 times pinnately dissected into irregular, elliptic to ovate or lance-shaped segments to 1.6 in. long that have rounded tips. The heads are small and narrow, the disk about 0.2-in. wide at flowering. Involucral bracts are green, linear, to 0.3-in. long. Ray flowers are absent to few that are yellow and less than 0.2-in. long. Achenes, from 0.4 to 0.7-in. long, are linear and needle-like with 3 or 4 barbed awns. Frequent. Moist to fairly dry disturbed areas, fields, roadsides, waste places. Widely scattered in TN. The extended range is from MA to NB to CA south to FL and Mexico. Jul-Oct.

Jack Carman

Jack Carman

Nodding Bur Marigold
Bidens cernua L.

Annual or short-lived perennial to 4 ft tall, usually with smooth stems. The leaves are sessile, often grown together at the base, lance-linear to lance-ovate, coarsely serrate to almost entire, from 2 to 8 in. long and 0.2 to 1.8 in. wide. The flower heads are nodding, at least in age, and have hemispheric disks from 0.5 to 1 in. wide and 6 to 8 yellow rays to 0.6-in. long, or none. Outer involucral bracts are leafy, consistently surpassing the disk. Occasional. Low wet places, sometimes in shallow water. Thinly spread across TN, but found in most of temperate North America. Aug-Nov.

Showy Bur Marigold (*B. laevis* (L.) BSP.) is similar, but the outer involucral bracts are not leafy, seldom surpassing the disk, ray flowers are longer, from 0.6 to 1.2 in. long, and the heads are erect. Low wet places. Listed as occurring in TN, but not officially recorded, chiefly a Coastal Plain species. Aug-Oct.

Ozark Tickseed Sunflower
Bidens polylepis Blake

Erect, branching, annual or biennial from 1 to 5 ft tall that is smooth or slightly hairy. The leaves, from 2 to 6 in. long, are opposite, stalked, once or twice pinnately-divided into lance-shaped, mostly toothed segments. The flowers are showy with a yellow disk from 0.3 to 0.6-in. wide and about 8 yellow rays from 0.4 to 1 in. long. The 12 to 25 outer involucral bracts are curled and twisted, usually hairy and longer than the inner. Frequent. Wet areas, mostly in full sun. Widespread in TN. A western species extending eastward into TN. Aug-Oct.

Midwestern Tickseed Sunflower (*Bidens aristosa* (Michaux) Britton) is similar, but the outer involucral bracts are fewer (8 to 10) and shorter than the inner. Occasional. Wet areas, most often in shade. Found in the western 2/3 of TN. U.S. range from ME to MN south to VA and TX. Aug-Nov.

Jack Carman

Jack Carman

False Aster
Boltonia asteroides (L.) L'Her.
Short-lived, much-branched perennial from 1 to 6 ft tall. Leaves are alternate, broadly linear to lance-shaped, from 2 to 6 in. long and 0.2 to 0.8-in. wide, reduced in size upward. Flower heads are usually numerous with yellow disk flowers and 25 to 35 white, pink or purplish rays from 0.3 to 0.6-in. long. Occasional. Moist or wet areas. Widely scattered in West and Middle TN, and found from NJ to ND south to FL and TX. Jul-Oct. The genus name is in honor of James Bolton, an 18th century English botanist.

Doll's Daisy (*Boltonia diffusa* Elliott) is similar, but the leaves are narrow (mostly less than 0.2-in. wide), and the white or lilac rays are less than 0.3-in. long. Occasional. Wet to moist to sometimes dry areas. Widely scattered in West and Middle TN. Extended range is se U.S., north to NC and s IL west to OK and e TX. Jul-Sep.

Genus *Cacalia*
Four species are found in Tennessee. The genus name is of ancient origin and uncertain meaning.

Great Indian Plantain   ***Cacalia muhlenbergii*** (Schultz-Bipontinus) Fernald
Stout smooth perennial to 10 ft tall with green and grooved stems. Leaves are alternate, irregularly toothed, often shallowly lobed, green on both sides, the lower somewhat reniform, to 32 in. wide and long stalked, the upper reduced and somewhat ovate. The inflorescence is broadly flat-topped with numerous flower heads that have 5 whitish disk flowers and no ray flowers. Occasional. Open woods. Thinly scattered in TN. U.S. range from NJ to s MN south to GA and MS. Jun-Sep.
Pale Indian Plantain (*C. atriplicifolia* L.) is similar, but the stem is glaucous and round, and leaves are pale green above and glaucous beneath. Frequent. Woods, pastures, open areas. Found in the Western Highland Rim, and from the Eastern Highland Rim east in TN, also in Weakley County. U.S. range from NJ to s MN south to w FL and OK. Jun-Sep.

Jack Carman

Tuberous Indian Plantain
Cacalia plantaginea (Raf.) Shinners
Stout smooth perennial with a mostly leafless grooved stem to 7 ft tall. Basal leaves are thick and firm, mostly entire, commonly elliptic and tapering to the long petioles, the blade from 3 to 8 in. long and 1 to 4 in. wide. The inflorescence is broadly flat-topped with numerous flower heads that have 5 whitish disk flowers and no ray flowers. Rare. Wet fields and pastures. Found in Davidson, Marshall and Rutherford counties in TN. U.S. range from OH to e SD south to AL and TX. May-Jun. *Cacalia tuberosa* Nuttall.

Sweet-Scented Indian Plantain (*Cacalia suaveolens* L.) has 20 to 40 disk flowers per head and the larger leaves are triangular-hastate and sharply toothed. Infrequent. Moist low ground. In TN, known only from the Western Highland Rim in Cheatham, Davidson, Dickson, Houston, Humphreys, Lawrence, Lewis, Perry, Stewart and Williamson counties. U.S. range from RI to MN south to MD and TN, and to GA in the mountains. Jul-Oct.

Jack Carman

Jack Carman

Thistles   *Carduus* and *Cirsium*
Both thistle genera are usually recognized from their prickly stems and leaves, and the large spiny heads with reddish flowers. The major difference between the two is not readily evident, but found in the pappus: feather-like bristles in *Cirsium*, and barbed, hair-like bristles in *Carduus.*

Nodding Thistle   *Carduus nutans* L.*
Smooth or thinly hairy biennial from 1 to 7 ft tall with a spiny-winged stem. The leaves, to 10 in. long and 4 in. wide, are mostly smooth and deeply lobed. The flower heads, about 2 in. wide, are usually nodding and solitary at the ends of very long stalks, and have numerous reddish-purple flowers. Involucral bracts are tipped with spreading spines. Occasional. Roadsides, pastures, and waste places. Found in Middle TN, also Knox, Jefferson, Sevier and Hamblen counties in East TN. A native of Eurasia, now spreading in TN and widely established in the U.S. and adjacent CAN. May-Nov. *Carduus* is the ancient Latin name for thistle.

Jack Carman

Genus *Centaurea*
Four species are found in TN. The genus name is from the ancient Greek plant name *Centaurie*.

Spotted Knapweed
Centaurea maculosa Lamarck*
Thinly-hairy, short-lived perennial that is 1 to 5 ft tall, widely branched. The leaves are alternate, pinnatifid with narrow lobes or entire upward, from 4 to 8 in. long. The heads are solitary and terminal on the many branches, and have numerous pinkish to lavender flowers. Involucres, from 0.4 to 0.5-in. high, are urn-shaped with overlapping and ribbed bracts that have blackish, fringed tips. Occasional. Fields, roadsides, waste places. Naturalized from Europe, found throughout TN and most of the e U.S. Jun-Oct.

Bachelor's Button (*Centaurea cyanus* L.*) is similar, but an annual with mostly linear leaves without lobes. The flowers are blue, infrequently pink, purple or white. Occasional. Fields, roadsides, waste places. Native to the Mediterranean, now found throughout TN and the e U.S. Apr-Jun.

Oxeye Daisy
Chrysanthemum leucanthemum L.*
Mostly smooth perennial from 8 to 32 in. tall, arising from a rhizome. Basal leaves, from 1.6 to 6 in. long, are oblanceolate or spatulate, stalked, usually lobed or cleft as well as toothed, and stem leaves are reduced in size upward, becoming sessile. Showy flower heads are solitary at the ends of leafless branches. The heads have a yellow disk from 0.4 to 0.8-in. wide, and 15 to 35 white rays from 0.4 to 0.8-in. long. Common. Fields, roadsides, waste places. Found throughout TN. Introduced from Eurasia and naturalized in most of temperate North America. May-Oct. The genus name is from the Greek *chrysanthemon* (golden flower).

Showy displays of Oxeye Daisy are common along Tennessee roadsides from late May to early June. The plant is disliked by farmers because it can produce an unwanted flavor in milk if eaten by cattle.

George Hornal

John MacGregor

Jack Carman

ireen-and-Gold
***hrysogonum virginianum** L.*
    var. *australe* (Alexander *ex* Small) Ahles
ibrous-rooted, hairy, creeping, mat-forming
erennial seldom over 4 in. tall, but **var.
irginianum** grows to 20 in. tall. Leaves are
pposite, shallowly toothed, long-stalked,
vate to almost round, from 1 to 4 in. long
nd 0.6 to 2.4 in. wide. Flowers are solitary
r few on slender stalks that are terminal or
om the leaf axils. Disks are yellow, from
.3 to 0.4-in. wide, and the 5 rays are bright
ellow, from 0.3 to 0.6-in. long. Rare. Rich
/oods. Found in Polk, Scott, Claiborne and
;reene counties in TN, and from s PA and
e OH south to FL and MS. Mar-Jul.

Chicory   *Cichorium intybus* L.*
Taprooted perennial 1 to 6 ft tall with a milky
sap. Leaves are alternate, the lower ones
toothed or pinnately lobed, oblanceolate,
from 3 to 10 in. long and 0.4 to 3 in. wide,
and the upper ones reduced, sessile, entire
or toothed. The flowers, to 1.6 in. wide, are
borne in the upper leaf axils and are usually
open only in the morning. Disk flowers are
absent and rays are pale blue (rarely white).
Occasional. Disturbed areas, roadsides,
fields. Widespread in TN and the e U.S.
Jun-Oct. Introduced from Eurasia. The root
is used as a flavoring for coffee in many
countries. The genus name was adapted
from the Arabian name for the plant.

Genus *Cirsium*
Seven species are found in TN. The genus
name is from *cirsos* (a swollen vein), alluding
to the supposed curative properties of thistle
for that malady.

Tall Thistle
Cirsium altissimum (L.) Sprengel
Robust, openly-branched, fibrous-rooted
perennial from 3 to 14 ft tall with a smooth to
spreading-hairy stem. The leaves are large,
to 20 in. long and 8 in. wide below but
reduced above, broadly oblanceolate to
obovate or elliptic, densely white-hairy
beneath, mostly spiny-toothed or coarsely
toothed, but sometimes with shallow lobes.
Flower heads several to numerous on more
or less leafy stalks, and the flowers are pink-
purple. Involucres, from 0.8 to 1.6 in. long,
have the middle and outer bracts tipped with
a spine. Occasional. Fields, waste places,
roadsides. Found in the eastern 2/3 of TN,
and throughout most of the e U.S. Jul-Oct.

Jack Carman

Jack Carman

Carolina Thistle
Cirsium carolinianum (Walter) Fernald & Schubert
Slender biennial from 2 to 5 ft tall, mostly smooth, but softly hairy when young. Leaves are smooth or hairy above, white-hairy beneath, entire with a spiny margin or pinnately lobed, from 3 to 6 in. long and 0.6 to 2 in. wide. From 1 to several heads, with numerous red-purple flowers, are borne on long leafless stalks that terminate the branches. Involucres are 0.6 to 0.8-in. high, and only the outer bracts bear short erect or spreading spines. Occasional. Roadsides, open woods, woods borders. Found in the southern Western Highland Rim and from the Cumberland Plateau east in TN. U.S. range from s OH south to the mountains of NC, GA and AL, and west to MO and TX. May-Jun.

Field Thistle
Cirsium discolor (Muhl. *ex* Willd.) Spreng.
Robust biennial from 3 to 7 ft tall with a hairy stem. Leaves are deeply divided into firm, narrow and spiny lobes, smooth to slightly rough above, densely white-hairy beneath, from 4 to 8 in. long. Heads are few to several atop long leafy stalks and have numerous pink-purple flowers. Involucres, from 1 to 1.5 in. long, have the middle and outer bracts tipped with a spine. Occasional. Open woodlands, thickets, roadsides, fields. Found throughout TN, and from Quebec to Manitoba south to NC, MS, LA and KS. Jul-Oct.

Jack Carman

Spiny Thistle, Yellow Thistle
Cirsium horridulum Michaux
Stout biennial from 1 to 5 ft tall, the stem simple or with short, stout, ascending, stalk-like branches. Leaves are strongly spiny, broad and pinnately lobed to seldom narrow and spiny-toothed, from 4 to 12 in. long. Heads are solitary to several with white, buff-yellow, lavender or red-purple flowers. The involucre, from 1.2 to 2 in. high, has spine-tipped outer bracts, and is surrounded by several erect, narrow, strongly-spiny leaves. Rare. Open places, roadsides. Found in Stewart, Hardin, McNairy, Wayne and Bradley counties in TN. Chiefly a Coastal Plain species found from ME to FL to TX. May-Aug.

Jack Carman

George Hornal

Swamp Thistle
Cirsium muticum Michaux
Biennial from 2 to 7 ft tall with a branching stem. Leaves, to 10 in. long and 2 in. wide, are deeply divided into lanceolate to oblong segments that are weakly spiny, usually toothed, entire or lobed. Involucres, from 0.8 to 1.4 in. long, have sticky hairy bracts usually without spines. Flowers are purple, red or lavender, rarely white. Infrequent. Swamps, wet meadows, moist woods. Thinly scattered from the Western Highland Rim east in TN. A mainly northern species extending south into TN. Jul-Oct.

Canada Thistle (*C. arvense* (L.) Scopoli*) is a colonial perennial with numerous small heads from 0.4 to 0.8-in. high, and involucral bracts without spines or only weakly spine-tipped. Flowers are pink-purple. Rare. Fields and waste places. Recorded from Knox, Davidson and Johnson counties in TN. A noxious weed widely introduced in the northern U.S. and southern CAN. Jul-Aug. Native of Eurasia.

Jack Carman

Bull Thistle
Cirsium vulgare (Savi) Tenore*
Biennial from 2 to 5 ft tall. The stem is mostly spreading-hairy and conspicuously spiny-winged by the decurrent leaf bases. Leaves, from 3 to 12 in. long and 1 to 4 in. wide, are strongly spiny, rough-hairy above, thinly hairy beneath, dissected or twice dissected into irregular, sometimes toothed lobes. Heads are usually several on leafy spiny stalks and have purple flowers. Involucres are 1 to 1.6 in. high and all bracts are spine-tipped. Occasional. Pastures, roadsides, and waste ground. Naturalized from Eurasia, scattered throughout TN, and widely established in North America. Jun-Oct.

George Hornal

Mistflower
Conoclinium coelestinum (L.) DC.
Perennial from 1 to 3 ft tall with a hairy stem. Leaves are opposite, stalked, shallowly to sharply toothed, broadly lance-shaped, from 1 to 4 in. long and 0.8 to 2 in. wide. The flower clusters are terminal or arise from the leaf axils. Each bell-shaped head, about 0.2-in. high, has 35 to 70 blue-purple disk flowers. Involucral bracts are awl-shaped, nearly smooth. Common. Moist woods, ditches, fields, low areas. Widespread in TN, and found from NY to IL and KS south. Jul-Oct. *Eupatorium coelestinum* L.

Pink Thoroughwort (*Fleischmannia incarnata* (Walter) King & H. E. Robinson) is similar, but the flowers are pink-purple and there are fewer flowers (18 to 24) per head. Frequent. Moist woods and thickets. Found throughout TN, and from se VA to s IN to OK south. Aug-Oct. *Eupatorium incarnatum* Walter.

Jack Carman

Lobed Tickseed   *Coreopsis auriculata* L.
Perennial to 2 ft tall with an erect stem that is leafy below. Leaves are petioled with ovate to broadly elliptic blades, to 3 in. long and 1.6 in. wide, that usually have a pair of small lateral lobes. Heads are mostly solitary on long leafless stalks, and have yellow rays to 1 in. long with the tips deeply notched. Occasional. Open woods. Found from the Eastern Highland Rim east in TN, also in Sumner County, and in most of the se U.S. Apr-Jun.

Lance-Leaf Coreopsis (*C. lanceolata* L.) is similar, but has slightly larger flowers, to 3 in. wide, and longer narrower leaves, to 8 in. long and 0.8-in. wide. Occasional. Dry, open, often sandy soils. Found in the western 2/3 of TN, also Scott and Knox counties, and in most of the e U.S. Apr-Jun.

Hairy Tickseed (*C. pubescens* Elliott) is similar, but 2 to 4 ft tall, usually hairy and leafy throughout. Occasional. Found in most of TN. U.S. range from VA to s IL to OK south to FL and LA. Jun-Sep.

Genus *Coreopsis*
Eight species are found in TN. The genus and common names are from the Greek *coris* (a bug) and *opsis* (appearance), alluding to the form of the achene.

Whorled-Leaf Coreopsis   *Coreopsis major* Walter
Perennial from 20 to 40 in. tall. Leaves, each usually with 3 lance-shaped leaflets to 3 in. long, are opposite and sessile, but appear whorled. Heads are from 1 to 2.5 in. wide. Disk flowers are yellow, sometimes aging to purplish, and rays are yellow, usually with rounded tips. Frequent. Dry open woods, roadsides. Found in East and Middle TN with few records from the Central Basin. U.S. range from PA and OH south to FL and TX. Jul-Sep. Another common name is Forest Tickseed.

Jack Carman

Jack Carman

Garden Coreopsis
Coreopsis tinctoria Nuttall

A smooth, leafy, branching annual from 1 to 4 ft tall. Leaves, from 2 to 4 in. long, are short-stalked to almost sessile, once or twice pinnately divided into mostly linear segments from 0.04 to 0.16-in. wide. Flower heads are numerous with a red-purple disk to 0.5-in. wide, and rays, from 0.4 to 0.8-in. long, that are yellow with a red-brown base, toothed at the tip. Occasional. Moist low places, open disturbed areas. Thinly scattered in TN. Primarily native to the Great Plains and south to TX and LA, but widely cultivated, escaped and irregularly established elsewhere. Jun-Aug. A root tea was used by American Indians for diarrhea and to cause vomiting.

Jack Carman

Tall Coreopsis   *Coreopsis tripteris* L.

Perennial from 3 to 10 ft tall. The solitary stems are usually smooth and somewhat glaucous. Leaves, with 3 lance-shaped leaflets from 2 to 4 in. long, are opposite, stalked, numerous. The flower heads, from 1 to 2.5 in. wide, have yellow disks aging brown to purplish, and round-tipped yellow rays. Occasional. Moist thickets, barrens, fields. Found throughout TN, but generally absent from the Central Basin. Extended range includes most of the central and eastern U.S. Jul-Sep.

Genus *Doellingeria*

Two species are found in Tennessee. The flat-topped asters are closely related to the true asters (genus *Aster*), but have outer pappus bristles that are less than 0.04-in. long and much shorter than the inner pappus bristles.

Tall Flat-Topped White Aster
Doellingeria umbellata (Miller) Nees
Mostly smooth perennial from 3 to 7 ft tall, branched above. Leaves are entire, mostly sessile, narrowly elliptic or lance-elliptic, from 1.6 to 6 in. long. The flower heads are borne at the tops of the stem and branches in a more or less flat-topped cluster. The heads have yellow disk flowers and 7 to 14 white rays from 0.2 to 0.3-in. long. The achenes are softly hairy. Occasional. Roadsides, fields, woodland borders. Scattered in TN, but most populations are found in the Eastern Highland Rim and Cumberland Plateau. A northern species extending south in the uplands to GA and n AL. Aug-Oct. *Aster umbellatus* Miller.

Appalachian Flat-Topped White Aster (*D. infirma* (Michaux) Greene) is similar, but less than 4 ft tall, usually with fewer and slightly longer rays, and the achenes are smooth. Occasional. Open woodlands. Widely scattered in the eastern 2/3 of TN, and found from MA to KY south to GA and AL. Aug-Oct. *Aster infirmus* Michaux.

Jack Carman

Jack Carman

Genus *Echinacea*
Primarily plants of western prairies, four species are found in TN. Plains Indians are believed to have used *Echinacea* more than any other plant group for medicinal purposes such as snakebites, spider bites, cancers, toothaches, burns, sores, wounds, flu and colds. Science confirms many traditional uses. Considered to be a nonspecific immune system stimulant. The genus name is from the Greek *echinos* (sea-urchin), alluding to the sharp chaffy scales of the achenes.

Pale Purple Coneflower
Echinacea pallida Nuttall
Perennial from 2 to 3 ft tall with coarsely spreading-hairy herbage. Leaves are entire, basally disposed, long, narrow, parallel-veined, stalked and have blades to 8 in. long. The disk, from 0.6 to 1.2 in. wide, has white pollen, and rays are narrow, pale lavender, drooping, from 1 to 3 in. long. Rare. Dry open places. Found in Coffee and Franklin counties in TN, it is a western species extending east into GA. Jun-Jul.

Jack Carman

Purple Coneflower *Echinacea purpurea* (L.) Moench
Perennial from 2 to 6 ft tall that arises from a crown, caudex or short stout rhizome. The leaves are alternate, mostly hairy, stalked, broadly lance-shaped, toothed, the blades to 6 in. long and 4 in. wide. The disk, to 1.4 in. wide, has orange disk flowers, and rays are purplish, drooping, to 3 in. long. Occasional. Woods edges, barrens. Found in McNairy County in West TN, in Wayne, Lewis, Perry, Dickson, Cheatham, Davidson, Sumner, Marion, Grundy and Warren counties in Middle TN, and in Roane, Anderson, Knox and Claiborne counties in East TN, but some records are likely garden escapes. Found in the prairie states, and irregularly east to MI, KY, TN and GA, and less commonly to NC and VA. Jun-Oct.

Jack Carman

Prairie Purple Coneflower
Echinacea simulata McGregor
Perennial to 3 ft tall with coarsely spreading-hairy herbage. The leaves are entire, long, narrow, parallel-veined, basally disposed, stalked, and have blades to 8 in. long. The disk, to 1.2 in. wide, has yellow pollen, and the rays, from 1 to 3 in. long, are narrow, pink (to purplish), strongly drooping. Rare. Cedar glades or glade-like sites. Found in Montgomery and Rutherford counties in TN. The U.S. range is from se MO to s IL south to ne AR and c TN. Jun-Jul.

Tennessee Coneflower
Echinacea tennesseensis (Beadle) Small
Endemic perennial to 3 ft tall with coarsely
spreading-hairy herbage. The leaves are
entire, long, narrow, parallel-veined, basally
disposed, stalked, and have blades to 8 in.
long. The disk, to 1.2 in. wide, has yellow
pollen, and the rays, to 2 in. long, are
narrow, purplish (to pinkish or white),
spreading-ascending. Rare. The first
species from Tennessee to qualify as a
federally endangered species, it is found
only in a few cedar glades of Davidson,
Rutherford, and Wilson counties in the TN
Central Basin. May-Jul.

Jack Carman

Yerba-De-Tajo   ***Eclipta prostrata*** (L.) L.*
Weedy, weakly ascending or spreading, branched, hairy annual that often roots at the nodes.
The leaves are opposite, lance-shaped, sessile or short-stalked, shallowly toothed, from 0.8
to 4 in. long. From 1 to 3 flower heads are borne in terminal or axillary clusters on the many
branches. The disk is yellow, about 0.25-in. wide, and the rays are white, tiny, numerous.
Frequent. Bottomlands and muddy places. Found throughout TN and most of the e U.S.
Aug-Oct. The genus name is from the Greek *ecleipo* (to be deficient), alluding to the
absence of the pappus.

Jack Carman

Jack Carman

Two *Elephantopus* species are found in TN
The genus name is from the Greek *elephas*
(elephant) and *pous* (foot), the translation o
an aboriginal name.

Leafy Elephant's Foot
Elephantopus carolinianus Raeusch.
Perennial from 1 to 3 ft tall with the stem
densely hairy and branched above. Basal
leaves few, stem leaves well developed bu
reduced upward, broadly elliptic to obovate
to 10 in. long and 4 in. wide, roundly toothed
softly hairy beneath. Heads with bluish
flowers are borne in clusters, surrounded by
leafy bracts, and terminate the spreading
branches. The involucres are about 0.4-in
high, and have triangular-ovate bracts that
are thinly hairy with a pointed tip and
resinous coating. Common. Open dry
woods. Found throughout TN and the e U.S
Aug-Sep.

Devil's Grandmother or Elephant's Foot (*E
tomentosus* L.) is similar, but has a basal
rosette of large leaves that lie flat on the
ground. The stem leaves are greatly
reduced, usually to small bracts. Frequent
Open woods. Found throughout TN and the
se U.S. Aug-Sep.

Jack Carman

Pilewort , Fireweed
Erechtites hieraciifolia (L.) Raf. *ex* DC.
Weedy erect annual from 1 to 8 ft tall that is
mostly smooth, but sometimes spreading-
hairy throughout. Leaves, from 2 to 8 in.
long, are alternate, irregularly lobed and
sharply serrate with firm teeth, the lower
mostly oblanceolate and stalked, and the
upper mostly elliptic, sessile or clasping.
Small cylindric flower heads with disk flowers
only (no rays) occur in flat-topped or long
clusters that terminate the stem and
branches. The pappus is composed of
numerous, very fine and soft, bright white
hairs persistent on the seeds which are
dispersed by the wind. Frequent. Old fields,
open woods, fire-swept areas, disturbed
places. Widespread in TN and found from
Newfoundland to FL west to NB and TX.
Aug-Sep. *E. hieracifolia* (L.) Raf. The genus
name is adapted from the ancient name
Erechthites, used by Dioscorides for some
species of groundsel.

Jack Carman

Common or Philadelphia Fleabane   *Erigeron philadelphicus* L.
A biennial to short-lived hairy perennial from 8 to 28 in. tall. Basal leaves are oblanceolate to obovate, coarsely toothed or lobed, less than 6 in. long. Stem leaves are alternate, clasping, oblong to ovate, usually toothed, reduced upward. The inflorescence is a corymb, usually with numerous heads. Flower heads, from 0.6 to 1.4 in. wide, have yellow disks, and 150 to 400 white to pink rays to 0.02-in. wide. Common. Fields, lawns, roadsides, waste areas. Widespread in TN and North America. Apr-Jul.

Daisy Fleabane (*Erigeron annuus* (L.) Persoon) is similar, but the stem has spreading hairs, and lanceolate, usually toothed leaves that are not clasping. Common. Disturbed areas. Widespread in TN, the U.S. and s CAN. Jun-Oct.

Fleabane   **Genus *Erigeron***
Four species are found in TN. The genus name is from the Greek *eri* (early) and *geron* (old man), adapted from an ancient name of an early-flowering plant with hoary down.

Jack Carman

Robin's Plantain
Erigeron pulchellus Michaux
Colonial perennial from 6 to 24 in. tall. Basal leaves are mostly oblanceolate and toothed, to 5 in. long and 2 in. wide. Stem leaves are lance-shaped and reduced upward. Flower heads, from 1 to 1.6 in. wide, usually solitary (or few), terminating the hairy stem. The 50 to 100 rays are white to lavender to violet, about 0.04-in. wide. Common. Woods, roadsides, stream banks. Found in the eastern 2/3 of TN, also Hardin, Shelby and Haywood counties, and in most of the e U.S. Apr-Jun.

Lesser Daisy Fleabane (*Erigeron strigosus* Muhlenberg *ex* Willdenow) is similar to Common Fleabane, but the stem has appressed hairs and narrow entire leaves that are not clasping. Common. Disturbed areas. Found throughout TN, the U.S. and southern CAN. May-Aug.

Tall Thoroughwort
Eupatorium altissimum L.

Stout perennial from 3 to 6 ft tall with a mostly hairy stem. Leaves are numerous, opposite, hairy, lance-elliptic, strongly 3-nerved to the base, toothed above the middle, from 2 to 6 in. long and 0.3 to 1.2 in. wide. Flowers are borne in a dense, flat-topped cluster at the top. Each head, about 0.25-in. high, has 5 white disk flowers and rounded involucral bracts. Occasional. Open woods, fields, roadsides. Found from the Western Highland Rim east in TN, also in Weakley County. The U.S. range is from NJ to s MN south to SC and TX. Aug-Oct.

White-Bracted Thoroughwort (*E. album* L.) has sharply-toothed leaves and pointed, white-edged involucral bracts. Occasional. Dry open woods. Western Highland Rim east in TN, also Henry County. Jul-Sep.

Small-Flower Thoroughwort (*Eupatorium semiserratum* DC.) has small heads. Leaves are toothed above the middle and 3-nerved, but the lateral veins arise from the midvein instead of the base. Infrequent. Low wet woods, clearings. A Coastal Plain species found in Middle and West TN. Aug-Oct.

Jack Carman

Jack Carman

Genus *Eupatorium*

Both the joe-pye weeds and thoroughworts are members of this genus. The small tube-like flower heads are usually borne in terminal, dense, flat-topped or rounded clusters. Sixteen species are found in TN. The genus is named in honor of Mithridates Eupator, 132-63 B.C., who is said to have used a species of this genus in medicine.

Dog Fennel
Eupatorium capillifolium (Lamarck) Small

Coarse perennial from 2 to 7 ft tall with hairy stems that are freely-branched above. The leaves are opposite below, alternate above, from 1 to 4 in. long, multi-divided into numerous, delicate, needle-like segments. The inflorescence is a long panicle with numerous heads about 0.1-in. high that are smooth and have 3 to 6 greenish-white disk flowers. Occasional. Open woods, fields, roadsides, pastures. Scattered in TN, mostly in the southern half. A mostly Coastal Plain species found from NJ to FL to TX, and interior to s AR and TN. Sep-Oct.

Hollow Joe-Pye Weed
Eupatorium fistulosum Barratt

Perennial from 2 to 10 ft tall with smooth, purple-glaucous, hollow stems. Leaves are in whorls of 4 to 7, stalked, mostly elliptic, bluntly toothed, smooth to hairy beneath, to 12 in. long and 4 in. wide. Inflorescence large and terminal, somewhat rounded. Flower heads, about 0.25-in. long, have 5 to 11 pink-purple disk flowers. Frequent. Wet meadows, marshes, woods borders. Found throughout TN and the e U.S. Jul-Sep.

Sweet Joe-Pye Weed (*Eupatorium purpureum* L.) has a green stem that is purplish at the leaf nodes, and leaves in whorls of 3 or 4. Frequent. Thickets, open woods. Widespread in TN, and found from NH to IA south to VA and OK, and south in the uplands to GA. Jul-Sep.

Spotted Joe-Pye Weed (*E. maculatum* L.) has solid stems, purple-speckled or evenly purplish, seldom glaucous. Inflorescence flat-topped and many-flowered. Infrequent. Moist calcareous areas. Scattered in TN, it is a northern species that extends south to TN and NC in the uplands. Jul-Sep.

Jack Carman

Jack Carman

Hyssop-Leaf Thoroughwort
Eupatorium hyssopifolium L.

Perennial from 12 to 40 in. tall with hairy stems, especially above. There is usually a whorl of 3 or 4 leaves at each node, but sometimes above, they are merely opposite or alternate. Leaves are linear to narrowly lance-shaped, sessile, smooth or sometimes hairy beneath, from 1 to 3 in. long and 0.04 to 0.4-in. wide. The principal leaf nodes have noticeable bundles of very small leaves. The inflorescence is flat-topped to somewhat rounded. The flower heads are about 0.25-in. high and have 5 white disk flowers. Frequent. Fields, roadsides, open areas, barrens. Found throughout TN, and in the Coastal Plain from MA to LA, and interior to KY and OH. Aug-Oct.

Justiceweed (*E. leucolepis* (DC.) T. & G.) has white-edged involucral bracts like *E. album*, but has small heads and opposite, narrow leaves usually folded along the midvein. Rare. Wet meadows. Known only from Coffee County in TN. A Coastal Plain species ranging from MA to FL to LA. Jul-Oct.

Jack Carman

Boneset   *Eupatorium perfoliatum* L.
Perennial from 1 to 5 ft tall with a spreading-hairy stem. Leaves are opposite and fused at the base (connate-perfoliate), gradually tapering to the tip, sparsely hairy above, evidently hairy beneath, coarsely toothed, from 3 to 8 in. long and 0.6 to 1.8 in. wide. The inflorescence is more or less flat-topped. Flower heads, about 0.2-in. high, have 9 to 23 dull-white disk flowers. Frequent. Moist or wet open areas. Found throughout TN, the eastern and central U.S., and se CAN. Aug-Oct. A leaf tea has been used to cause sweating for fevers, flu and colds, and also has been used to treat malaria, pneumonia, rheumatism and muscular pain. A common home remedy for 19th century American settlers and extensively used by Native Americans.

Jack Carman

Round-Leaf Thoroughwort
Eupatorium rotundifolium L.
Perennial from 1 to 5 ft tall with a soft-hairy stem. Leaves are hairy, mostly sessile, opposite, broadly ovate, evenly toothed, from 0.8 to 5 in. long and 0.4 to 2.4 in. wide. The inflorescence is more or less flat-topped and its upper branches are mostly opposite. Flower heads, about 0.25-in. high, have 5 white disk flowers. Frequent. Woodlands, fields, meadows. Found in the eastern 2/3 of TN. U.S. range from ME to s OH south to FL and TX. Aug-Oct.

Hairy Thoroughwort (*Eupatorium pilosum* Walter) is similar, but the leaves are mostly less broad and more unevenly toothed, and the upper leaves and inflorescence branches are usually alternate. Occasional. Moist open areas. Found in the eastern half of TN, and from MA to VA to FL west to e KY, s TN and MS. Aug-Sep.

Upland Boneset (*E. sessilifolium* L.) is similar but smooth below the inflorescence. Leaves are lance-shaped, mostly tapering to a pointed tip. Frequent. Found in the eastern 2/3 of TN, also Madison County, and from NH to MN south to GA and AR. Aug-Sep.

Late-Flowering Thoroughwort
Eupatorium serotinum Michaux

Perennial from 1.5 to 7 ft tall with a soft-hairy stem, especially above. The leaves are opposite, sharply toothed, thinly hairy to almost smooth, lanceolate to ovate but tapering to the tip, from 2 to 8 in. long and 0.6 to 4 in. wide, on stalks from 0.4 to 1.6 in. long. The inflorescence is flat-topped to rounded and loosely spreading. Flower heads, about 0.15-in. high, have 9 to 15 white disk flowers. Common. Moist to dry open woods, fields, roadsides, waste areas. Widespread in TN, and found throughout the e U.S. from s NY south. Aug-Oct.

Genus *Euthamia*

Three species are found in TN. The flat-topped goldenrods are closely related to the goldenrods (genus *Solidago*), but the leaves of *Euthamia* species are dotted with resinous glands.

Jack Carman

Jack Carman

Mississippi Valley Flat-Topped Goldenrod
Euthamia leptocephala (T. & G.) Greene

Highly-branched, smooth perennial to 40 in. tall. Leaves to 0.25-in. wide are mostly 10 to 20 times as long, and usually 3-nerved. The flower clusters are flat-topped. Flower heads are small and numerous, the 10 to 14 rays short and yellow. Rare. Open, moist sites. Found in Coffee, Lincoln, Obion and Shelby counties in TN, and from s MO to s IL south to TX and w FL. Aug-Oct. *Solidago leptocephala* Torrey and A. Gray.

Great Plains Flat-Topped Goldenrod (*E. gymnospermoides* Greene) is similar, but copiously resinous. Rare. Open moist to dry areas. Found in Hardeman, Lawrence and Coffee counties in TN, generally more northern in distribution. Aug-Oct. *Solidago gymnospermoides* (Greene) Fernald.

Common Flat-Topped Goldenrod (*Euthamia graminifolia* (L.) Nuttall *ex* Cassini) is similar, but leaves are mostly wider with 5 to 7 nerves. Occasional. Open moist ground. Western 2/3 of TN, and most of the U.S. and adjacent s CAN from TN north. Aug-Oct. *Solidago graminifolia* (L.) Salisbury.

Firewheel, Blanket Flower
Gaillardia pulchella Foug.*

An annual or short-lived perennial from 4 to 24 in. tall that is hairy and usually freely-branched. Leaves are alternate, toothed or pinnately lobed, mostly lance-shaped, from 1 to 6 in. long. The showy flower heads are borne on long leafless stalks. Rays, from 0.4 to 0.8-in. long, are usually reddish-purple with a yellow tip, sometimes all yellow or all purplish. The disk, from 0.4 to 1 in. wide, has the same color as the base of the rays. Rare. Dry sandy areas, fields, roadsides. In TN, reported only from Warren County, but also observed in Bedford and Maury counties. U.S. range from MO to CO south to TX, and along the coast from TX to FL to se VA. May-Sep. The genus name is in honor of Gaillard de Charentonneau, a French botanical amateur.

The author is Auguste Denis Fougeroux de Bondaroy.

Jack Carman

Jack Carman

Genus *Gnaphalium*
Three species are listed for TN. The name is from the Greek *gnaphallon* (lock of wool).

Rabbit Tobacco, Sweet Everlasting
Gnaphalium obtusifolium L.

Erect fragrant annual from 4 to 40 in. tall with a white-woolly stem. Leaves are woolly beneath, sessile, lance-shaped, to 4 in. long. Numerous flower heads occur in dense terminal clusters. The heads are bell-shaped, whitish or yellowish, to 0.3-in. long with white bracts. Common. Pastures fields, open woods, disturbed places. Found throughout TN and the e U.S. Aug-Oct.

Purple Cudweed (*G. purpureum* L.) is similar, but the bracts of the flower head are brown to purplish. Basal leaves spatulate or oblanceolate. Common. Sandy soil and waste places. Found throughout TN and the U.S. May-Oct.

Cudweed (*G. helleri* Britton) is similar to *G. obtusifolium*, but has greenish, glandular sticky stems. Rare. Franklin, Grundy Roane, Blount and Polk counties in TN. U.S range from ME to IN south to GA, AR and TX. Aug-Oct.

Lance-Leaf Gumweed
Grindelia lanceolata Nuttall
Short-lived perennial from 1 to 5 ft tall. Leaves are alternate, scarcely glandular-dotted, usually sharply toothed with the teeth bristle-tipped, linear to linear-oblong, to 4 in. long and 1 in. wide. The flower heads are terminal on the stem and branches. The disk is yellow, from 0.6 to 0.8-in. wide, and the 15 to 30 rays are yellow, from 0.4 to 0.65-in. long. Involucral bracts are loose but not abruptly spreading-reflexed or markedly overlapping. Infrequent. Dry, open places, often on limestone. Found in Chester, Maury, Williamson, Davidson, Rutherford, Franklin and Knox counties in TN. U.S. range from s IN to KS south to TN and NM. Jun-Sep. Genus name in honor of David Grindel, a 19th century Russian botanist.

Curly-Top Gumweed (*Grindelia squarrosa* (Pursh) Dunal*) is similar, but the leaves have blunt or rounded teeth, and are abundantly glandular-dotted. The involucral bracts are distinctly spreading-reflexed and overlapping. Rare. Dry, open sites. Known from Knox County in TN. A northern and western species introduced in TN. Jul-Sep.

George Hornal

Bitterweed   *Helenium amarum* (Rafinesque) H. Rock
Taprooted, smooth annual to 20 in. tall, much branched from a single stout stem. Leaves are numerous, linear to linear-filiform, to 3 in. long, seldom over 0.08-in. wide. Heads are on short leafless stalks that extend above the leaves. Disk yellow and spherical, to 0.5-in. wide. The yellow rays, from 0.2 to 0.5-in. long, are slightly reflexed and wedge-shaped, each with 2 or 3 shallow notches at the tip. Frequent. Pastures, fields, roadsides, waste places. Found throughout most of TN, except for northeastern counties. U. S. range from VA to MO south to FL and TX. Aug-Oct. *Helenium tenuifolium* Nuttall. Cows that graze on the foliage usually produce bitter-tasting milk.

George Hornal

Jack Carman

Autumn or Common Sneezeweed   *Helenium autumnale* L.
Freely-branched perennial from 2 to 5 ft tall with winged stems. Leaves are numerous, alternate, usually toothed, lance-shaped, mostly sessile, from 1.6 to 6 in. long and from 0.2 to 1.6 in. wide. Heads are on leafless stalks that are terminal or from the leaf axils. Disk yellow and spherical, from 0.3 to 0.8-in. wide. The yellow rays, from 0.6 to 1 in. long, are slightly reflexed and wedge-shaped, each with 2 or 3 shallow notches at the tip. Frequent. Low moist places. Recorded from the Western Highland Rim east in TN, and found throughout the eastern and central U.S. Sep-Oct.

Dried powdered leaves induce sneezing. American Indians used dried, powdered, disk flowers as a snuff for head colds. Flower tea has been used as a folk remedy for fevers.

Jack Carman

Four *Helenium* species are found in TN. The genus name is said by Linnaeus to be in honor of Helena (Helen of Troy), wife of King Menelaus of Sparta.

Purple-Headed Sneezeweed
Helenium flexuosum Rafinesque
Leafy perennial to 3 ft tall with a mostly hairy winged stem. Leaves are mostly oblong to lanceolate, sessile, from 1 to 5 in. long and 0.2 to 0.8-in. wide, little reduced upward. The heads are usually numerous in an open, corymb-like, leafy-bracted inflorescence. The disk is mostly spherical, to 0.6-in. wide, red-brown or purplish. The 8 to 13 bright yellow rays are about 0.6-in. long. Common. Moist soil in waste areas, fields, ditches. Found throughout TN but mostly absent from the Central Basin. U.S. range from NH to WI south to FL and TX. June-Aug. *Helenium nudiflorum* Nuttall.

Short-Leaf Sneezeweed (*H. brevifolium* (Nuttall) A. W. Wood) is similar, but the lower stem is smooth, and flower heads are few and borne on long leafless stalks. Rare. Swamps, moist woods. Found in Morgan County in TN, and from se VA to TN south to FL and LA. May-Jun.

Sunflowers   Genus *Helianthus*

Mostly tall, stout, coarse plants found in open woods and barrens in TN. The flowers are usually large and ray flowers are yellow, sterile, typically overlapping. Twenty species are listed in TN. The genus name is from the Greek *helios* (the sun) and *anthos* (a flower).

Narrow-Leaf Sunflower
Helianthus angustifolius L.

Perennial to 5 ft tall from a crown bud with stem solitary but highly branched, mostly hairy, especially below. Leaves are dark green, narrow, linear, revolute-margined, sessile, alternate above, opposite below, from 2 to 8 in. long and 10 to 30 times as long as wide. The small disks, to 0.8-in. wide, are purplish. The 8 to 21 yellow rays are narrow, from 0.6 to 1.2 in. long. Frequent. Moist to wet open areas. Widely scattered in TN and found mostly near the coast in the eastern U.S., but inland to the southern part of OH, IN and MO. Aug-Oct.

Jack Carman

George Hornal

Common Sunflower
Helianthus annuus L.*

Coarse, rough-hairy annual from 3 to 10 ft tall. Leaves are mostly alternate, rough, heart-shaped or spade-shaped, toothed, long-stalked, from 1.6 to 8 in. long. Flower heads are large and showy. Disks are reddish-brown, seldom less than 1.2 in. wide, and the 12 to 35 rays are yellow, from 1 to 2.5 in. long. Occasional. Moist low ground and disturbed sites. Recorded in West and Middle TN, also Bradley, McMinn, Loudon and Knox counties. Widespread in the U.S. Jul-Oct. A flower tea was used by American Indians for lung ailments and malaria, and a leaf tea for high fever. Seeds were used for bread flour and seed oil for cooking. In the 19th century, it was believed that plants growing near a home would protect it from malaria. Widely cultivated.

Tennessee Sunflower, Eggert's Sunflower
Helianthus eggertii Small
Perennial from 3 to 6 ft tall with a smooth and usually glaucous stem that arises from a long rhizome. Leaves are sessile, mostly opposite, lanceolate, entire or serrate, smooth (or nearly so) above, below very smooth and strongly glaucous, from 3 to 6 in. long and 0.6 to 1.4 in. wide. Heads are usually few on long stalks, large and showy (to 3 in. across) with a yellow disk and 10 to 14 yellow rays. Involucral bracts are firm, tapering, about equaling the disk, marginally hairy. Infrequent. Dry rocky areas and barrens. Endemic to the Highland Rim and Cumberland Plateau regions of TN and south-central KY. Found in Williamson, Dickson, Davidson, Maury, Lawrence, Lewis, Coffee, Franklin and Marion counties. Aug-Sep.

Pale-Leaf Wood Sunflower (*H. strumosus* L.) is similar, but has stalked leaves that are weakly glaucous beneath. Occasional. Woods and open places. Found throughout TN and the e U.S. Jul-Aug.

Jack Carman

Jack Carman

Stiff-Haired Sunflower
Helianthus hirsutus Rafinesque
Perennial from 2 to 6 ft tall from lon rhizomes, the stems densely spreading hairy. The leaves are mostly opposite, shor stalked with 3 prominent veins from th base, coarsely hairy on both sides, ovate t lanceolate, serrate to entire, from 3 to 6 ir long and 0.8 to 2.5 in. wide. Heads, from to 3 in. wide, are usually several on sti branches, and have a yellow disk and 10 t 15 yellow rays. Involucral bracts slende long-pointed, often with loose or reflexe tips, conspicuously hairy on the margins an often on the back. Common. Dry wooded c open places, especially barrens. Foun throughout TN and the se U.S. Jul-Oct.

Woodland Sunflower (*H. divaricatus* L.) ha smooth, often glaucous stems. Leaves ar opposite, rough above, mostly sessile, lance shaped, usually toothed, from 2 to 7 in. long Heads, from 2 to 3 in. wide, have a yello disk and 8 to 15 yellow rays. Involucra bracts pointed, loose. Frequent. Dry woods open places. Found in the eastern 2/3 c TN, also Weakley County, and throughou much of the e U.S. Jul-Sep.

Maximilian's Sunflower
Helianthus maximilianii Schrader
Perennial from 2 to 10 ft tall with crown buds and short rhizomes. Stems are pubescent with short appressed white hairs, especially upwards. Leaves, from 3 to 8 in. long and 0.4 to 1.2 in. wide, are lanceolate, short-stalked, strongly scabrous, entire or slightly toothed with at least some partially folded along the midrib. Usually several heads are present with the inflorescence tending to be long. Involucral bracts are narrow, firm, loose, often much exceeding the disk and with short white hairs. Disk yellow to 1 in. wide. Rays 10 to 25, yellow, to 1.6 in. long. Occasional. Prairies, barrens and waste ground. This species, primarily from the Great Plains, has been recorded from the Western Highland Rim east in TN, as an extension of its natural range, or introduced. Jul-Oct. The seeds are valuable as a food source for wildlife. It was named in honor of Prince Maximilian of Wied Neuwied, a naturalist who led an expedition into the American West in the 1830's.

Jack Carman

Jack Carman

Small-Headed Sunflower
Helianthus microcephalus T. & G.
Perennial from 3 to 7 ft tall with short rhizomes and crown buds, the stem smooth and usually glaucous. The leaves, from 3 to 6 in. long and 0.8 to 2 in. wide, are mostly scabrous above, resin-dotted, usually short-hairy beneath, entire or toothed, lanceolate to lance-ovate, abruptly narrowed to about a 1 in. petiole. Many small heads on long slender stalks have a yellow disk to 0.4-in. wide, and 5 to 8 yellow rays to 0.6-in. long. Involucral bracts are few, slender, smooth or hairy on the margins. Common. Roadsides and woods. Found throughout TN, and from NJ to s MN south to nw FL and se LA. Aug-Sep.

Jack Carman

Hairy Sunflower, Downy Sunflower
Helianthus mollis Lamarck
Colonial perennial densely and softly hairy throughout, from 2 to 3 ft tall, arising from a stout rhizome. Leaves are sessile, mostly opposite, ascending, broadly lanceolate to broadly ovate or oblong, from 2 to 6 in. long. The disk is yellow, from 0.8 to 1.2 in. wide. The 16 to 35 rays are yellow and from 0.6 to 1.4 in. long. Involucral bracts are often glandular and densely white-hairy, the upper ones loose and spreading. Occasional. Dry fields, roadsides, barrens. In TN, it is found from the Eastern Highland Rim west, also in Meigs, McMinn, Blount and Scott counties. The U.S. range is from OH to WI to e KS south to GA and TX. Jul-Sep.

Jack Carman

Western Sunflower
Helianthus occidentalis Riddell
Perennial from 2 to 5 ft tall arising from a rhizome. Leaves are basally disposed, long-stalked, the lower with spade-shaped to lance-shaped, almost entire blades from 3 to 6 in. long. Stem leaves are few and greatly reduced. Flower heads from 2 to 3 in. across terminate the stem and branches. Disk yellow, 10 to 15 yellow rays. Involucral bracts are hairy on the margins, at least the inner array with loose, slender tips. Infrequent. Dry soil and barrens. Found in Weakley, Stewart, Montgomery, Rutherford, Franklin, Bledsoe, Hamilton, Meigs, Roane and Knox counties in TN, and throughout much of the e U.S. Aug-Oct.

Ozark Sunflower
Helianthus silphioides Nuttall

Perennial to 10 ft tall, usually with several stems rising from a short rhizome or crown. Lower stem leaves have broad blades that are mostly less than 1.7 times as long as wide, and hairy petioles that are mostly 1/3 or less the length of the blades, seldom wing-flared upward. Leaves often extend above the middle of the stem, but are reduced in size upward. Flowering heads several on long naked stems, showy and large (to 3 in. wide) with purplish disks, 10 to 15 yellow rays. Occasional. Dry open woods. In TN, found as far east as the Cumberland Plateau. U.S. range from s MO to s IL south to c LA and TN. Jul-Oct.

Appalachian Sunflower (*H. atrorubens* L.) is similar, but the stems are usually solitary. The leaves are more basally disposed with petioles that are longer than 1/3 the length of the blade and noticeably wing-flared upward. Frequent. In TN, found in the Western Highland Rim, also Henderson County, and from the Cumberland Plateau east. The U.S. range is from VA to w TN south to c GA and se LA. Jul-Oct.

Jack Carman

Jack Carman

Jerusalem Artichoke
Helianthus tuberosus L.

Stout rough perennial from 3 to 10 ft tall, more or less spreading-hairy. Leaves, from 4 to 10 in. long, are alternate (upper), opposite (lower), thick, toothed, broadly lance-shaped with winged petioles to 3 in. long. The disk is yellow, from 0.6 to 1 in. wide. Rays are 10 to 20, yellow, from 0.8 to 1.6 in. long. Common. Disturbed sites. It is found throughout TN and most of the e U.S. Aug-Oct. The large underground stem is edible, nutritious and contains no starch. It can be boiled or roasted like a potato.

Tall Sunflower (*H. giganteus* L.) is similar, but the leaves are narrowly lance-shaped and mostly sessile. Rare. Moist places. Scott, Davidson, and Rutherford counties in TN. Aug-Oct.

Saw-Tooth Sunflower (*H. grosseserratus* Martens) is similar, but the stems are smooth and often glaucous below the inflorescence and leaves are narrowly lance-shaped. Rare. Bottomlands, moist places. Shelby, Henderson, Carroll, Meigs and Hamblen counties in TN. Jul-Oct.

Oxeye
Heliopsis helianthoides (L.) Sweet
Robust erect perennial from 2 to 5 ft tall with a smooth stem. Leaves are opposite, toothed, spade-shaped, from 2 to 6 in. long on stalks from 0.2 to 1.4 in. long. The flower heads are solitary or several, sometimes numerous, borne on leafless stalks. The disk is yellow, from 0.4 to 1 in. wide. Rays are 8 to 16, pale yellow, from 0.6 to 1.6 in. long, and unlike those of sunflowers, fertile. Frequent. Thickets, barrens, woods, stream banks. Widespread in TN and found from Quebec to British Columbia south to GA and NM. Jul-Sep. Also called False Sunflower. The genus name is from the Greek *helios* (sun) and *opsis* (appearance), alluding to the likeness to the sunflower.

Jack Carman

Jack Carman

Golden Asters   Genus *Heterotheca*
Seven species are found in TN. In the past, some golden asters have been assigned to other genera, particularly *Chrysopsis*, but also in some instances *Pityopsis*. Therefore, when consulting reference material, be sure not to overlook these possibilities. The genus name is from the Greek *heteros* (different) and *thece* (case), in reference to the differences in achenes.

Prairie Golden Aster
Heterotheca camporum (Greene) Shinners
Robust, coarsely but often thinly hairy perennial from 16 to 40 in. tall with slender creeping rhizomes as well as a taproot. Leaves are alternate, more or less lance-shaped, to 3 in. long and 0.8-in. wide, mostly entire, but sometimes with a few small sharp teeth. The disks, from 0.5 to 1 in. wide, are yellow and the 21 to 34 rays are yellow, about 0.4-in. long. Frequent. Roadsides, fields, barrens. Widespread in Middle and East TN, it is a prairie species of MO to IL to IN recently introduced into the se U.S. Jul-Sep. *Chrysopsis camporum* Greene.

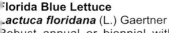
Jack Carman

False Boneset　***Kuhnia eupatorioides*** L.
Perennial from 1 to 4 ft tall with a short-hairy to nearly smooth stem. Leaves mostly alternate, entire or toothed, sessile or short-stalked, narrowly lanceolate to broadly rhombic-lanceolate, from 1 to 4 in. long and 0.4 to 1.5 in. wide, gland-dotted beneath. Heads are in small corymb-like clusters that terminate the upper branches. Each head is from 0.28 to 0.56-in. high with creamy white disk flowers and no rays. Occasional. Dry open woods, glades, barrens. Found throughout TN and most of the eastern and central U.S. Aug-Oct. The genus name is in honor of Dr. Adam Kuhn of Philadelphia, who carried a living plant to Linnaeus. This plant resembles many *Eupatorium* species, thus accounting for the species name.

Genus *Lactuca*
Six species are found in Tennessee. The genus name is the ancient name of Lettuce (*Lactuca sativa* L.), and is derived from *lac* (milk), in reference to the milky sap.

Jack Carman

Florida Blue Lettuce
Lactuca floridana (L.) Gaertner
Robust annual or biennial with milky sap, from 2 to 7 ft tall with a smooth leafy stem. Leaves mostly smooth, alternate, stalked, lance-shaped to triangular-ovate, from 3 to 12 in. long and 1 to 8 in. wide, pinnately-lobed or merely toothed. The inflorescence is long and panicle-like with numerous heads having 11 to 17 blue (to white) ray flowers. Involucres are from 0.36 to 0.56-in. high. Frequent. Moist open woods, thickets, open areas. Found throughout TN and from NY to MN south to FL and TX. Jun-Sep.

Wild Lettuce (*L. canadensis* L.) is similar, but the flowers are pale yellow. Frequent. Fields, waste places, roadsides. Found throughout TN and the e U.S. Jul-Sep. Its milky sap was used by American Indians to treat poison ivy and other skin irritations.

Prickly Lettuce (*L. serriola* L.*) is similar, but has prickly stems and leaves, and pale yellow flowers. Occasional. Fields, waste places. Widespread in TN and most of the U.S. Jul-Sep.

Jack Carman

Rough Blazing Star *Liatris aspera* Michx.
Leafy perennial from 1.5 to 5 ft tall that may be short-hairy or smooth throughout. Leaves are narrowly elliptic, stalked, the lowest from 2 to 16 in. long and 0.4 to 2 in. wide, the others progressively decreased in size upward. The inflorescence is long and spike-like with many roundish, mostly sessile heads that are about 0.75-in. high and have 14 to 35 lavender flowers. Involucral bracts are broadly rounded with thin margins that are hyaline (translucent to transparent), white or pink, rolled inward and often tattered. Occasional. Open woods, barrens, roadsides. In TN, mostly found in the Cumberland Plateau, and Ridge and Valley, thinly scattered west. The U.S. range is from ND to TX east to MI and MS, and occasionally further east to n FL, w VA and OH. Aug-Oct.

Jack Carman

Genus *Liatris*
Perennials growing from a thick, usually corm-like rootstock. Leaves are alternate, gradually reduced in size upward. The flower heads are borne in a long spike-like inflorescence, consist of disk flowers only, and bloom from the top down rather than from the bottom up. Seven species are found in TN. The derivation of the genus name is unknown.

Cylindric Blazing Star
Liatris cylindracea Michaux
Perennial from 8 to 24 in. tall, usually smooth but sometimes short-hairy. Leaves firm, mostly linear, the lower from 4 to 10 in. long and 0.1 to 0.5-in. wide, the others reduced upward. The inflorescence is spike-like with a few cylindric, sessile or stalked heads that are about 1 in. high and have 10 to 35 lavender flowers. The involucral bracts are firm and rounded with a short, pointed tip. Infrequent. Limestone glades and barrens. Found in Decatur, Rutherford, Marion, Meigs, Rhea and Roane counties in TN. A northern species, irregularly extending south to TN and AL. Jul-Sep.

Small-Headed Blazing Star
Liatris microcephala (Small) K.Schumann
Smooth perennial from 12 to 32 in. tall.
Leaves are numerous and linear, the lower
from 1 to 6 in. long and 0.04 to 0.2-in. wide,
the others gradually reduced upward. The
inflorescence is raceme-like, the heads often
attached along one side of the stem. Heads
are numerous, slender, stalked, about 0.3-in.
high, and have 4 to 6 lavender flowers.
Involucral bracts are green, narrow, mostly
blunt-tipped. Occasional. Open rocky
areas, barrens, meadows. In TN, found in
the Eastern Highland Rim and Cumberland
Plateau, also Roane, Hamilton and Polk
counties. U.S. range from the uplands of KY
to SC, GA and AL. Aug-Sep.

Jack Carman

George Hornal

Dense Blazing Star
Liatris spicata (L.) Willdenow
Perennial from 2 to 7 ft tall that is usually
smooth, rarely hairy. Leaves are linear, the
lower from 4 to 16 in. long and 0.2 to 0.8-in.
wide, the others reduced upward. The
inflorescence is long and spike-like with
many cylindric to bell-shaped, sessile heads
that are about 0.5-in. high and have 5 to 14
lavender (rarely white) flowers. Involucral
bracts have rounded or pointed tips, and are
often purple-tinged. Occasional. Wet to dry
meadows and open areas, barrens. Found
from the Western Highland Rim east in TN,
also in Carroll County, and in all of the e U.S.
from NY south. Jul-Sep.

Scaly Blazing Star
Liatris squarrosa (L.) Michaux

Perennial from 12 to 30 in. tall that may be smooth or hairy. Leaves are firm, mostly linear, the lower from 3 to 10 in. long and 0.2 to 0.5-in. wide, the others gradually reduced upward. Heads are solitary or few, short-stalked or sessile, about 1 in. high, and usually have 20 to 45 lavender flowers. Involucral bracts are green and firm with a pointed, spreading or reflexed tip and hairy margins. Occasional. Dry open places, barrens. Widespread in TN. U.S. range from DE to SD south to FL and TX. Jul-Aug.

Jack Carman

Jack Carman

Southern Blazing Star
Liatris squarrulosa Michaux

Perennial from 1 to 5 ft tall, usually with a soft-hairy stem. Leaves are mostly smooth and elliptic, the lower are stalked, from 4 to 14 in. long and 0.5 to 2 in. wide, the others reduced upward and becoming sessile. Heads are often more than 20, sessile or stalked, about 0.75-in. high, and with 14 to 24 lavender flowers. Involucral bracts are spreading to reflexed with a broadly rounded or pointed tip. Frequent. Dry open woods, roadsides, barrens. Found from the Western Highland Rim east in TN, the U.S. range from s WV to s OH to s MO south to FL and LA. Jul-Sep.

Northern Blazing Star (*Liatris scariosa* (L. Willdenow) is similar, but less robust (to 3 ft tall). Heads are seldom more than 20, and each head has from 25 to 80 lavender flowers. Infrequent. Dry open places. Found in Wayne, Decatur, Rutherford, Franklin, Van Buren, Cumberland, Morgan, Roane, Polk and Monroe counties in TN. U.S. range from ME to MI south to s PA and AR, and in the uplands to TN and n GA. Aug-Sep.

Jack Carman

Broad-Leaf Barbara's Buttons
Marshallia trinervia (Walter) Trelease *ex* Branner & Coville

Smooth, mostly colonial perennial from 16 to 32 in. tall that arises from short-creeping rhizomes. Stem leaves evenly distributed, alternate, mostly sessile, broadly lance-shaped, strongly triple-nerved, from 2 to 4 in. long. Flower heads are terminal and solitary on long stalks rising above the leaves, and have white or pale lavender disk flowers and no ray flowers. Rare. Stream banks and woods. Found in Coffee, Grundy and Lewis counties in TN. U.S. range from VA to SC, TN and LA. May-Jun.

Appalachian Barbara's Buttons (*Marshallia grandiflora* Beadle & Boynton) is similar, but the stem arises from a crown, has fewer internodes (5 to 12), and the leaves are more basally disposed. Rare. Wet places in woods, meadows, and along streams. In TN, found in Cumberland, Morgan, Roane and Scott counties. U.S. range in the Appalachian region from s PA to NC and TN. Jun-Aug. The genus name is in honor of Dr. Moses Marshall, at the request of Gotthilf Henry Ernest Muhlenberg.

Climbing Hempweed
Mikania scandens (L.) Willdenow

Perennial twining vine to 17 ft long that is smooth to softly hairy. Leaves are opposite, narrowly heart-shaped or somewhat triangular with entire or wavy margins, palmately veined, from 1 to 5 in. long and 0.6 to 3.5 in. wide, on stalks to 4 in. long. Numerous small dense clusters of flower heads arise from the leaf axils on long stalks. Each slender head is about .2-in. high and has 4 whitish to pinkish disk flowers. Occasional. Moist open woods and woods borders, thickets. Found throughout West TN, thinly scattered in Middle and East TN. A chiefly Coastal Plain species found from ME to FL to TX, and locally inland as far north as IL. Jul-Oct. The genus name is in honor of Joseph Gottfried Mikan, a professor at the University of Prague in the late 18th and early 19th centuries.

Jack Carman

Jack Carman

Wild Quinine
Parthenium integrifolium L.
Bitter aromatic perennial from 1 to 3 ft tall
that is usually branched above.   Basal
leaves are sometimes few, coarsely toothed
and sometimes lobed near the base, long
stalked, lance-elliptic to broadly ovate with
blades from 3 to 8 in. long and 1.6 to 4 in.
wide.   The stem leaves are reduced in size
upward and have progressively shorter
stalks, the uppermost often sessile and
clasping.   Flat-topped clusters of flower
heads terminate the stem and branches.
Each flower head has a white disk about
0.25-in. wide, and 5 white rays that are less
than 0.1-in. long. Disk flowers are staminate
and sterile, ray flowers pistillate and produce
achenes. Frequent. Barrens, fields, and dry
woods. Found in Middle and East TN, also
Decatur County. The U.S. range is from VA
to se MN south to GA and AR.   Jun-Sep.
The genus name is from the Greek
parthenos (virgin), probably alluding to only
some of the flowers being fertile.

Marsh Fleabane
Pluchea camphorata (L.) DC.
Annual or short-lived perennial from 1 to 5 ft
tall with a camphor-like odor.   Leaves are
alternate, lanceolate to elliptic or ovate,
sharply toothed, petioled, to 6 in. long. The
inflorescence is densely flowered and
usually round-topped.   Flower heads, from
0.1 to 0.2-in. wide, are pink and without ray
flowers. Frequent. Wet woods, marshes,
ditches. Found throughout TN (except far
eastern counties), and in the U.S. from DE to
s OH to e OK south to n FL and TX. Aug-
Sep. Other common names are Stinkweed
and Camphorweed. The genus name is in
honor of Pluche, a French naturalist of the
18th century.

Jack Carman

Cut-Leaf Coneflower
Rudbeckia laciniata L.

Perennial from 3 to 10 ft tall with a smooth, often glaucous stem that is freely-branched above. Leaves, from 2 to 8 in. long, are stalked, deeply divided to almost the midrib into 3 to 7 lobes that are irregular, toothed, sharply-pointed. The disk, from 0.4 to 0.8-in. wide, is greenish-yellow and hemispheric at first, but usually lengthening with age. Rays are 6 to 16, lemon yellow, drooping, to 2.5 in. long. Frequent. Bottomlands, stream banks, rich moist soils. Found from the Western Highland Rim east in TN, and throughout most of the U.S. Jul-Sep. Another common name is Green-Headed Coneflower. The genus name is in honor of Professors Olaf Rudbeck (father and son), predecessors of Linnaeus at Uppsalla.

Jack Carman

Jack Carman

Thin-Leaf Coneflower, Brown-Eyed Susan
Rudbeckia triloba L.

Short-lived perennial from 2 to 5 ft tall with stems that are highly branched and usually hairy. Leaves, from 1.6 to 4 in. long, are thin, sharply toothed to almost entire with the lower ones broadly ovate and long-stalked, and the upper ones more narrow and short-stalked to sessile. Usually some of the larger leaves are deeply trilobed. Flowering heads are several to numerous. The disk is dark purple or brown, hemispheric or egg-shaped, from 0.3 to 0.6-in. wide. Rays are 6 to 13, yellow or orange, from 0.4 to 1 in. long. Frequent. Moist thickets and woods borders. Found from the Western Highland Rim east in TN, also in Shelby and Tipton counties, and throughout much of the central and eastern U.S. Jun-Oct.

Rugel's Indian Plantain
Rugelia nudicaulis Shuttlew. *ex* Chapm.
Perennial from 1 to 2 ft tall. Leaves are mostly basal, alternate, ovate, coarsely-toothed, long-stalked, to 7 in. long. Stem leaves are very small and clasping. Nodding flower heads are borne in loose terminal clusters. The heads are bell-shaped, from 0.4 to 0.6-in. long and without rays. Rare. Found in open areas at high elevation in Blount, Cocke and Sevier counties in TN. Endemic to the Great Smoky Mountains of TN and NC. Jul-Aug. *Cacalia rugelia* (Shuttleworth *ex* Chapman) T.M. Barkley & Cronquist, *Senecio rugelia* Gray. Also called Rugel's Ragwort, from earlier placement in the genus *Senecio*.

Genus *Senecio*
Eight species are listed for TN. The genus name is from *senex* (an old man), in reference to the hoariness of many species, or to the white hairs of the pappus.

Jack Carman

Jack Carman

Southern Ragwort
Senecio anonymus A. W. Wood
Perennial from 1 to 3 ft tall that is mostly smooth upward but woolly at the base. Basal leaves are mostly toothed and elliptic, long-stalked, to 12 in. long. Stem leaves are deeply cleft, reduced in size and sessile upward. From 20 to 100 yellow flowers, about 0.75-in. wide, are borne at the top of the stem. Common. Meadows, pastures, roadsides, dry open woods. Widespread in the eastern 2/3 of TN. U.S. range from s PA and s OH south to FL, chiefly in the uplands. May-Jun. *Senecio smallii* Britton.

Balsam Ragwort (*S. pauperculus* Michaux) is similar, but has few heads (mostly less than 20), and is usually smooth at the base. Infrequent. Moist meadows, fields. Thinly scattered in TN (Montgomery, Dickson, Coffee, Bledsoe, Cumberland, Fentress, Morgan and Johnson counties). A northern species extending south to TN and GA. May-Jul.

Jack Carman

Golden Ragwort   *Senecio aureus* L.
Mostly smooth perennial from 1 to 3 ft tall. Basal leaves are long-stalked, somewhat heart-shaped with blades to 4 in. long and about as wide as long. Stem leaves are reduced, mostly pinnatifid, becoming sessile upward. Heads several to many, the yellow disk from 0.2 to 0.5-in. wide, yellow rays from 0.25 to 0.5-in. long. Frequent. Moist woods, wet areas, stream banks. Found in Middle and East TN and from Labrador to MN south to n GA and c AR. Apr-Aug.

New England Groundsel (*Senecio schweinitzianus* Nuttall) is similar, but basal leaves are mostly lanceolate, acute, and truncate to cordate at the base, much longer than wide. Rare. A northern species with disjunct populations in the TN mountains. Carter and Unicoi counties. May-Aug.

Round-Leaf Ragwort (*Senecio obovatus* Muhlenberg *ex* Willdenow) is similar, but has runners (stolons), and the basal leaves, to 8 in. long, are long-stalked with rounded blades. Common. Rich woods and rocky outcrops, especially limestone. Widely scattered in TN. Found from VT to KS south to FL and TX. Apr-Jun.

Butterweed   *Senecio glabellus* Poiret
Fibrous-rooted, mostly smooth annual or winter annual from 6 to 32 in. tall, usually with a single unbranched stem. Basal leaves are mostly pinnatifid with rounded lobes and teeth, to 8 in. long and 3 in. wide. Stem leaves are similar and gradually reduced in size upward. The inflorescence is a showy terminal cluster with numerous flower heads. The disks are yellow, from 0.2 to 0.4-in. wide and the rays are yellow, from 0.2 to 0.5-in. long. Frequent. Moist open woods, pastures, fields. Found in Middle and West TN, also Rhea County. U.S. range from NC to SD south to FL and TX. May-Jul.

Jack Carman

Jack Carman

Narrow-Leaf White-Topped Aster   *Sericocarpus linifolius* (L.) BSP.
Smooth perennial from 8 to 24 in. tall. Leaves are entire, linear, to 0.5-in. wide, more than 5 times as long as wide. The densely-flowered inflorescence is flat-topped. Flower heads have white bracts with green tips, yellowish to white disk flowers, 3 to 6 narrow white rays to 0.4-in. long. Frequent. Dry woods, open ground. Found throughout most of TN. U.S. range from MA to w KY south to GA and LA. Jul-Sep. *Aster solidagineus* Michaux.

Toothed White-Topped Aster (*S. asteroides* (L.) BSP.) is similar, but the leaves, from 0.4 to 1.8 in. wide, have hairy margins and at least some are toothed. Occasional. Open dry woods. Found from the Eastern Highland Rim east in TN. U.S. range from ME to s OH south to e AL and GA. Jun-Sep. *Aster paternus* Cronquist.

Jack Carman

Rosinweeds   **Genus *Silphium***
Eleven species are found in TN. Although similar in appearance to sunflowers, one major difference is rosinweed ray flowers produce seed and disk flowers do not, while sunflower disk flowers produce seed and ray flowers do not. The genus name is from the Greek *silphion*, an ancient name of some resinous plant transferred by Linnaeus to this genus.

Southern Rosinweed
***Silphium asteriscus* L.**
Coarse leafy perennial from 20 to 48 in. tall that is densely to sparsely spreading-hairy. Leaves are alternate or opposite, mostly coarsely toothed but sometimes entire, lance-shaped, from 3 to 6 in. long and 0.6 to 2 in. wide, the lower usually stalked and the upper sessile. Flowers are from 2 to 3 in. wide with a yellow disk and from 10 to 20 pale yellow rays. Occasional. Roadsides, woods borders, barrens. Found in Middle and East TN, also Benton and Hardin counties. U.S. range from VA to MO south to n FL and TX. Jun-Sep.

Prairie Rosinweed
Silphium integrifolium Michaux

Perennial from 2 to 5 ft tall. Leaves are firm, opposite, entire or toothed, sessile and often clasping, ovate to elliptic, to 6 in. long and 2.4 in. wide. Flowers are clustered at the top of the stem, and have yellow disks from 0.6 to 1 in. wide and 16 to 35 yellow rays from 0.8 to 2 in. long. Infrequent. Roadsides, fields. Shelby, Fayette, Gibson, Weakley, Carroll, Henry, Stewart, Montgomery, Houston and Davidson counties in TN. U.S. range from s MI to NB south to AL and TX. Jul-Sep.

Cup Plant (*S. perfoliatum* L.) has a square stem and large connate-perfoliate leaves, i.e., the fused bases of the blades surround the stem. Flowers are 2 to 4 in. wide. Occasional. Moist open woods, low ground. Found in Middle and West TN, also Knox and Hancock counties, and from s Ontario to ND south to NC and LA. Jul-Sep.

Jack Carman

Jack Carman

Jack Carman

Shaggy Rosinweed
Silphium mohrii Small

Perennial from 2 to 5 ft tall that is densely bristly-hairy throughout. Leaves are mostly ovate, to 12 in. long and 8 in. wide, the lower ones stalked, the upper ones sessile and reduced in size. Disk yellow to 1 in. wide and about 13 yellow rays to 0.8-in. long. Infrequent. Barrens, open woods. Found in southern Middle TN, also Cumberland County, and in the Interior Low Plateau and Cumberland Plateau regions of KY, TN, AL and GA. Jul-Oct.

Cutleaf Prairie Dock
Silphium pinnatifidum Elliott

Smooth perennial from 2 to 10 ft tall. Basal leaves (shown left) are large, deeply cleft, long-stalked. Stem leaves are few and very small with the long flower stalks appearing leafless. The flower heads are 2 to 4 in. wide with a yellow disk and 13 to 21 yellow rays (and similar to Prairie Dock shown on the following page). Infrequent. Roadsides, barrens. Found in Middle TN, also Bradley County, and from IN and OH south to AL and GA. Jul-Sep. *Silphium terebinthinaceum* Jacquin var. *pinnatifidum* (Elliott) A. Gray.

Jack Carman

Jack Carman

Prairie Dock
Silphium terebinthinaceum Jacquin
Smooth perennial to 10 ft tall. Basal leaves large (to 1 ft wide), long-stalked, entire and spade-like. Stem leaves are few and very small, the long flowering stalks appearing leafless. Flower heads large (2 to 4 in. wide) with a yellow disk and 13 to 21 yellow rays. Infrequent. Barrens. Found in the Ridge and Valley Province in TN. Jul-Sep.

Lesser Prairie Dock (*Silphium compositum* Michaux) is similar, but flowers are smaller and have only 5 to 10 rays. Infrequent. Found in East TN, primarily in dry open woods and clearings. Jun-Sep.

Jack Carman

Whorled Rosinweed
Silphium trifoliatum L.
Smooth, leafy, often glaucous perennial from 3 to 6 ft tall. The leaves are lance-shaped, toothed to entire, from 3 to 8 in. long. Flowers have yellow disks from 0.4 to 0.8-in. wide and 8 to 13 yellow rays that are 0.6 to 1.2 in. long. Two varieties occur in TN. In West and Middle TN, **var. *latifolium*** A. Gray (a more southern variety) has opposite leaves. Occasional. In East and Middle TN, **var. *trifoliatum*** (photo, a more northern variety) has 3 whorled leaves. Frequent. Open woods, barrens, and disturbed open places. Jun-Sep.

Cumberland Rosinweed (*S. brachiatum* Gattinger) has smooth and glaucous stems. The leaves are lanceolate with heart-shaped to truncate bases, coarsely toothed, the lower and middle ones on long petioles. Flowers numerous and relatively small, to 1.6 in. wide. Rare. Open woods. Found in Franklin and Marion counties in TN, and in the Cumberland Plateau region of KY, TN, AL and GA. Jul-Sep.

Dan Pittillo

Jack Carman

Silverrod, White Goldenrod
Solidago bicolor L.

Erect perennial from 1 to 4 ft tall. The stem leaves are downy, usually elliptic, toothed, from 3 to 8 in. long. The inflorescence is terminal, long and narrow, somewhat leafy below. The flower heads, to 0.2-in. long, have whitish bracts with a light green tip, yellow disk flowers and silvery white rays. Occasional. Dry woods and open rocky areas. In TN, it is found from the Western Highland Rim east, also in Carroll and McNairy counties. The extended range is from Nova Scotia to WI south to GA and LA. Jul-Oct.

Jack Carman

Blue-Stem or Axillary Goldenrod
Solidago caesia L.

Perennial with slender, round, ascending, bluish-glaucous stems to 3 ft long. Leaves are alternate, lance-shaped, to 5 in. long. Clusters of small yellow flowers are borne in the upper leaf axils. Common. Moist woods. Widespread in TN and the e U.S. Aug-Oct.

Curtis's Goldenrod (*S. curtisii* T. & G.) is similar, but the stem is angled and marked with fine, more or less parallel lines and is not glaucous. Occasional. Woodlands. In TN, found from the Western Highland Rim east, also in Carroll County, and from VA and WV south to GA. Aug-Oct.

Goldenrods　　　　　　　　Genus *Solidago*

Showy perennials with many small flower heads borne in clusters. The ray and disk flowers are yellow with a few exceptions. Goldenrod pollen is commonly believed to cause hay fever, but little of it is carried by the wind. Ragweed pollen is carried by the wind and the common cause of hay fever. Thirty-one species are found in TN.

Erect Goldenrod
Solidago erecta Pursh

Erect perennial from 1 to 4 ft tall that is smooth below and downy above, and arises from a caudex. Lower stem leaves, from 3 to 12 in. long, are smooth, toothed, broadly obovate to elliptic. Middle and upper stem leaves are progressively reduced upward. Inflorescence terminal, long and narrow. Flower heads, about 0.25-in. long, have 6 to 10 yellow disk flowers and 5 to 9 yellow rays. Frequent. Dry woods. Found from the Western Highland Rim east in TN, and from MA to IN south to GA and MS. Aug-Oct.

Jack Carman

Zigzag Goldenrod, Broad-Leaf Goldenrod   *Solidago flexicaulis* L.
Perennial from 1 to 4 ft tall with a slender, smooth, zigzag stem. Leaves are stalked, sharply toothed, ovate or elliptic, from 3 to 6 in. long. The inflorescence is mostly a series of short flower clusters in the upper leaf axils and terminal. The heads have 5 to 9 yellow disk flowers and 3 or 4 yellow ray flowers. Frequent. Moist woods. Found from the Western Highland Rim east in TN, it is a more northern species extending south to TN and GA in the uplands. Jul-Nov. The genus name is from the Latin *solidus* (whole) and the suffix *ago*, likely derived from reputed wound-healing properties of some plants.

Jack Carman

Great or Late Goldenrod
Solidago gigantea Aiton
Perennial from 1 to 7 ft tall with a smooth, purplish-glaucous stem. Leaves are mostly smooth, sharply toothed, lance-shaped, parallel veined, from 2 to 7 in. long. The inflorescence is terminal and plume-like with the yellow flowers attached along only one side of the recurved branches. Frequent. Moist thickets, woodland edges. Found throughout TN, and in most of the U.S. and southern CAN. Jul-Sep.

Common or Canada Goldenrod (*Solidago canadensis* L.) is similar, but the stem is downy and not glaucous, and leaves are downy beneath. Common. Moist or dry open places. Found throughout TN, and most of the U.S. and s CAN. Jul-Sep.

Downy Goldenrod (*S. puberula* Nuttall) has both stem and leaves downy, and long, slender, arching clusters of yellow flowers. Infrequent. Open sandy or rocky areas. Found in the eastern mountains of TN, and from Nova Scotia to southern Quebec south to FL and LA. Aug-Oct.

Early Goldenrod   *Solidago juncea* Aiton
Smooth perennial from 1 to 4 ft tall with
basally disposed, narrowly elliptical, net-
veined, toothed leaves, from 6 to 16 in. long,
tapering into a long petiole. Stem leaves are
reduced in size upward, becoming entire,
and have bundles of very small leaves in the
axils. The inflorescence is terminal and
plume-like, about as broad as long, and has
yellow flowers attached along only one side
of the recurved branches. Occasional. Dry
open places, dry woods. It is thinly scattered
throughout most of TN. Extended range
from Nova Scotia to MN south to northern
GA and northern MS. Jun-Aug.

Rough-Stem Goldenrod (*S. rugosa* Aiton) is
similar, but grows to 5 ft tall and has rough-
hairy stems. The leaves are numerous,
prominently veined, mostly sessile, hairy,
sharply toothed, broadly lance-shaped, from
.4 to 5 in. long. Frequent. Meadows,
barrens, low open woods. Found throughout
TN, the eastern U.S. and se CAN. Jul-Oct.

Jack Carman

Jack Carman

Gray Goldenrod
***Solidago nemoralis* Aiton**
Perennial from 1 to 3 ft tall with densely hairy
stems, appearing gray. The oblanceolate
leaves are progressively smaller up the stem
with small leaf bundles in the axils. The
inflorescence may be narrow or plume-like
with yellow flowers on one side of the
branches. Common. Dry woods and open
places. Found throughout TN, and in most
of the eastern and central U.S. and s CAN.
Sep-Nov.

Short-Pappus Goldenrod (*S. sphacelata*
Rafinesque) grows to 4 ft tall. The basal
leaves, to 5 in. long, are prominently cordate
at the base and conspicuously petioled. The
stem leaves are progressively reduced
upward, less cordate and on shorter petioles.
Inflorescence panicle-like with a few
spreading secund (flowers on one side)
branches. The pappus bristles are very
short and firm, much shorter than the
achene. Frequent. Open woods and rocky
places, especially calcareous soil. Found
from the Western Highland Rim east in TN,
and from VA to IL south to GA and AL. Aug-
Sep.

Sweet Goldenrod
Solidago odora Aiton

Perennial from 2 to 5 ft tall. Stem leaves are anise-scented, narrow, sessile, smooth, entire, without prominent veins, to 4 in. long. The inflorescence is terminal and plume-like with the yellow flowers attached along only one side of the recurved branches. Frequent. Open woods, roadsides, barrens. Scattered throughout TN. U.S. range from VT to MO south to FL and TX. Jun-Sep. Tea made from the leaves is pleasant-tasting.

Elm-Leaf Goldenrod (*Solidago ulmifolia* Muhlenberg) is similar, but the inflorescence has long spreading branches. The leaves are pinnately veined and somewhat wider, and do not have the anise scent. Common. Widespread in TN except for the Blue Ridge. Extended range from Nova Scotia to MN south to FL and TX. Aug-Oct.

Jack Carman

Jack Carman

Hard-Leaf Goldenrod   *Solidago rigida* L.

Perennial from 1 to 5 ft tall that is usually hairy. The basal leaves have broad blades to 10 in. long and stalks often longer than the blades. Stem leaves are small, elliptic, sessile, firm. The inflorescence is terminal and flat-topped, to 10 in. wide, with many yellow flowers. Infrequent. Dry open areas, barrens. Thinly scattered from the Western Highland Rim east in TN. Extended range from MA to Alberta south to GA and NM. Aug-Oct. Stiff Goldenrod and Prairie Goldenrod are other common names for this species.

Jack Carman

Common Dandelion
Taraxacum officinale Weber*

Perennial with alternate, oblanceolate, pinnately-lobed, basal leaves to 16 in. long that are smooth above and sometimes sparsely hairy beneath. A single head of yellow ray flowers terminates a leafless flowering stalk from 2 to 20 in. tall. Outer involucral bracts are reflexed and about as long as the inner bracts. The fruit is a conspicuous ball formed from the brown achenes and whitish pappus. Frequent. Lawns, disturbed sites. A native of Eurasia, now widely naturalized in TN and the U.S. Apr-Dec. The genus name is adapted from the Arabic *Tharakhchakon.*

Red-Seeded Dandelion (*T. laevigatum* (Willdenow) DC.*) is similar, but the leaves are very deeply cleft and the outer involucral bracts are spreading and only about half as long as the inner bracts. Achenes are red to reddish-brown. Rare. In TN, recorded from Hickman, Davidson, Knox and Blount counties. Widely established in the U.S. and s CAN. Mar-Dec. *T. erythrospermum* Andrzejowski*.

Yellow Goatsbeard   *Tragopogon dubius* Scopoli*

Erect biennial from 1 to 3 ft tall. Leaves are alternate, linear, entire, clasping, somewhat grass-like, to 12 in. long. Large flower heads are solitary at the end of the stem and branches. The flower heads are somewhat bell-shaped with numerous lemon yellow rays and several long, pointed, pale green bracts much longer than the rays. The flowers are open in the morning but close by noon. Fruiting heads are large, dandelion-like. Occasional. Roadsides, open dry areas. Widely scattered in TN and found in most of the U.S. May-Jul.

Showy Yellow Goatsbeard (*T. pratensis* L.*) is similar, but the bracts are shorter than the ray flowers. May-Aug. Oyster Plant (*T. porrifolius* L.*) is similar, but has purple rays. Rare. Grainger and Knox counties. May-Jul. Both are widely established in much of the U.S.

George Hornal

Jack Carman

Coltsfoot   *Tussilago farfara* L.
Perennial from a creeping rhizome. Flowering occurs before the leaves develop, and solitar
flower heads are terminal on leafless flowering stalks from 2 to 20 in. tall. Each flower hea
has a yellow disk to 1.2 in. wide and numerous narrow yellow rays. Leaves are long-stalked
cordate to nearly round, firmly toothed and shallowly lobed, smooth above and densel
white-hairy beneath, from 2 to 8 in. wide and long. Rare. Disturbed areas and waste places
Found in Scott, Anderson, Union, Hancock and Carter counties in TN, and throughout mos
of the ne U.S. and se CAN. Mar-Apr. A native of Europe. The genus name is adapted fron
tussis (a cough) for which the plant has long been a reputed remedy.

Wingstem   *Verbesina alternifolia* (L.) Britton
Coarse perennial from 3 to 10 ft tall. Leaves, from 4 to 10 in. long, are alternate, lance
shaped with winged stalks that extend downward as wings on the stem. Flower heads are
10 to 100 in an open inflorescence. The disk, to 0.6-in. wide, has loose, spreading, yellov
flowers, and the 2 to 10 ray flowers, from 0.4 to 1.2 in. long, are yellow, drooping. Frequen
Moist thickets, woods borders. Widespread in TN and most of the e U.S. Aug-Oct.

Ozark Wingstem (*V. helianthoides* Michaux) is similar, but seldom over 3 ft tall. Flowe
heads are mostly less than 10, the disk usually over 0.6-in. wide and rays are spreading
Occasional. Found in West and Middle TN. U.S. range from OH to IA south to GA and TX
Jun-Oct.

Jack Carman

Jack Carman

ellow Crownbeard   ***Verbesina occidentalis*** (L.) Walter

'erennial from 3 to 7 ft tall, the stem leafy and glabrous below, softly hairy above. Leaves, om 3 to 7 in. long, are sharply toothed, opposite, ovate with winged stalks that extend down he stem. The heads are numerous in an open, mostly flat-topped inflorescence. The flower isk is about 0.25-in. wide with yellow flowers, and the 2 to 5 rays are yellow, to 0.8-in. long.)ccasional. Bottomlands, woods, thickets, waste places. In TN, found from the Eastern lighland Rim east, also in Clay, Macon, Trousdale, Smith, Davidson and Montgomery ounties. Extended range from PA to MO south to FL and TX. Aug-Oct.

Jack Carman

Genus *Verbesina*

'our species are found in Tennessee. The enus name is believed to be transposed om *Verbena*.

White Crownbeard, Frostweed
Verbesina virginica L.

:oarse perennial from 3 to 7 ft tall with a airy and leafy stem. Leaves, from 3 to 8 in. >ng, are alternate, toothed to almost entire, vate to lance-elliptic with winged stalks that 'ften, but not always, extend down the stem. 'lower heads are 20 to 100+ in a dense, sually flat-topped inflorescence. The disk is :ss than 0.3-in. wide and has white flowers, nd the 1 to 5 rays are white, to 0.4-in. long. requent. Bottomlands, woods, roadsides, 'aste places. Found throughout TN, and om VA to KS south to FL and TX. Aug->ct.

George Hornal

Tall Ironweed   *Vernonia gigantea* (Walter) Trelease *ex* Branner & Coville
Perennial from 3 to 10 ft tall with mostly smooth stems. Leaves are thin, alternate, mostly
toothed, smooth above and hairy beneath, lance-shaped, from 4 to 12 in. long and 1 to 3 in
wide, gradually narrowed to the base. Heads are borne in loose and open clusters and have
from 13 to 30 purplish disk flowers. The involucre is less than 0.3-in. high with overlapping
purplish bracts that have a rounded tip. Common. Moist or wet open woods, pastures
meadows. Widespread in TN. U.S. range from w NY to e NB south to FL and TX. Aug-Oct
Vernonia altissima Nuttall. Genus name in honor of William Vernon, an English botanist.

New York Ironweed (*V. noveboracensis* (L.) Michaux) is similar, but involucral bracts taper to
a very long, slender tip. Occasional. Moist open areas. East and Middle TN. Aug-Sep.

Tennessee Ironweed (*V. flaccidifolia* Small) has a smooth and glaucous stem. Rare. Upland
woods. Found in Franklin, Coffee, Grundy, Marion and Hamilton counties in TN. Jul-Aug.

Broomweed   *Xanthocephalum dracunculoides* (DC.) Shinners
Annual from 1 to 3 ft tall with a thin, brittle, resinous, broom-like stem. It is freely and
profusely branched above, the plants appearing bush-like. Leaves are numerous, alternate
linear (to 2.5 in. long and 0.1-in. wide), entire, and dotted with glandular pits. The yellow
flowers are numerous and small (to 0.5-in. wide), and have 5 to 10 rays each. Infrequent. A
plant of the southwestern U.S. naturalized in the cedar glades and other dry calcareou
habitats of Middle TN. Jul-Oct. *Amphiachyris dracunculoides* (DC.) Nuttall.

Jack Carman

Jack Carman

A small family of marsh or aquatic herbs with 3 genera and 10 species found in TN.

Water Plantain
Alisma subcordatum Rafinesque
An aquatic perennial to 3 ft tall that has numerous arching basal leaves. Leaf blades are elliptic to ovate to heart-shaped, from 2 to 6 in. long on stalks that are several inches long. Flowering scapes extend well above the leaves and are highly branched. Each flower has 3 white petals about 0.1-in. long. Frequent. Edges of streams, swamps, ponds, wet areas. Scattered in TN and sometimes locally abundant. Widespread in the e U.S. Jun-Sep. The genus name is an adaptation of a Greek name for a water plant, but its derivation is of uncertain origin.

Genus *Echinodorus*
Two species are found in Tennessee. The genus name is from the Greek *echinus* (rough husk) and *doros* (a leathern bottle), likely from the form of the ovary and fruit.

George Hornal

Creeping Burhead
Echinodorus cordifolius (L.) Grisebach
Perennial with erect or arching basal leaves, from 2 to 8 in. long, that have long petioles and heart-shaped blades from 1.2 to 6 in. wide. The flower scapes, at first erect but soon prostrate, are leafless, to several ft long. The flowers occur in whorls of 5 to 15 at widely-spaced nodes, and are on slender pedicels about 1 in. long. Each flower has 3 white petals from 0.25 to 0.5-in. long, and many stamens and pistils. Styles, shorter than the ovaries, persist on the achenes, forming a bur-like fruit about 0.4-in. wide. Occasional. Shallow water of ditches, swamps, and reservoir shorelines. Found in Middle and West TN, it is a Coastal Plain species extending inland in the Mississippi River drainage. Jun-Aug.

Tall Burhead (*E. rostratus* (Nutt.) Engelm.) is similar, but the scapes are erect (to 2 ft) and the styles are longer than the ovaries. Rare. Similar habitat and general distribution. Found in Obion County in TN. Jun-Oct. *Echinodorus berteroi* (Sprengel) Fassett.

Jack Carman

Genus *Sagittaria*
Seven species are found in Tennessee. The genus name is derived from *sagitta* (an arrow), alluding to the prevalent shape of the leaves.

Grass-Leaf Arrowhead
Sagittaria graminea Michaux
Aquatic perennial with long-stalked, linear-lanceolate to elliptic-ovate (rarely sagittate) leaves from 2 to 12 in. long and 0.2 to 4 in. wide. The flower scape is usually simple, but sometimes branched, from 4 to 20 in. tall with 2 to 12 whorls of 3 flowers each. The upper flowers are usually male on slender erect stalks, and the lower female on thicker ascending stalks. The 3 white (to pink) petals are 0.4 to 0.8-in. long and often as wide. The achenes have a very short beak, and are winged on the margins, also with one or more facial wings. Rare. Swamps, marshes and ponds, in mud or shallow water. Only known from Dickson, Fentress and Coffee counties in TN. Extended range from se CAN south to the Gulf Coastal Plain. Jul-Sep.

Jack Carman

Broad-Leaf Arrowhead, Duck Potato
Sagittaria latifolia Willdenow
Aquatic perennial with mostly arrowhead-shaped leaf blades that are 6 to 16 in. long and about half as wide, and on long petioles. The flowering scape is erect, from 4 in. to 4 ft tall, with 2 to 15 whorls of flowers. Flowers have 3 white petals to 0.8-in. long. The upper flowers are on short stalks, and male with many stamens. The lower flowers are on long ascending stalks, and female with many pistils. The fruit is a cluster of beaked achenes, each with the beak set at a right angle to the achene body. Frequent. Shallow water or mud of swamps, ponds, streams. Found throughout TN, the U.S. and s CAN. Jul-Sep. Tubers are edible.

Southern Arrowhead (*S. australis* (Smith) Small) is similar, but the achene beak is ascending. Occasional. Shallow water or mud of swamps, ponds, streams. Found throughout TN. The U.S. range is from NY to s IN to se MO south to GA and MS, mainly inland. Jul-Sep.

HYDROCHARITACEAE : FROG'S BIT FAMILY

Five genera and seven species of the Frog's Bit Family are found in Tennessee.

American Frog's Bit
Limnobium spongia (Bosc) Steudel

Aquatic perennial with creeping or free-floating stems. Leaves are long-stalked with floating or emergent blades from 1.2 to 3 in. long that are broadly heart-shaped to nearly round, but usually with a pointed tip. Flowers are long-stalked with 3 sepals and 3 narrow, linear-oblong, white petals to 0.4-in. long. Male flowers have the stamens united into a central column with the anthers spreading in the upper half. Female flowers have 6 to 9 styles with conspicuous stigmas from 0.4 to 0.6-in. long. Rare. Shallow ponds, swamps, marshes. Found in Lake and Obion counties in TN, and in the Gulf Coastal Plain from FL to TX, along the Atlantic Coastal Plain from FL to NJ, and up the Mississippi River basin to s IL. Jun-Sep. The genus name is from the Greek *limnobius* (living in pools).

Jack Carman

Jack Carman

ARACEAE : ARUM FAMILY

Five genera and seven species of the Arum Family are found in Tennessee.

Sweetflag, Calamus
Acorus americanus (Raf.) Rafinesque

Aquatic perennial from a thick rhizome with basal sword-shaped leaves from 20 to 80 in. tall and 0.3 to 1 in. wide. The flower scape, from 8 to 24 in. tall, resembles a leaf. The spadix, from 2 to 4 in. long, extends laterally from the top of the scape and has very small yellowish-brown flowers. The erect green spathe extends upward from the top of the scape another 3 to 20 in. Occasional. Marshes, swamps, shallow water. Thinly scattered in TN. The extended range is from e CAN south to the Carolinas and west to TX. May-Jul. *Acorus calamus* L. Underground roots have a sweet odor and flavor, and were once used for making candy. The genus name is the Latin name for an aromatic plant.

Jack Carman   Jack Carman

Green Dragon   *Arisaema dracontium* (L.) Schott

Perennial with a single compound leaf atop a stalk from 8 to 40 in. tall. The leaf is divided into 7 to 15 dark green leaflets that form a horizontal "U." A single stalked flower arises from a basal sheath. The green spathe is about 1 to 2 in. long and surrounds the spadix flowers. The tapered sterile tip of the spadix, the *dragon's snout*, extends from 2 to 4 in. beyond the spathe. The fruit is a cluster of orange-red berries. Common. Damp low woods and along streams. Found throughout TN and most of the e U.S. May-Jun.

Genus *Arisaema*

Three species are found in Tennessee. The genus name is from the Greek *aris* (a kind of Arum) and *haima* (blood), alluding to the spotted leaves of some species.

Jack Carman

Jack-in-the-Pulpit, Indian Turnip, Pepper Turnip
***Arisaema triphyllum* (L.) Schott**

Perennial arising from a corm. The stem is 1 to 2 ft tall at flowering and topped with one or 2 compound leaves with 3 leaflets. The solid green or purple-striped spathe (*pulpit*), from 1.6 to 3.2 in. long, is borne under the leaves, expanded above, arching over and surrounding the spadix (*jack*) with its numerous small flowers. The fruit is a cluster of bright red berries. Common. Rich moist woods. Found throughout TN and most of the e U.S. Apr-May. American Indians used the dried, aged root for colds and dry coughs, but it may be intensely irritating if eaten uncooked.

Arisaema quinatum (Nuttall) Schott is similar, but lateral leaflets are deeply bilobed, and leaves appear to have 5 leaflets. Infrequent. Habitat and flowering are similar, general distribution southern. Found in Sequatchie, Polk, Monroe, Blount, Sevier and Knox counties in TN. Variously considered as a species, variety or not distinct in different botanical treatments.

Jack Carman

Goldenclub, Bog Torch   ***Orontium aquaticum*** L.
Perennial from a thick rhizome with long-stalked, elliptic, basal leaves from 10 to 20 in. long
that are often floating. The white flower scape, from 8 to 16 in. long, is erect in flower,
prostrate in fruit. The spadix, about 1 to 2 in. long, terminates the scape and is covered with
tiny golden yellow flowers. The spathe surrounds the base of the scape. Infrequent. Wet
soil, shallow ponds, quiet streams. Thinly scattered in TN, recorded in Lewis, Fentress,
Scott, Morgan, Roane, Johnson, Carter and Washington counties, also observed in Greene
County. Abundant in the Atlantic and Gulf Coastal Plains, less frequent inland. Mar-Jun.
The genus name is said to have belonged to a plant growing in the Orontes River of Syria.

Jack Carman

Arrow Arum, Tuckahoe
Peltandra virginica (L.) Schott
Aquatic perennial with long-stalked, oblong
to broadly triangular leaves, from 4 to 12 in.
long at flowering, but then becoming larger.
The flower scape is from 8 to 16 in. tall and
found below the leaves. The spathe, from 4
to 8 in. long, is green with a pale margin and
tapers to a pointed tip. The spadix is
cylindric, enclosed by but nearly as long as
the spathe. The flower scape is prostrate in
fruit with a cluster of green berries turning
brown. Occasional. Swamps, shallow
water. Found in West and East TN, absent
in Middle TN except for Robertson County.
Extended range mostly throughout the
eastern U.S. May-Jun. The genus name is
from the Greek *pelte* (a small shield) and
aner (stamen), from the shape of the
stamen.

ARACEAE : ARUM FAMILY

Skunk Cabbage
Symplocarpus foetidus (L.) Nuttall

Perennial with a skunk-like odor. The flower appears in late winter, well before the leaves. The spathe is fleshy, egg-shaped but abruptly pointed, green, purple, striped or spotted, about 3 to 6 in. long, and surrounds the spadix. The spadix is about 1 to 1.4 in. wide and covered with tiny flowers. Leaves are all basal, heart-shaped with conspicuous veins, to 20 in. long and 16 in. wide, on stalks to 12 in. long. Rare. Moist low ground, swamps. In TN, only known from Carter, Johnson and Sullivan counties in East TN. A northeastern species extending south to TN and NC in the mountains. Feb-Mar. Also called Polecat Weed and Swamp Cabbage. The heat produced by the rapid growth of the flower can actually melt snow. The strong fetid odor lures insects for pollination. The genus name is from the Greek *symploce* (connection) and *carpos* (fruit), alluding to the joining of the ovaries into a compound fruit.

Jack Carman

Jack Carman

XYRIDACEAE
YELLOW-EYED GRASS FAMILY

Seven species of this family occur in TN, al in the genus *Xyris*. The genus name is from the Greek *xyron* (a razor), alluding to the sharp-edged leaves.

Wide-Leaf Yellow-Eyed Grass
Xyris laxifolia Martius
var. *iridifolia* (Chapman) Kral

Perennial with 4 to 10 basal leaves that are flat, erect, linear, usually reddish-purple a the base, from 16 to 28 in. long, and from 0. to 1 in. wide. The inflorescence is a head like spike, from 0.8 to 1.4 in. long, atop a naked, very smooth scape that may be 3 t tall. One or two small, 3-petaled, yellov flowers are usually open for about two hour in the early morning. Rare, but often locally abundant. Shallow water, pond margins marshes, ditches. Found in Grundy, White Franklin, Warren and Coffee counties in TN A southeastern Coastal Plain specie extending north into TN. Jul-Sep. *Xyri iridifolia* Chapman.

XYRIDACEAE
YELLOW-EYED GRASS FAMILY

Twisted Yellow-Eyed Grass
Xyris torta Smith

The narrow, ascending, basal leaves, from 8 to 20 in. tall and 0.08 to 0.2-in. wide, are usually spiraled or twisted. The naked scape, from 0.5 to 3 ft tall, is more or less twisted, ribbed below but usually flat above. The inflorescence is an egg-shaped spike from 0.4 to 1 in. long. One or two small, 3-petaled, yellow flowers open during the morning. Occasional. Damp to wet soil, but more terrestrial than aquatic. Found in the Cumberland Plateau, the Eastern Highland Rim and the Western Highland Rim, but mostly absent elsewhere in TN. Found throughout most of the e U.S. Jun-Aug.

Since 4 of the 7 *Xyris* species found in TN are rare, collection is discouraged!

COMMELINACEAE : SPIDERWORT FAMILY
Three genera and nine species of the Spiderwort Family are found in TN.

Jack Carman

Asiatic Dayflower   *Commelina communis* L.*

Annual from fibrous roots with branched stems at first erect, later spreading and rooting at the lower nodes. Leaves are lanceolate-ovate, from 2 to 5 in. long, and sheath the stem. Flowers are borne on slender pedicels from a spathe that has edges open to the base. The flowers are open for a single morning and have 3 petals. The upper two petals are larger, from 0.3 to 0.6-in. long, showy and dark blue, and the lower is white, much smaller. Frequent. Found in moist shaded ground, and often considered a weed. Introduced from eastern Asia, now widespread in TN and the eastern U.S. May-Oct.

Jack Carman

Jack Carman

Four *Commelina* species are found in TN. Dayflowers always arise from spathes, have 3 petals that are not necessarily the same size and color, and last for one day. The genus name refers to 3 Dutch brothers named Commelin. Two became well-known botanists (large petals), but the other died with no botanical recognition (small petal).

Slender Dayflower   *Commelina erecta* L.
Perennial from thickened fibrous roots with slender, succulent, erect or ascending, branched stems from 6 to 36 in. tall. The stems often weaken and recline with age. Leaves, from 2 to 6 in. long, are narrow with each base forming a white-hairy sheath around the stem. Several flowers arise on slender stalks from a folded bract (spathe). Each branch usually has one to many terminal spathes that have the edges fused for about the lower third. The flowers have 3 petals with the upper 2 petals larger, from 0.4 to 1 in. long, showy and pale blue (rarely pink), and the lower white, much smaller. Flowers fade fast in the morning sun. Occasional. Dry soil. Roadsides, woods edges. Found throughout TN (especially the Central Basin), and the e U.S. Jun-Oct.

Virginia Dayflower
***Commelina virginica* L.**
Rhizomatous perennial often forming dense colonies. Stems are erect, widely branched, stout, to 4 ft tall. The leaves, from 4 to 8 in. long and 1 to 2 in. wide, are sheathing, the sheath margins with coarse reddish hairs. The spathes are usually clustered toward the summit of the branches and have margins that are fused in the lower third. The flowers arise from the spathes on slender stalks and have 3 showy pale blue petals, the lower scarcely reduced. As with all dayflowers, a flower is open for a single day. Frequent. Moist or wet woods. Found in West and Middle TN, and Knox and Blount counties east. Extended range throughout the e U.S. from NJ south. Jun-Oct.

Creeping Dayflower (*C. diffusa* Burman f.) is a diffusely branched, reclining annual. The flowers have 3 small blue petals. Spathes are sickle-shaped (falcate) and the margins are not fused. Occasional. Wet woods and river banks. Found in West and Middle TN, also Blount and Hawkins counties. A mostly southeastern species occasionally extending north from MN east to DE. Jun-Oct.

Jack Carman

Jack Carman

Ohio Spiderwort
Tradescantia ohiensis Rafinesque

Perennial with a straight, slender, smooth, glaucous, often branched stem 16 to 40 in. tall. Leaves are flat and firm, linear, smooth, glaucous, to 0.4-in. wide, conspicuously dilated into a sheath at the base. Cymes are solitary, terminating the stem and branches. Pedicels, to 1 in. long, are without hairs, and the flowers have 3 petals to 0.8-in. long, blue to rose to white. Occasional. Meadows, thickets, forests, and along railroad right-of-ways. Thinly spread across TN, and found throughout most of the e U.S. Apr-Jul.

Harsh Spiderwort (*T. subaspera* KerGawler) is a stout perennial to 3 ft tall with leaves wider than the opened flattened sheath. Frequent. Rich moist woods. Found throughout TN, and from VA and WV south in the uplands to AL and FL. Jun-Jul.

Hairy Spiderwort (*T. hirsuticaulis* Small) has densely hairy stems. Rare. Dry woods and rocky places. Found in Lawrence, Hickman and Cheatham counties in TN. A mainly Gulf Coastal Plain species that extends north from NC to AR. Apr-Jul.

Genus *Tradescantia*

Four species are found in TN. Spiderwort flowers never arise from spathes, and the 3 petals are always uniform in size and color. The genus name is in honor of John Tradescant, gardener to Charles the First of England in the 17th century.

Virginia Spiderwort
Tradescantia virginiana L.

Perennial with erect stems from 2 to 16 in. tall at flowering. Leaves are from 6 in. to over 1 ft long with blades from 0.2 to 0.6-in. wide that are narrower than the opened flattened sheath. The bracts below the inflorescence are often wider and longer than the leaves. The inflorescence is a terminal cyme, usually solitary. The slender, sparsely-hairy pedicels are about 1 in. long, the sepals are densely pubescent, and the 3 bluish-purple petals are from 0.5 to 0.7-in. long. Occasional. Moist woods. Most often found in Middle TN, but widespread across the state. A ne U.S. species extending south to GA and MO. Apr-Jul.

George Hornal

344

JUNCACEAE : RUSH FAMILY
Represented by 2 genera and 32 species in Tennessee.

Coriaceus Rush
Juncus coriaceus Mackenzie
Perennial to 3 ft tall, forming a dense clump of erect, green shoots which are round in cross-section. The basal leaves are sheaths to 8 in. long, and the involucral leaf resembles the stem (except channeled) such that the inflorescence appears to be lateral. The inflorescence, to 1.6 in. long, is sparsely branched, and has a few small flowers with 6 tepals (3 similar sepals and petals) that are green to light brown. The fruits are roundish and shiny brown. Common. Marshes, swamps and wet ground. Found throughout TN, and in the Coastal Plain from NJ to FL to TX, north in the interior to KY and OK. May-Jun. *Juncus* is the classical name for rush.

Soft Rush (*Juncus effusus* L.) is similar, but has a larger, many-flowered inflorescence. Common. Marshes, wet meadows. Found throughout TN, the eastern U.S. and southeastern CAN. Jun-Sep.

Jack Carman

Jack Carman

CYPERACEAE : SEDGE FAMILY
Members are often grass-like in aspect, but usually have solid stems that are triangular in cross-section. Grass stems are usually round and hollow between joints. Fourteen genera and 231 species are found in TN.

Genus *Carex*
The largest plant genus in TN with over 125 species. The genus name is the classical Latin name for sedge, but derived by some from the Greek *keirein* (to cut) in reference to the sharp leaves.

Plantain-Leaf Sedge
Carex plantaginea Lamarck
Perennial to 2 ft tall with numerous leaves to 2 ft long and 0.4 to 1.0 in. wide that are strongly red-purple tinged at the base. The flowering stem is usually leafless with a terminal male spike (0.8-in. long) on a long stalk, and 3 to 4 mostly sessile female spikes spaced along the stem. Occasional. Rich moist woods. Found from the Eastern Highland Rim east in TN, also in Sumner Wayne and Macon counties. A northeastern species extending south in the uplands to TN and n GA. Apr-May.

Alan S. Heilman

Genus *Cymophyllus*

A monotypic genus, that is, with only one known species. The genus name is from the Greek *cyma* (a wave) and *phyllon* (a leaf), alluding to the minutely undulate leaf margin.

Fraser's Sedge
Cymophyllus fraserianus (KerGawler) Kartesz & Gandhi
Somewhat colonial perennial from a short thick rhizome. A single flower stalk, from 4 to 16 in. tall, is sheathed by a single, thick, oblong-linear, pale green leaf from 8 to 20 in. long and 0.8 to 2 in. wide. The inflorescence is a terminal spike, about 0.4-in. wide, that is white and showy with male (staminate) flowers above, female (pistillate) flowers below. Infrequent. Rich mountain woods. In TN, restricted to the mountains near the NC border (Polk, Monroe, Blount, Sevier, Cocke, Unicoi, Carter and Johnson counties). U.S. range from s PA to VA south to SC and TN. Mar-May. *Cymophyllus fraseri* (Andrews) Mackenzie.

Jack Carman

Genus *Cyperus*

Twenty nine species are found in TN. The genus is often called umbrella sedge, since the inflorescence somewhat resembles the spokes of an umbrella. The genus name is adapted from the ancient Greek name *ypeiros*.

False Nutsedge   *Cyperus strigosus* L.
Coarse perennial herb with stems from 4 to 24 in. tall, sometimes taller in robust plants. Basal leaves, from 0.1 to 0.4-in. wide, are about the same length as the stems. Several stalked, cylindric spikes occur in a terminal umbel, each made up of 5 to 15 flowering spikelets to 1 in. long. The inflorescence is subtended by several long leafy bracts. Common. Open wet places. Found throughout TN and most of the U.S. Jul-Oct.

Jack Carman

Genus *Dulichium*
A monotypic genus, that is, with only one known species. The genus name is of uncertain origin.

Three-Way Sedge
Dulichium arundinaceum (L.) Britton
A stout rhizomatous perennial from 1 to 3 ft tall, often forming large colonies. The stem leaves, to 3 in. long and 0.25-in. wide, are numerous and conspicuously 3-ranked, i.e. the leaves spiral around the stem forming 3 vertical ranks. Flowering spikes arise from the leaf axils, and are about 1 in. long with several spikelets from 0.4 to 1.0 in. long. Occasional. Swamps, marshes, ponds. Thinly scattered in TN, and found in most of the e U.S. Jul-Oct.

Jack Carman

Genus *Scirpus*
Fourteen species are found in Tennessee. The genus name is the classical Latin name for bulrush.

Wool Grass
Scirpus cyperinus (L.) Kunth
Coarse tufted perennial to 6 ft tall from a short rhizome, often forming large dense colonies. The grass-like basal leaves are numerous and curving, from 0.1 to 0.4-in. wide and to 2 ft long. The inflorescence is terminal with many branches, and several long, spreading, often drooping, leafy bracts are present just below the inflorescence. The mature spikelets appear woolly. Frequent. Wet meadows, marshes, ditches. Found throughout TN, and most of the eastern and central U.S. and s CAN. Jul-Sep.

large family represented by 73 genera and
03 species in TN. Members have long
arrow leaves that are parallel-veined and
ostly arranged in two vertical rows, and
sually have split leaf sheaths. The culms
owering stems) are usually round in cross-
ction and hollow between joints.

ig Bluestem, Turkeyfoot
ndropogon gerardii Vitman

obust, bluish-green, tufted, erect, often
aucous perennial from 3 to 10 ft tall that is
ometimes shortly rhizomatous or sod-
rming. Long leaf blades are mostly 0.2 to
4-in. wide, the lower leaves sometimes
airy. The inflorescences are solitary and
rminal on long stems that extend well
oove the leaves. The flowering raceme,
om 2 to 4 in. long, has 3 branches arising
om a common point (the Turkeyfoot), and
aired spikelets with one stalked and the
her sessile. Frequent. Barrens, prairies,
lds, roadsides. Found throughout TN, and
om Quebec to Saskatchewan south to FL
d AZ. Aug-Oct. A principal inhabitant of
e midwestern Tallgrass Prairie. Related to
ommon Broomsedge (*A. virginicus* L.) and
ree other broomsedge species in TN.

Jack Carman

Jack Carman

Genus *Chasmanthium*

In addition to River Oats, two other species
with narrow inflorescences are found in TN
forests. River Oats closely resembles Sea
Oats (*Uniola paniculata* L.) found on coastal
sand dunes.

River Oats, Spangle Grass
Chasmanthium latifolium (Michaux) Yates

Loosely colonial perennial from 3 to 5 ft tall
that arises from short stout rhizomes.
Leaves, from 4 to 8 in. long and 0.4 to 0.8-in.
wide, have smooth sheaths and flat, sharply-
toothed blades. The inflorescence is a large,
open, drooping, terminal panicle extending
well above the leaves. Spikelets, from 0.6 to
1.6 in. long, are green, flattened, broadly
lance-shaped, nodding on slender stalks.
Common. Moist woods, streambanks,
roadsides, barrens. Found throughout TN,
and from NJ to IL to KS south to FL and TX.
Jun-Oct. *Uniola latifolia* Michaux.

Jack Carman

Sugar-Cane Plumegrass *Erianthus giganteus* (Walter) Muhlenberg
Tall, coarse, tufted perennial with long leaves and a long culm (flowering stem) from 3 to 10 ft
tall. Leaf blades, from 0.25 to 0.6-in. wide, may be smooth or hairy, and sheaths are hairy at
the summit. The flowering panicles, from 6 to 16 in. long, are narrow, tawny or purplish
usually conspicuously silky. Spikelets, about 0.25-in. long, are sparsely long-hairy and borne
in pairs with one sessile and one stalked. The awns, from 0.6 to 1 in. long, are round, and
straight or slightly twisted. Occasional. Moist ground, old fields, barrens. Found throughout
TN, and from NJ to AR south to FL and TX. Sep-Oct.

Genus *Erianthus*
Four species are found in Tennessee. The genus name is from the Greek *erion* (wool) and
anthos (flower).

Jack Carman

Silver Plumegrass (*E. alopecuroides* (L.)
Elliott) is similar to Sugar-Cane Plumegrass
but has a flattened, spirally twisted awn, and
the panicle is silvery to tawny. Frequent.
Found throughout TN. Sep-Oct.

Genus *Panicum*
Thirty seven species with 18 additional
varieties are found in TN. The genus name
is from the Latin *panus* (an ear of millet).

Switchgrass *Panicum virgatum* L.
Stout erect perennial from 3 to 7 ft tall that
arises from a hard scaly rhizome and often
forms large tufts. The leaf blades, from 4 to
20 in. long and to 0.6-in. wide, are mostly
smooth but sometimes hairy near the base.
The inflorescence, from 8 to 16 in. long and
one third to one half as wide, is open and
freely-branched, spreading, pyramidal. The
spikelets, from 0.1 to 0.2-in. long, are egg-
shaped and grow on both sides of the
inflorescence branches. Occasional. Moist
barrens, open woods, prairies, marshes.
Found throughout TN, and most of the
eastern two-thirds of North America. Jun-
Oct. A principal inhabitant of the midwestern
Tallgrass Prairie.

Jack Carman

Genus *Sorghastrum*
Two species are found in Tennessee. The genus name is from the resemblance to *Sorghum.*

Indian Grass
Sorghastrum nutans (L.) Nash
Erect perennial arising from a short rhizome and occurring in loose tufts. Long leaves, from 0.2 to 0.4-in. wide, taper to the base, and culms (flowering stems) are 3 to 8 ft tall. The panicle, from 4 to 12 in. long, is terminal, narrow, freely-branched, golden with nodes and smaller branches more or less hairy. Spikelets, about 0.3-in. long, are lanceolate and hairy. Frequent. Barrens, fields, open woods, roadsides. Found throughout TN and the eastern 2/3 of North America. Sep-Oct. A principal inhabitant of the midwestern Tallgrass Prairie.

Genus *Sorghum*
Two species are found in Tennessee. The genus name is an old oriental name.

Johnson Grass
Sorghum halepense (L.) Persoon*
Robust perennial from 2 to 5 ft tall that is colonial by long rhizomes. Leaves are long, from 0.4 to 0.8-in. wide. The inflorescence is an open terminal panicle from 6 to 16 in. long. The spikelets, about 0.25-in. long, are paired with one silky and sessile, and the other stalked and smooth. Both have awns from 0.4 to 0.6-in. long. Frequent. Fields, pastures, roadsides. Found throughout TN and most of the eastern U.S. May-Oct. A native of the Mediterranean region that was introduced as a forage crop, but has escaped and become well established as a weed. Under some conditions, the plant becomes **poisonous to livestock** through the production of prussic acid. It is related to and will hybridize with the cultivated sorghum (*Sorghum bicolor* (L.) Moench).

George Hornal

Jack Carman

SPARGANIACEAE : BUR REED FAMILY

Two species are found in TN. *Sparganium* is from the Greek *sparganon* (swaddling band) alluding to the ribbon-like leaves.

American Bur Reed
Sparganium americanum Nuttall

Few-branched colonial perennial with leafy stems from 1 to 3 ft tall. Leaves are flat and thin, to 3 ft long and from 0.2 to 0.5-in. wide. Flowers are small and grouped into dense, unisexual, roundish heads along the stem and branches. Male flowers are uppermost. Fruiting heads, about 0.8-in. wide, are bur-like when mature. Occasional. Shallow water, wetlands, ditches. Widespread in TN, but more frequent in the Cumberland Plateau. Found throughout the e U.S. July. Seeds are eaten by marsh birds and waterfowl, and the entire plant by muskrats.

Branching Bur Reed (*S. androcladum* (Engelmann) Morong) is similar, but has stiffer leaves and the fruiting head is about 1.2 in. wide. Rare. Muddy shores and shallow water. Found in Blount and Carter counties in TN, it is a more northern species extending south to TN. Summer.

George Hornal

TYPHACEAE : CATTAIL FAMILY

Two species are found in Tennessee. *Typha* is derived from *Typhe*, the old Greek name for cattail.

Common Cattail   *Typha latifolia* L.

Colonial perennial from 3 to 10 ft tall. Leaves, from 0.4 to 1 in. wide, are linear, erect and mostly basal, sheathing the base of the stem. Flowers are tiny and occur in dense, unisexual, cylindric spikes. The slender terminal spike has male flowers uppermost that fall soon after pollination. The female flower spike is directly below, rarely separated by more than 0.16-in. The cattail, 4 to 6 in. long and 0.8 to 1.3 in. wide, is the fruit formed by the female flower spike, and is fuzzy-brown at maturity. Occasional. Ponds, ditches, and marshes. Found throughout TN and the U.S. May.

Narrow-Leaf Cattail (*Typha angustifolia* L.) is similar, but the leaves are less than 0.4-in. wide, and the male and female flower spikes are separated about 2 in. Infrequent. Ponds, ditches marshes. Found in Shelby, Lewis, Crockett, Carroll, Hickman, Wilson, Blount and Hawkins counties in TN, and throughout the e U.S. May.

aquatic or marsh herbs, usually perennial. Water Hyacinth (*Eichhornia crassipes* Martius) Solms in A. DC.*), a beautiful pest found in more southern areas (and in Shelby County), is a member of this family. Three genera and 6 species are found in TN.

Blue Mud Plantain, Duck Salad
Heteranthera limosa (Swartz) Willldenow
Annual that has oblong to ovate leaf blades from 0.4 to 2 in. long on petioles to 6 in. long. Terminal spathes bear a single flower that is white to light blue, about 1 in. wide. Rare. Shallow ponds, ditches, reservoir margins, mud flats. Found in Henry, Montgomery, Stewart, Humphreys and Davidson counties in TN. Extended range includes most of the Mississippi River drainage. Jul-Oct.

Water Stargrass (*H. dubia* (Jacquin) MacMillan) is perennial and has narrow grass-like leaves to 6 in. long, yellow flowers to 0.8-in. wide. Occasional. Thinly scattered in TN, and found from VA and WV south to AL and MS. Jul-Oct. *Zosterella dubia* (Jacquin) Small.

Jack Carman

Jack Carman

Genus *Heteranthera*
Four species are found in Tennessee. The genus name is from the Greek *hetera* (different) and *anthera* (anther), in reference to the different anthers of the original species.

Mud Plantain
Heteranthera reniformis Ruiz & Pavon
Low plant that creeps in mud or floats in shallow water, often forming large colonies. Leaves have petioles to about 5 in. long and reniform blades from 0.4 to 2 in. wide that float or extend above the water. From 2 to 8 white to bluish flowers about 0.5-in. wide are produced on a spike that arises from a spathe. All flowers open on the same day, but sometimes only the terminal one extends outside the spathe. Occasional. Shallow water or mud. Scattered in Middle and West TN, also found in Knox and Greene counties, and most of the e U.S. Aug-Oct.

PONTEDERIACEAE
PICKERELWEED FAMILY

Pickerelweed   *Pontederia cordata* L.
Stout, erect, usually aquatic perennial from
16 to 40 in. tall that arises from a thick,
creeping rhizome, often colonial. The basal
and lower stem leaves, to 7 in. long, have
long petioles and heart-shaped to narrow
blades. The upright flowering stem has one
leaf with an expanded blade, and above it, a
bladeless sheath. The inflorescence is a
terminal, crowded, hairy spike to 6 in. long.
The flowers are funnelform, to 0.4-in. long,
and 2-lipped with violet-blue to whitish lobes,
the upper marked with yellow. Infrequent.
Muddy shores or shallow water of lakes,
streams, and ponds. Thinly scattered in TN
(Lake, Obion, Crockett, Lewis, Rutherford,
Warren, Coffee, Franklin and Cocke
counties). Found throughout the eastern
U.S. and se CAN. Jun-Oct. Dense stands
may be found in Reelfoot Lake. The genus
name is in honor of Guilio Pontedera, a
professor at Padua in the 18th century.

Jack Carman

Jack Carman

LILIACEAE : LILY FAMILY
The Lily Family is represented by 29 gener
with 67 native and 10 introduced species i
Tennessee.

Colicroot, White Stargrass
Aletris farinosa L.
Perennial arising from a thick short rhizome
the flowering stem from 20 to 40 in. tal
Leaves in the basal rosette are 3 to 8 in. lon
and narrowly lanceolate to oblanceolate wit
acuminate tips. Stem leaves are few, muc
reduced and bract-like. The inflorescence i
a terminal, spike-like raceme from 4 to 8 ir
long. White flowers, from 0.3 to 0.4-in. long
are tubular with triangular lobes to 0.1-i
long. Occasional. Open woods, barrens
fields. Found from the Eastern Highland Ri
east in TN, also in Lewis County, and
most of the e U.S. Apr-Jun. Until the 19
century, the roots were collected and used
treat colic. The genus name was taken fro
Aletris, a female slave who ground corn, ar
apparently alludes to the mealiness of th
flowers.

George Hornal

Genus *Allium*

Perennial with a strong odor of onion or garlic that arises from a coated bulb. Leaves are usually narrow, basal or near the base of the stem. The scape-like stem is erect and topped by an umbel. The flowers have six tepals that generally wither and persist below the fruit. Eight species are found in TN.

Wild Garlic, Canada Garlic
Allium canadense L.

Perennial with the odor of onion, the stem leafy in the lower third, from 1 to 2 ft tall. Leaves are flat, to 12 in. long and 0.25-in. wide. The terminal umbel is usually a mixture of bulblets and flowers. The small white (to pinkish) flowers occur on stalks to 1.2 in. long, the tepals less than 0.25-in. long and tapering to a slender point. Frequent. Fields, waste places, barrens. Found throughout TN and the e U.S. Apr-May.

Small Ramp (*Allium burdickii* (Hanes) A.G.Jones) is similar to Ramp, but the leaves, from 0.8 to 1.6 in. wide, are usually without stalks and whitish at the base. Infrequent. Rich woods. Thinly scattered in TN. Jun-Jul.

Nodding Wild Onion
Allium cernuum Roth

Perennial to 2 ft tall with the odor of onion. Leaves several, mostly basally disposed, glaucous, flat, to 16 in. long and 0.33-in. wide. The flower stalk is noticeably bent at the top so the flowering umbel droops downward. Rose (to white) flowers are borne on pedicels to 1.0 in. long. Tepals are less than 0.25-in. long, usually rounded at the tip. There are no bulblets in the umbel. Occasional. Open woods, rocky places. Western Highland Rim east in TN. Jul-Sep.

Glade Onion (*Allium stellatum* KerGawler) is similar, but has few, very narrow leaves (less than 0.08-in. wide) and the umbel does not nod. Rare. Limestone glades. Davidson, Wilson and Rutherford counties. Jul-Sep.

Ramp (*Allium tricoccum* Aiton) has the odor of leek. Large flat leaves, from 2 to 3 in. wide and to 12 in. long, have a reddish stalk and wither before flowering. The umbel has many flowers with pale yellow to white tepals. Occasional. Rich coves. Found in the Blue Ridge and occasionally west to Middle TN. Jun-Jul.

Jack Carman

Jack Carman

Jack Carman

Field Garlic, Wild Onion   *Allium vineale* L.*

Perennial with the odor of garlic that arises from a bulb. Leaves are glaucous, slender, cylindric, hollow. The flower stalk is solid, slender, from 12 to 40 in. tall with few to several sheathing leaves, and is terminated by an umbel of all bulblets or all flowers, or a mixture of both. The bulblets are egg-shaped but pointed, and often tipped with a long, fragile, rudimentary leaf. The flowers are few to numerous, small, urn-shaped, red-purple to lavender to greenish or white, from 0.12 to 0.2-in. long on stalks from 0.4 to 1 in. long. The inner stamens have 2 white hair-like appendages that protrude from the corolla. Frequent. Disturbed sites, lawns, fields, pastures. Found throughout TN, the e U.S., and se CAN. May-Jun. Native of Europe, now well established as a noxious weed.

Wild Leek (*Allium ampeloprasum* L.*) is similar, but the leaves are few, linear and flat, sharply keeled, from 0.2 to 0.8-in. wide, the bases strongly sheathing. The flower umbel is always without bublets. Infrequent. Waste places, roadsides, fields. Found in Hardeman, Shelby, Fayette, Roane, Washington and Union counties in TN, and in most of the e U.S. May-Jul. Native of Europe. *Allium* is the ancient Latin name of garlic.

Jack Carman

Fly Poison
Amianthium muscaetoxicum (Walt.) Gray

Poisonous perennial to 3 ft tall arising from a bulb. Leaves are mostly basal and densely clustered, to 16 in. long and 0.8-in. wide. The showy inflorescence is a terminal raceme with white flowers to 0.4-in. wide. The flowers are without glands and the persistent tepals turn light green as they age. Occasional. Open woodlands. Found in the Blue Ridge, Ridge and Valley, and widely scattered in southern Middle TN. Extended range from s NY to OK south. May-Jul. A monotypic genus, i.e., containing only one species. The plant contains a **poisonous** alkaloid that can kill livestock. Pulp from a crushed bulb mixed with sugar is used to kill flies. The species name is from the Latin *muscae* (flies) and *toxicum* (poison). Genus name from the Greek *amiantos* (unspotted) and *anthos* (flower).

Wild Hyacinth
Camassia scilloides (Rafinesque) Cory
Perennial that arises from a coated bulb from
0.4 to 1.2 in. thick. Basal leaves are several,
narrow, grass-like, from 8 to 16 in. long and
0.2 to 0.4-in. wide. The flower scape, from 1
to 3 ft tall, is stout and terminated by a loose
many-flowered raceme from 4 to 12 in. long.
The flowers are borne on spreading pedicels
from 0.4 to 0.8-in. long that are subtended by
filiform bracts. Tepals are pale blue to white,
linear-elliptic, from 0.3 to 0.5-in. long. As
they wither, the tepals are persistent at the
base of the fruit. Stamens are from 1/2 to
3/4 the length of the tepals. Occasional.
Shady rich coves and slopes, moist woods.
Found predominately in Middle TN, also in
Roane, Knox and Sullivan counties in East
TN. Extended range from PA to WI south.
Apr-May. The genus name is adapted from
the native American Indian name *quamash*
or *camass*.

Jack Carman

Jack Carman

Fairy Wand, Devil's Bit
Chamaelirium luteum (L.) Gray
Perennial from a short stout rhizome.
Leaves, in a nearly evergreen basal rosette,
are spatulate, to 8 in. long and 2.5 in. wide.
Stem leaves are smaller and reduced
upward. Male and female flowers occur in
spikes on separate plants with female plants
to 4 ft tall and male plants to 28 in. tall. The
male spikes may be 5 in. long and are at first
erect, but the tip usually droops with age.
The male flowers, white at first but turning
yellowish with age, have tepals to 0.2-in.
long and showy stamens about the length of
the tepals. The female spike is erect and
less than 2 in. long when flowering begins,
but continues to lengthen after flowering, up
to 12 in. long as the fruits are developing.
The female flowers are greenish-white,
smaller and much less conspicuous than
male flowers. Frequent. Rich moist open
woods. Found throughout TN, and most of
the e U.S. and se CAN. May-Jul. The
genus name is from the Greek *chamai* (on
the ground) and *leirion* (lily), the genus
having been founded on a dwarf
undeveloped specimen.

Genus *Clintonia*

Two species are found in Tennessee. Both the genus and common names are in honor of former New York governor Dewitt Clinton.

Yellow Clintonia, Bluebead Lily
Clintonia borealis (Aiton) Rafinesque

Erect perennial with 2 to 5 (usually 3) glossy dark-green basal leaves, from 4 to 16 in. long, that are oblong to elliptic or obovate with hairs on the margin. The inflorescence is a terminal raceme on a leafless stalk from 6 to 15 in. tall. The flowers are nodding, and have sepals and petals that are similar, greenish-yellow, from 0.6 to 0.7-in. long. The fruits are blue berries. Infrequent. Rich moist woods. Found in TN only at high elevation in the eastern mountains (Carter, Cocke, Greene, Johnson, Sevier and Unicoi counties). A northeastern species extending south to GA in the mountains. May-Jun.

Alan S. Heilman

Jack Carman

Speckled Wood Lily, White Clintonia
Clintonia umbellulata (Michaux) Morong

Erect perennial with 2 to 5 (usually 3) basal leaves, from 6 to 12 in. long and 1 to 3.5 in. wide, that are oblong to elliptic or obovate with long hairs on the margin. Inflorescence a terminal umbel on a leafless flowering stalk from 8 to 15 in. tall. The flowers have similar sepals and petals, from 0.3 to 0.4-in. long, that are white but often speckled with purplish-brown. The fruits are black berries. Occasional. Mountain or upland woods. Found at low elevation in the East TN mountains and westward to the Cumberland Plateau in Middle TN. The U.S. range is from n GA to c NY in the uplands. Apr-May.

Lily-of-the-Valley
***Convallaria montana* Rafinesque**

Smooth, loosely-colonial perennial with a short stem bearing mostly 2 or 3, widely elliptic to oblanceolate leaves from 6 to 12 in. long and 2 to 5 in. wide. The flower scape has a bracted raceme of hanging flowers and does not extend above the middle of the lowest leaf. The flowers, from 0.25 to 0.4-in. long, are bell-shaped and have 6 white tepals with recurved tips and 6 stamens. Raceme bracts are linear, at least as long as any individual flower stalk. Occasional. Rich upland woods. Found from the Eastern Highland Rim east in TN, and in VA, WV and NC. Apr-May. The genus name is from *convallis* (a valley).

European Lily-of-the-Valley (*Convallaria majalis* L.*) is similar, but densely colonial. Leaves are smaller, to 6 in. long and 2 in. wide, and the raceme extends above the middle of the lowest leaf. Raceme bracts are lanceolate, much shorter than the longest individual flower stalk. Infrequent. Rich woods. Commonly cultivated and escaped. Widely scattered in TN. Apr-May. Introduced from Europe.

Jack Carman

Yellow Mandarin, Fairy Bells   ***Disporum lanuginosum* (Michaux) Nicholson**

Erect branched perennial from 16 to 36 in. tall. Leaves are sessile, thin, ovate or lance-ovate, from 2 to 5 in. long and 0.8 to 2 in. wide. Flowers in clusters of 1 to 3 hang down from the end of the branches on stalks from 0.6 to 1.2 in. long. The 6 tepals are spreading, pale yellow to yellowish-green, narrowly lance-shaped, from 0.5 to 0.8-in. long. Fruits are smooth, reddish, elliptic-shaped berries from 0.3 to 0.6-in. long. Frequent. Rich moist woods. Found from the Eastern Highland Rim east in TN, also in Sumner, Davidson, Williamson, Maury and Stewart counties. Extended range from s CAN to n AL and n GA, mostly in the highlands. Apr-May.

Jack Carman

Jack Carman

Genus *Disporum*
Two species are found in TN. Genus name from the Greek *dis* (double) and *spora* (seed).

Spotted Mandarin   *Disporum maculatum* (Buckley) Britton
Erect branched perennial from 8 to 32 in. tall. Leaves are sessile, thin, oblong or ovate-oblong, commonly abruptly acuminate, from 1.6 to 4 in. long. Flowers in clusters of 1 to 3 hang down from the end of the branches on stalks from 0.24 to 0.6-in. long. The 6 tepals are spreading, white spotted with purple, lance-ovate, clawed, from 0.6 to 1.0 in. long. Fruits are densely-hairy, trilobed, yellow berries from 0.3 to 0.6-in. long. Occasional. Rich upland woods. Found from the Eastern Highland Rim east in TN, and from s OH to n AL and n GA, mostly in the mountains. Apr-May.

George Hornal

Genus *Erythronium*
Perennials with almost no above ground stem that arise from a deep solid corm and have one leaf when juvenile and two when mature. Leaves are mostly oblong, tapering to the base, fleshy, shining, usually mottled with brown, to 8 in. long and 3 in. wide. The flowers are solitary on a scape from 4 to 8 in. tall, nodding, always on mature plants. Tepals are strongly recurved or spreading on bright days. Common names include Trout Lily, Dogtooth Violet, Fawn Lily and Adder's Tongue.

White Trout Lily
Erythronium albidum Nuttall
Extensively colonial. Flower stalk stout, from 4 to 8 in. tall. Tepals, 1 to 2 in. long, are strongly recurved, bluish-white, but may be yellowish at the base within, and greenish or brownish-striped outside. Anthers yellow. Occasional. Rich moist woods. Found in Middle TN, also Shelby and Fayette counties. U.S. range from MN to s Ontario south to MD, AL and OK. Mar-Apr.

Jack Carman

Yellow Trout Lily
Erythronium americanum KerGawler
Extensively colonial. Flowering stalk stout, from 4 to 8 in. tall. Tepals, from 0.6 to 2 in. long, are yellow, often spotted with red inside, darker-colored outside, strongly recurved. Inner tepals have a small rounded auricle (ear) about 0.1 to 0.2-in. above the base. Anthers are yellow or red. The fruit capsule is usually held above the ground and the tip may be rounded, flat or pointed. Common. Rich moist wooded slopes. Found from the Western Highland Rim east in TN, also in Fayette, Benton and Henry counties, and throughout most of the e U.S. and se CAN. Mar-May.

Dimpled Trout Lily (*Erythronium umbilicatum* Parks & Hardin) is similar, but not colonial, the inner tepals lack the auricle, and the mature capsule is indented at the top and rests on the ground. Occasional. Rich moist woods, rocky slopes. Found in East TN, also in Sumner and Davidson counties, and from WV, MD and VA south to AL and n FL. Mar-May.

Beaked Trout Lily
Erythronium rostratum W. Wolf
Extensively colonial. Flowering stalk stout, from 4 to 8 in. tall. Flowers are usually held more erect and the tepals, about 1 to 2 in. long, are spreading to weakly recurved. Tepals and anthers are yellow. The top of the mature capsule has a prominent beak. Rare. Rich moist woods. Found in Henderson, Hickman, Wayne, Lawrence and Marion counties in TN and primarily restricted to TN, n AL and nw AR. Mar-Apr.

Trout lilies were likely so named because of the resemblance of the leaf markings to those on brown or brook trout. The genus name is from the Greek *erythros* (red) that was first applied to the purplish-flowered European species.

Jack Carman

Jack Carman

Orange Daylily, Common Daylily   *Hemerocallis fulva* (L.) L.*
Smooth, often colonial perennial with numerous spreading, linear, basal leaves to 3 ft long
and 1 in. wide. The flowering stalk, to 4 ft tall, is leafless and bears a terminal cluster of large
flowers. Flowers are 3 to 5 in. wide, and tepals are tawny orange, occasionally yellow,
spreading outward at the tip from a tube-like base. The stamens and style are long and
slender, extending just outside the tepals. Flowers are not fragrant, last for only one day
and fruit does not develop. Occasional. Widely cultivated and freely escaped. Abandoned
home sites, roadsides, pasture and field edges. Introduced from Eurasia, and naturalized
throughout TN and most of the e U.S. May-Jul. The genus name is from the Greek *hemera*
(a day) and *callos* (beauty).

George Hornal

Genus *Lilium*
Tall erect perennials that arise from a scaly
bulb. Sepals and petals are separate, but
usually similar and called tepals. Six species
are found in TN. *Lilium* is the classical Latin
name for Lily.

Canada Lily   ***Lilium canadense*** L.
Perennial from 2 to 5 ft tall with a smooth
stem, branched above. Leaves are mostly in
6 to 11 whorls of 4 to 12 each, lance-shaped,
widest at or below the middle, tapering to
both ends, coarse or rough on the margins
and midvein beneath, from 3 to 6 in. long
and 0.3 to 0.8-in. wide. Flowers are borne at
the top of the stem on long stalks and
nodding. Tepals, from 2 to 3 in. long, are
slightly recurved or spreading from a tube-
like base, widest toward the middle, orange
to red (although yellow over much of its
range) and heavily spotted with purple on the
inside. Anthers are held close together,
extending little past the tepals. The flower
buds are almost round in cross-section.
Occasional. Open moist woods, meadows.
Thinly scattered in Middle and East TN. A
northeastern species ranging south in the
uplands to GA and AL. Jun-Jul.

Gray's Lily   *Lilium grayi* S. Watson
Perennial from 2 to 4 ft tall with a smooth and stout stem. Leaves, in 3 to 8 whorls of 4 to 8 each, are lance-oblong to narrowly elliptic, tapering to an acute or obtuse tip, to 4 in. long and 1 in. wide. Leaf margins are coarse or rough. From 1 to 8 narrowly bell-shaped flowers on long stalks are borne at the top of the stem and held nearly horizontal. The tepals, from 1.6 to 2.4 in. long, are oblong-spatulate but not recurved or widely spreading at the tip. The corolla is dark red outside, and the inside is lighter red becoming yellowish in the throat and marked with many purple spots. Anthers are usually not visible in a side-view of the flower. Rare. Balds, open areas at high elevation. In TN, known from Johnson and Carter counties. Endemic to the high mountains of VA, NC and TN. Jun-Jul. Also called Bell Lily, Roan Lily or Roan Mountain Lily.

Jack Carman

Carolina Lily   *Lilium michauxii* Poiret
Perennial from 2 to 4 ft tall with a stout and erect stem. The principal leaves are in whorls of 3 to 7 each with the upper leaves sometimes alternate. The leaves are rather fleshy, glaucous, smooth and oblanceolate (widest distinctly beyond the middle), from 2 to 5 in. long and 0.6 to 1 in. wide, the upper progressively smaller. Flowers are usually 1 or 2, nodding from long stalks at the top of the stem. Tepals are orange-red becoming yellow in the throat, purple spotted within, strongly recurved, narrowly lance-shaped, tapering to the tip, from 3 to 4 in. long. The stamens extend well beyond the tepals. Infrequent. Bogs, dry to moist upland woods and thickets. In TN, only recorded from the counties in the Blue Ridge. Extended range along the Coastal Plain from VA to LA, also in the mountains from VA and WV south. Jul-Aug.

Dan Pittillo

Michigan Lily
Lilium michiganense Farwell

Stout erect perennial to 8 ft tall. Principal leaves are in whorls of 5 to 20 each with the upper leaves sometimes alternate. Leaves lanceolate, tapering to both ends, coarse or rough on the margin and midvein beneath, to 7 in. long and 1.2 in. wide. Flowers terminal, usually 3 to 25, nodding from long ascending or erect stalks. Tepals, to 3.6 in. long, are lance-shaped, strongly recurved, orange to red, heavily spotted with purple. Anthers, to 0.6-in. long, are well separated on long divergent filaments. Flower buds are 3-angled. Occasional. Moist open woods, wet meadows. Found in Middle TN, also Shelby and Anderson counties, and from w NY to Manitoba south to TN and AR. Jun-Jul.

Dan Pittillo

Jack Carman

Jack Carman

Jack Carman

Wood Lily   ***Lilium philadelphicum*** L.
Smooth erect perennial from 1 to 3 ft tall that arises from a bulb. Leaves are mostly in 2 to 6 whorls of 4 to 7 each, oblanceolate to lanceolate, tapering to the tip, to 4 in. long and 1 in. wide. From 1 to 5 open, erect, bell-shaped flowers terminate the stem. The 6 tepals, from 2 to 3.5 in. long, are broadly lance-shaped, reddish-orange, dark-spotted within, distinctly clawed at the base spreading at the tip. Rare. Open woods, meadows, thickets. Found in Sequatchie, Grundy, Hamilton and Claiborne counties in TN, and from ME to s Ontario south to DE and KY, and in the uplands to GA. Jun-Jul.

Turk's-Cap Lily   ***Lilium superbum*** L.
Stout erect perennial to 8 ft tall. Principal leaves are in whorls of 5 to 20 each with the upper leaves sometimes alternate. Leaves are lance-shaped, tapering to both ends, smooth or minutely rough on the margins, to 7 in. long and 1.2 in. wide. Flowers terminal, usually 3 to 25 (potentially 65 to 70), nodding from long ascending or erect stalks. The 6 tepals are lanceolate, from 2.4 to 3.6 in. long, strongly recurved, orange to red densely spotted with purple. The flower tube is conspicuously marked inside with a green "star." Anthers are greater than 0.6-in. long well separated on long divergent filaments. Flower buds are 3-angled. Infrequent. Moist open woods, meadows, balds. Found in the Blue Ridge in TN, and from MA to NH south to GA and AL in the uplands. Jul-Sep. The flower shape somewhat resembles an early Turkish cap, hence the common name.

anada Mayflower
aianthemum canadense Desfontaines

rect perennial from 2 to 8 in. tall with
branched stems. Leaves are few (1 to 3),
ssile or short-stalked, ovate to ovate-
long, from 1.2 to 4 in. long. Flowers are
rne in an erect terminal raceme from 0.8
2 in. long, and the 4 tepals are white,
reading, from 0.08 to 0.12-in. long. Fruits
e red berries, but green dotted with red just
ior to maturity. Infrequent. Rich moist
land woods and thickets. Found in
hnson, Carter, Unicoi, Greene, Sevier,
ount, Monroe and Polk counties in TN. A
rthern species extending south to GA in
e mountains. Apr-May. Other common
mes are Wild Lily-of-the-Valley and False
ly-of-the-Valley. The genus name is from
e Latin *Maius* (May) and the Greek
themon (a flower).

Jack Carman

Jack Carman

Indian Cucumber Root
Medeola virginiana L.
Erect perennial from 12 to 28 in. tall that
arises from a thick tuber-like rhizome. The
thin wiry stems have sparse, woolly clumps
of hair. Leaves occur in one or two whorls
with juvenile and non-flowering plants having
only the lower leaf whorl. The lower whorl
has 5 to 11 narrowly elliptic to oblanceolate
leaves to 5 in. long that taper to both ends.
Flowering plants have an upper whorl of
three smaller ovate leaves that usually have
a red base. From one to several flowers with
6 greenish-yellow tepals about 0.3-in. long
hang from the upper leaf whorl on stalks
from 0.6 to 1 in. long. Stamens are purple,
about 0.25-in. long. The fruits are round,
purplish-black berries about 0.3-in. wide.
Occasional. Rich upland woods. Found
from the Eastern Highland Rim east in TN,
also in Hardeman, Hardin, Henderson and
Henry counties. The extended range is from
ne MS, n AL and GA north to s CAN. Apr-
May. The root is white with a brittle texture.
It tastes and smells somewhat like a
cucumber, and was used as a food source
by American Indians.

Broad-Leaf Bunchflower
Melanthium hybridum Walter

Erect, stout, **poisonous** perennial from 2 to 5 ft tall from a thick rhizome, the stem mostly downy above and smooth below. The basal leaves are linear-oblanceolate, from 1.2 to 2.4 in. wide and 8 to 32 in. long. Stem leaves are similar but reduced upward. The inflorescence is a panicle of loose racemes with the terminal raceme much longer than the lateral. The 6 tepals, to 0.28-in. long, are greenish-white, ovate but narrowed to a claw at the base. Blades of the tepals have a pair of glands at the base and ruffled-wavy margins with the tip turned inward. Rare. Rich woods. In TN, recorded from Coffee, Polk, Sevier and Unicoi counties. Extended range from CT south to GA and TN. Jul-Aug. *Melanthium latifolium* Desrousseaux.

Jack Carman

Jack Carman

Genus *Melanthium*
Two species are found in Tennessee. Th genus name is from the Greek *melas* (blac and *anthos* (flower), alluding to the dark color that the persistent perianth assume after expanding.

Virginia Bunchflower
Melanthium virginicum L.

Erect, stout, **poisonous** perennial from 2 5 ft tall from a thick rhizome, the stem hai above. The basal leaves are linear, taperir to the tip, narrowed at the base, from 0.4 1.2 in. wide and 8 to 32 in. long. Ste leaves are similar but reduced upward. Th inflorescence is a terminal, hairy, eg shaped panicle from 8 to 12 in. long. The tepals, from 0.2 to 0.5-in. long, are whitish pale green, spreading, flat, oblong obovate, glandular at the base, each blac about twice as long as the claw. Rare. Ric woods, meadows, low thickets. Found Hardin and Lincoln counties in TN, and fro NY to IN to MN south FL and TX. Jun-Jul.

Jack Carman

Coastal False Asphodel
Tofieldia racemosa (Walter) BSP.
Perennial herb arising from a rhizome. Basal leaves are erect, from 8 to 16 in. long and to 0.2-in. wide. The flowering stem, to 28 in. tall, has short, stout, spreading hairs and a single bract-like leaf below the middle. The inflorescence is a dense terminal raceme from 2 to 6 in. long. Flowers are yellowish-white, the terminal ones opening first. The 6 tepals are mostly oblong, spreading, to 0.16-in. long. Stamens have flattened filaments and rotund anthers. The ovary is superior with 3 short, awl-shaped styles. Rare. Wet barrens. A Coastal Plain species found from NJ to FL to TX with a disjunct population in TN (Coffee County). Jul. The genus name is in honor of Thomas Tofield, an 18th century English botanist.

Genus *Uvularia*
Four species are found in Tennessee. The genus name is "from the flowers hanging like the uvula, or palate."

Jack Carman

arge-Flowered Bellwort
vularia grandiflora Smith
rect perennial from 8 to 20 in. tall that is rked above, and has 1 or 2 leaves (or one) below the fork, 4 to 8 leaves on the erile branch, and several leaves and 1 to 4 owers on the fertile branch. Leaves are erfoliate, broadly oval to oblong, minutely airy below, from 2 to 5 in. long. The flowers ang from the upper leaf axils, and have 6 arrow tepals that are pale to golden yellow, visted, overlapping, pointed at the tip, mooth within, from 1 to 2 in. long. ommon. Rich moist woods, chiefly in alcareous soils. Found throughout TN, and om n AL and n GA north to s CAN in most the e U.S. Apr-May.

erfoliate Bellwort (*Uvularia perfoliata* L.) is milar, but leaves are smooth below. The pals, from 0.7 to 1 in. long, are twisted, verlapping, straw-yellow with a noticeable ange, rough, inner surface. Frequent. pen woods and lowlands, preferring acid ils. Found in Middle and East TN, also ardin and McNairy counties, and in most of e e U.S. Apr-May.

Jack Carman

Wild Oats, Sessile-Leaf Bellwort   *Uvularia sessilifolia* L.
Smooth erect perennial from 4 to 12 in. tall with a forked stem. The leaves are few,
alternate, sessile, elliptic, glaucous beneath, from 1.6 to 2.8 in. long. One or two solitar
flowers hang from the upper leaf axils. The 6 tepals are overlapping, pale yellow, smoot
within, from 0.5 to 1.0 in. long. Styles are separate only in the upper third or fourth
Occasional. Open alluvial woods. Found throughout TN and the e U.S. Mar-May.
Mountain Bellwort (*Uvularia puberula* Michaux) is similar, but the stems are hairy in line
below the leaf bases, and leaves are shiny but not glaucous below. Styles are separate t
below the middle. Rare. Dry to moist, open, upland woods. Found in Blount, Sevier, Cocke
Carter and Johnson counties in TN and mainly in the highlands from PA south to GA. Mar
May. *Uvularia pudica* (Walter) Fernald.

Small False Hellebore
Veratrum parviflorum Michaux
Coarse **poisonous** perennial from 2 to 5 ft
tall, arising from a stout rhizome. Basal and
lower leaves are smooth, elliptic to broadly
oblanceolate, only slightly or not at all
pleated, stalked, from 6 to 13 in. long and 2
to 6 in. wide. The stem leaves are linear and
much reduced upward. The inflorescence is
a large, loose panicle with numerous flowers
on 0.5-in. stalks. The 6 tepals, from 0.16 to
0.3-in. long, are greenish or yellowish-green,
narrowed to the base, without glands.
Occasional. Rich woods. Found from the
Cumberland Plateau east in TN, also in
Cannon County. Extended range from WV
to TN and GA in the mountains. Aug-Sep.
Melanthium parviflorum (Michaux) S.
Watson.

Wood's False Hellebore (*Veratrum woodii*
J.W. Robbins) is similar, but the tepals are
dark maroon in color. Rare. Moist woods.
Found in Wayne, Hickman, Franklin and
Grundy counties in TN, and from OH to OK
south to TN. Jul-Aug.

Jack Carman

Genus *Veratrum*
Three species are found in Tennessee. *Veratrum* is the Latin name for the hellebore.

False Hellebore, Indian Poke
Veratrum viride Aiton
Coarse, **poisonous**, perennial from 2 to 7 ft tall, the stem stout, erect and leafy to the top. The leaves are mostly sessile, somewhat clasping and folded, oval or elliptic, to 1 ft long and half as wide, gradually reduced upwards, noticeably pleated. The flowers are borne in a terminal, freely-branched, hairy panicle with individual flowers on stalks to 0.16-in. long. Tepals are hairy on the edges, yellowish-green, tapering to the base, without glands, to 0.5-in. long. Infrequent. Open wet woods and fields. Found in Marion, Polk, Blount, Sevier, Claiborne, Hawkins, Carter and Johnson counties in TN, it is a northern species that extends south in the uplands to GA. Jun-Jul.

Jack Carman

Bob Hale

Turkeybeard
Xerophyllum asphodeloides (L.) Nuttall
Erect perennial that arises from a stout caudex-like rhizome, and has a dense cluster of long, slender, arching, persistent, firm and sharp-tipped basal leaves to 16 in. long and less than 0.1-in. wide. The flowering stem, from 2.5 to 5 ft tall, has numerous needle-like leaves to 6 in. long that are progressively reduced upward. The flowers, about 0.4-in. wide, are borne in a dense terminal raceme from 2 to 2.5 in. wide that is at first compact, but later may grow to 12 in. long. The 6 tepals are spreading, white, oblong-elliptic, without glands or claws, persistent on the fruit as they wither. Infrequent. Rich upland woods, pine barrens. Found in the Blue Ridge in TN (Washington, Unicoi, Greene, Blount, Polk and Monroe counties), and in the pinelands from NJ south to NC, and in the mountains from VA south to GA. May-Jun. The genus name is from the Greek *xeros* (dry) and *phyllon* (leaf).

Death Camas
Zigadenus leimanthoides Gray
Erect **poisonous** perennial from 2 to 8 ft tall, arising from a bulb. The leaves are linear and mostly crowded near the base, from 8 to 20 in. long and 0.16 to 0.5-in. wide, reduced upward. The inflorescence is a branched panicle of dense racemes with the terminal one longer than the few spreading or ascending side raceme(s). The flowers are stalked, white to greenish white or yellowish with 6 ovate-elliptic tepals to 0.2-in. long that have a small yellow gland at the base. Rare. Wet woods and fields. Found in Coffee, Franklin, Warren and Grundy counties in TN. A primarily Coastal Plain species found from s NY to GA to LA, and also in the southern uplands. Jun-Jul.

White Camas (*Zigadenus glaucus* Nuttall) is similar, but shorter (to 2 ft tall) and glaucous. The inflorescence is panicle-like. Flowers are larger, from 0.6 to 1 in. wide, and the tepals are usually purplish toward the base with a lobed gland. Rare. Wet calcareous places. Found in Johnson County in TN. Jul-Aug.

George Hornal

Three *Zigadenus* species are found in Tennessee. The genus name is from the Greek *zygos* (a yoke) and *aden* (a gland), alluding to the glands being sometimes in pairs.

Sweet Betsy   *Trillium cuneatum* Rafinesque
Erect perennial from 8 to 16 in. tall that arises from a stout rhizome. The 3 leaves are whorled, sessile, broadly elliptic, mottled, from 3 to 6 in. long. The flower is sessile and banana-scented, rarely musk-scented. Petals are more or less erect, narrowly to broadly elliptic-obovate, maroon, bronze, green or yellow, more than twice as long as the stamens. The anthers are blunt and without beaks. Frequent. Rich woods. Found from the Western Highland Rim east in TN and south to the Coastal Plain of MS and AL, north to the Highland Rim of KY, and east to the Piedmont of NC, SC and GA. Mar-May.

Jack Carman

Jack Carman

Trailing Trillium
Trillium decumbens Harbison

Mostly prostrate perennial with a reclining stem. The 3 broad, sessile, mottled, whorled leaves nearly lay flat on the ground. The flower is sessile with erect, maroon to brown-purple petals. Stamens are about one fourth the length of the petals. Rare. Rich woods. Only recorded in Polk County in TN, it ranges from se TN and n GA southwest into c AL. Mar-Apr.

One author has made an interesting observation. Since plants of the genus *Lilium* are called lilies, why are those of the genus *Trillium* not called "trillies?"

Genus *Trillium*
Seventeen of the 30 trillium species found in the eastern U.S. are found in Tennessee and photographs of all TN species are included. Trilliums are classified in two major groups:

Jack Carman

Toadshades have a sessile flower that rises above a whorl of 3 mottled green leaves (7 are found in TN and are presented first), and

Wakerobins have a stalked flower that rises above a whorl of 3 solid green leaves (10 are found in TN and are presented last).

Hybrids commonly occur among some species when their natural ranges overlap. The genus name is from *tres* (three) since all parts of the plants occur in threes. Juvenile plants commonly have a single leaf-blade terminating a stem-like petiole.

Lanceleaf Trillium
Trillium lancifolium Rafinesque
Erect perennial from 4 to 16 in. tall. The 3 leaves are whorled, narrow, mottled, elliptic to lanceolate, somewhat declining, to 3 in. (or more) long. The flower is sessile and sepals are spreading to recurved between the leaves. Petals are erect, slightly twisted, mostly maroon, at least four times as long as wide. Rare. Rich moist woods. Known from Marion and Hamilton counties in TN. Extended range from se TN to SC, GA, AL and FL. Apr-May.

Jack Carman

Yellow Trillium
Trillium luteum (Muhlenberg) Harbison
Erect perennial from 8 to 16 in. tall that
arises from a stout rhizome. The 3 leaves
are whorled, sessile, broadly elliptic, mottled
from 3 to 6 in. long. The flower is sessile
and lemon-scented. Petals are more or less
erect, narrowly to broadly elliptic-obovate
greenish-yellow aging to rich yellow, more
than twice as long as the stamens. The
ovary and stamens are greenish-white at the
time of flowering. Frequent. Rich woods.
Found from Warren and Jackson counties
east in TN, but noticeably showy in the
Smoky Mountains. Mostly found in the
southern Appalachians, it ranges from s KY
to w NC south to n AL and n GA. Apr-May.

Prairie Trillium   *Trillium recurvatum* Beck
Erect perennial from 6 to 18 in. tall that arises from a slender rhizome. The 3 leaves are
whorled, mottled, mostly ovate, from 2 to 4 in. long with a distinct stalk from 0.4 to 0.8-in.
long. The flower is sessile and the sepals are usually reflexed between the leaves. Petals
are normally maroon, lance-shaped but clawed at the base, from 2 to 3 times as long as
wide, usually spreading from the base but arching inward at the tip. Frequent. Rich moist
woods. Found from the Cumberland Plateau west in TN, also in Loudon County, and the
only trillium recorded from West TN. It is mainly a midwestern species ranging southward to
AL and e TX. Mar-Apr.

Jack Carman

Jack Carman

Sessile Trillium   ***Trillium sessile* L.**
Erect perennial from 4 to 12 in. tall that arises from a stout rhizome. The 3 leaves are
whorled, sessile, broadly ovate, vaguely or not at all mottled, from 2 to 4 in. long. The flower
is sessile and has a fetid odor. The petals are erect, usually maroon, rarely yellowish-green,
no more than twice as long as the stamens. Anthers are prominently beaked. Occasional.
Rich moist woods. Found in Middle TN, also Scott County. Generally a more northern
species extending south through c TN into n AL. Mar-Apr.

Jack Carman

Twisted Trillium
***Trillium stamineum* Harbison**
Erect perennial from 4 to 12 in. tall, the
upper stem often hairy. The 3 leaves are
whorled, sessile, broadly ovate, mottled,
from 2 to 4 in. long. The flower is sessile
and has an extremely fetid odor. The petals
are maroon (rarely yellow), narrow, twisted,
and spread horizontally. Occasional. Rich
moist limestone woods. Found in Middle TN,
also Decatur and Hardin counties, and
southward into AL and MS. Mar-Apr.

Jack Carman

Catesby's Trillium, Rose Trillium
Trillium catesbaei Elliott

Erect perennial from 6 to 16 in. tall that arises from a stout rhizome, the stem often purple-tinged at the node. The 3 leaves are green, whorled, ovate to widely elliptic, from 2.5 to 6 in. long, tapering at the base to a short stalk. The flower is borne on a stalk from 0.4 to 2.5 in. long and usually nods beneath the leaves. The petals are white or pink, turning roseate with age, elliptic recurved, often with a wavy margin, from 1.4 to 2.2 in. long. The anthers are curved and somewhat twisted, and have yellow pollen. The ovary is white. Infrequent. Rich upland woods. Found in Franklin, Marion, Polk, McMinn, Monroe, Blount and Sevier counties in TN. The extended range is from sw GA and e AL to se TN and c NC. Apr-May. Named for Mark Catesby, an English naturalist.

Red Trillium, Stinking Benjamin   *Trillium erectum* L.

Erect perennial from 4 to 16 in. tall that arises from a stout rhizome. The 3 leaves are green, whorled, sessile, broadly rhombic, from 3 to 7 in. long. The flower is borne above the leaves on a stalk from 1 to 3 in. long, usually faces horizontally, and has the odor of a wet dog. The petals are widely spreading, lance-shaped, maroon, white, green or yellow, from 1.0 to 2.4 in. long. The stamens are no longer than the pistil and the ovary is purple-black. Rare. Rich moist woods. Officially recorded in Polk, Monroe, Sevier, Cocke and Carter counties in TN. A more northeastern species ranging from se CAN to TN, NC and GA in the mountains. Apr-May. Early herbalists used this foul-smelling plant to treat gangrene, since according to the Doctrine of Signatures, plants were used to cure ailments they resembled in some fashion.

Jack Carman

Bent Trillium, White Trillium
Trillium flexipes Rafinesque
Erect perennial from 8 to 16 in. tall. The 3 leaves are green, whorled, sessile, broadly rhombic, from 3 to 6 in. long. The flower has a weakly sweet to stale musty odor, and is borne on a stalk from 1.6 to 5 in. long that may extend above or bend under the leaves. The petals are white (rarely maroon) but aging brown, spreading, broadly lance-shaped, from 0.8 to 2.0 in. long. The ovary is white to pink and the stamens have creamy white anthers that are more than twice as long as the filaments. Occasional. Rich moist or wet woods, often in limestone regions. Found in Middle TN, also Hamilton, Polk, Knox and Sullivan counties. A mostly northern species extending south into TN, AL, and GA. Apr-May.

Jack Carman

Jack Carman

Large-Flowered Trillium
Trillium grandiflorum (Michaux) Salisbury
Erect perennial from 8 to 16 in. tall that arises from a stout rhizome. The 3 leaves are green, whorled, sessile, broadly ovate or rhombic, from 3 to 5 in. long. The flower is borne on a more or less erect stalk from 2 to 3 in. long. The petals are white, turning pink with age, ascending from the tube-like base and widely spreading at the tip, mostly elliptic, from 1.6 to 3.0 in. long. Stamens, from 0.6 to 1 in. long, have noticeable yellow anthers that are readily visible within the floral tube. Frequent. Rich moist woods. Found in the eastern half of TN, it is a mostly northern species extending south to ne AL and n GA in the highlands. Apr-May.

Jack Carman

Least Trillium, Dwarf Trillium
Trillium pusillum Michaux

Erect perennial from 4 to 8 in. tall that arise from a slender rhizome. The 3 leaves are green, whorled, sessile, narrowly lance shaped, from 1 to 3 in. long. The flower is borne on an erect stalk to 1.2 in. long. The petals are white, turning roseate with age ascending from the tube-like base and widely spreading at the tip, ruffled along the margin, broadly lance-shaped, from 0.6 to 1.2 in. long. Infrequent. Rich alluvial woods Found in Cumberland, Sumner, Coffee Lincoln, Franklin and Putnam counties in TN and from n AL to c KY west to the Ozark and east to the Atlantic coast. Mar-Apr.

Several varieties are recognized based on geographic distribution.

Jack Carman

Southern Nodding Trillium
Trillium rugelii Rendle

Erect perennial to 2 ft tall. The 3 large leaves are green, whorled, broadly elliptic to obovate, tapering at the base to a short stalk. The flower has a somewhat green-apple fragrance and is borne on a long stalk that nods beneath the leaves. The petals are white aging to brown, ovate to elliptic, recurved. The stamens have white filaments and vivid purple anthers. Infrequent. Rich woods. Found in Blount, Sevier, Cocke, Unicoi, Carter and Washington counties, and from TN and NC south in the Blue Ridge and Piedmont, and in AL, GA, and SC in the Coastal Plain. Apr-May.

Jack Carman

weet White Trillium
illium simile Gleason

rect perennial to 2 ft tall. The 3 large
aves are green, whorled, broadly elliptic,
ually overlapping. The flower is borne
ove the leaves on a long stalk, usually
ces horizontally, and has the odor of green
ples. The petals are white, ovate, large
d usually overlapping, ascending from the
se and widely spreading at the tip. The
amens are longer than the pistil and the
ary is purple-black. Rare. Rich mountain
oods. Found in Polk, Monroe, Blount,
evier and Cocke counties in TN, and also in
e southeastern Blue Ridge of GA, NC and
C. Mar-Apr.

Jack Carman

Southern Red Trillium
Trillium sulcatum Patrick

Erect perennial from 8 to 24 in. high that
arises from a stout rhizome. The 3 leaves
are green, whorled, sessile, broadly obovate,
from 3 to 7 in. long. The flower is borne
above the leaves on a stalk from 2 to 4 in.
long, usually faces horizontally, and has an
odor somewhat like fresh mushrooms.
Sepals are usually purple-tinged, grooved at
the tip. Petals are deep maroon to creamy
white, ovate and sometimes overlapping,
ascending from the tube-like base and
widely spreading to recurved at the tip. The
ovary is purple-black. Occasional. Rich
moist woods. Found in the Ridge and
Valley, Cumberland Plateau, and Eastern
Highland Rim in TN, and in the southern
Appalachian region from AL and GA to KY,
VA and WV. Apr-May.

Painted Trillium
Trillium undulatum Willdenow
Erect perennial from 8 to 16 in. tall. The 3 leaves, from 2 to 4 in. long, are green, whorled, thin, ovate, broadly rounded at the base to a 0.2 to 0.4-in. stalk. The flower is borne on an erect stalk from 0.8 to 2 in. long and usually faces upward. The petals, from 0.8 to 1.6 in. long, are ruffled on the margin, white with a streaky red crescent near the base. Infrequent. Rich moist or wet woods and stream banks. Found in Polk, Monroe, Blount, Sevier, Cocke, Greene, Unicoi, Carter, Sullivan and Johnson counties in TN. A mostly northern species extending south to TN and GA in the mountains. Apr-May.

Jack Carman

Jack Carman

Vasey's Trillium
Trillium vaseyi Harbison
Erect perennial to 2 ft tall. The 3 large leaves are green, whorled, broadly elliptic tapering at the base to a short stalk. The large flower has a funereal, somewhat pungent, rose-like fragrance, and is borne on a long stalk that nods beneath the leaves. The petals are maroon, veiny, sometimes overlapping at the base, and usually strongly recurved. The stamens have yellow to maroon anthers, and are much longer than the small purple-black ovary. Infrequent. Rich upland woods. Found in Anderson, Morgan, Loudon, Bradley, Polk, Blount and Sevier counties in TN, and in the mountains of n GA, sw NC and nw SC south to sw GA and e AL. Apr-Jun.

he Iris Family is represented by 4 genera
nd 17 species in Tennessee.

lackberry Lily
***elamcanda chinensis** (L.) DC.*
'erennial from 1 to 2 ft tall that arises from a
orizontal rhizome. The leaves, from 12 to
8 in. long, are iris-like and clasping at the
ase, and rapidly reduced upward. The
ıflorescence is widely branched and cyme-
ke. The flowers, from 1.2 to 2.0 in. wide,
ıst for only one day, and have 3 sepals and
petals that are similar, widely spreading,
range with crimson or purple spots. The
ıass of round, black, fleshy seeds of the
uit pod somewhat resembles a blackberry.
)ccasional. Thickets, roadsides, barrens,
edar glades. Widespread in TN and the
astern U.S. Jun-Jul. A native of Asia, now
rell established as an escape. The genus
ame was adopted from the East Indian
ame for this species.

Jack Carman

Jack Carman

Genus *Iris*
Iris flowers are large and showy. The
flowers consist of 3 spreading or reflexed,
petal-like sepals, 3 erect or arching petals,
and a stigma with 3 petal-like branches that
arch over and hide the 3 stamens. Nine
species are listed for Tennessee. The genus
name is from *iris* (the rainbow).

Lamance Iris
***Iris brevicaulis** Rafinesque*
Perennial with sword-shaped leaves to 28 in.
long, and a strongly zigzag, often reclining
stem to 16 in. long. Flowers, to nearly 4 in.
wide, are light violet to lavender, and the
sepals have a white variegated area at the
base of the blade, surrounding a yellow
crest. Rare. Swamps and low woods in the
Tennessee River valley separating West and
Middle TN. Found in Hardin, Humphreys,
Madison and Stewart counties. Extended
range from OH and e KS south to LA and
KY. Jun.

Jack Carman

Dwarf Crested Iris *Iris cristata* Aiton

Perennial with basal leaves from 4 to 8 in. long that are curved and arching. The pale to deep lavender (rarely white) showy flowers about 3 in. wide occur on flower stalks less than 6 in. tall. The 3 sepals each have a ridged yellow crest bordered with white and outlined in purple. Common. Moist hillsides, ravines, slopes and ledges in rich woods. Widespread in TN and the eastern U.S. Apr-May.

Iris is the "Official State Flower" of Tennessee, and important horticulturally with numerous species and hybrids in cultivation. The flower colors essentially represent all the colors of the rainbow. The bearded irises (see *Iris x germanica* L.*) are very popular, but the Japanese Iris (*Iris kaempferi* Siebold*), Tangerian Iris (*Iris tingitana* Boiss. & Reut.*), Spanish Iris (*Iris xiphium* L.*, described below), and English Iris (*Iris xiphioides* Ehrh.*) are also well known.

Jack Carman

Copper Iris *Iris fulva* KerGawler
Perennial from a horizontal rhizome with sword-shaped leaves from 20 to 40 in. long and flower stalks from 2 to 5 ft tall. Copper to reddish-brown (rarely yellow) flowers may be as large as 3.6 in. wide. Infrequent Swamps, ditches. Found in the lower Mississippi River valley from eastern MO and southern IL south. In TN, it is found in Shelby, Lauderdale, Fayette, Dyer, Lake Obion and Gibson counties, all located near the Mississippi River. May-Jun.

Spanish Iris (*Iris xiphium* L.*) is one of the oldest cultivated irises and a popular florist iris. Leaves to 1 ft long are deeply furrowed linear, glaucous. The flowers are violet purple. Each sepal has an orbicular blade about 1 in. wide, and is narrowed, fiddle-form and streaked or patched with yellow or orange toward the base. Petals are erect oblong, about as long as the sepals, and 0. to 0.75-in. wide. Rare. Cultivated and sometimes persistent in ditches and waste areas. It has been recorded in Wilson County in TN. Spring.

Slender Blue Flag
Iris prismatica Pursh
Perennial from widely creeping rhizomes with narrow erect leaves to 28 in. long and 0.12 to 0.28-in. wide. The flowering stalks to 3 ft tall have blue-violet (to white) flowers to 3.2 in. wide. Rare. Wet woods, roadside ditches, and power line barrens. Found in Coffee and Warren counties in TN, and along the Atlantic Coastal Plain from Nova Scotia to GA, and interior in the southern Appalachian highlands. May.

Garden Iris (*Iris x germanica* L.*) has sword-shaped, glaucous leaves from 0.8 to 1.6 in. wide and 8 to 18 in. long. Stems are stout and branched at the top, to 3 ft tall. Flowers, from 3 to 4 in. wide, have broad, recurved, ovate, violet sepals with yellow, white and brown veins at the base, the median line long-bearded. The petals are light violet and arching, slightly smaller than the sepals. Rare. Commonly cultivated and sometimes persistent in ditches and waste areas. It has been recorded in Shelby, Stewart, Sumner and Williamson counties in TN. Apr-May. Likely representative of a series of hybrids from several European species.

Jack Carman

Jack Carman

Vernal Iris, Dwarf Iris
Iris verna L.
var. *smalliana* Fernald *ex* Edwards
Perennial from a densely-scaly rhizome. Grass-like leaves are mostly straight, to 4 in. long and 0.5-in. wide at flowering, later lengthening. The lavender showy flowers, to 2.5 in. wide, terminate stalks to 6 in. tall. Each of the 3 sepals of the flower has a hairy yellowish-orange band, bordered with white, but not ridged. Occasional. Sandy or rocky thin woods. Found from the Cumberland Plateau to the east in TN, and throughout the eastern U.S. May.

Any of the cultivated irises may occasionally escape by free seeding or from discarded garden material.

Jack Carman

Southern Blue Flag   *Iris virginica* L.
Perennial from a creeping rhizome tha
forms dense colonies. The leaves ar
sword-shaped, from 16 to 44 in. long and 0.
to 1.2 in. wide. Stems from 20 to 40 in. ta
usually have 1 or 2 branches. Blue-violet t
lilac flowers, from 2.4 to 3.2 in. wide, have
bright yellow patch at the base of the oblonç
ovate sepals. Occasional. Open swamp
woods and marshes. Widely scattered i
TN, and found in most of the east an
central U.S. Jun.

Yellow Flag (*Iris pseudacorus* L.*) has flowe
stalks to 3 ft tall. The yellow flowers, to 4 ir
wide, have a brownish patch at the base c
the sepals. Infrequent. A native of Europ
escaped from cultivation to wetlands an
shallow water along streams. Found i
Robertson, Cheatham, Knox, Lawrence
Claiborne, Greene, Unicoi, Carter, Silliva
and Johnson counties in TN, and wide
scattered in the eastern U.S. Apr-Jun.

The name "Flag" is from the middle Englis
flagge, meaning rush or reed.

Jack Carman

Genus *Sisyrinchium*
Grass-like perennials, usually tufted from
fibrous roots. The 3 sepals and 3 petals of
the flowers are alike (known as tepals), each
with an abruptly pointed tip. Four species
are found in TN. Genus name an old name
for another plant transferred to this genus.

Pale Blue-Eyed Grass
Sisyrinchium albidum Rafinesque
Pale green, grass-like perennial that is 4 to
16 in. tall and has linear, mostly basal
leaves. Flowers arise from a pair of sessile
spathes atop the stalk (scape). The scapes
are winged, and are 0.06 to 0.16-in. wide.
Flowers are white or pale blue with a yellow
eye, from 0.6 to 1 in. wide. Frequent. Open
places, dry woods. Found in Middle and
East TN, and most of the e U.S., but not
recorded from West TN. Apr-May.

Slender Blue-Eyed Grass (*S. mucronatum*
Michaux) is similar, but dark green with wiry,
narrow scapes to 0.06-in. wide, leaves to
0.06-in. wide, and solitary red-purple
spathes. Infrequent. A mostly northeastern
species found in Morgan, Polk, Bradley,
Hamilton, Rhea and Franklin counties in TN.
May-Jun.

IRIDACEAE : IRIS FAMILY

Eastern Blue-Eyed Grass
Sisyrinchium atlanticum E.P.Bicknell
Light-green, glaucous, spreading, grass-like perennial with leaves of similar length and width as the scapes. The 4 to 18 in. long flower scapes are narrowly winged, less than 0.08-in. wide, and terminated by a leaf-like bract from which arise 2 or 3 stalked flower-bearing spathes. The flowers, from 0.6 to 1.0 in. wide, are violet-blue with a yellow eye. Occasional. Low wet places. Widely scattered in Middle and East TN. A mostly Coastal Plain species found locally inland. May-Jul.

Stout Blue-Eyed Grass (*S. angustifolium* Miller) is quite similar, but the plants are bright green, and the broadly-winged flowering scapes are more than 0.10-in. wide. Common. Moist places. Found throughout TN and the e U. S. May-Jul.

Jack Carman

Jack Carman

ORCHIDACEAE : ORCHID FAMILY

Puttyroot
Aplectrum hyemale (Muhlenberg *ex* Willdenow) Nuttall
Perennial from stout side-by-side corms that produce a single elliptic basal leaf in late summer which is dark green with whitish veins, from 4 to 8 in. long. The leaf lasts until spring and withers about the time the 1 to 2 ft flower scape appears. The scape has sheathing non-green bracts and few to 15 flowers in a loosely-arranged raceme near the summit. Petals and sepals, from 0.4 to 0.6-in. long, are purplish and brownish. The lip, also 0.4 to 0.6-in. long, is white marked with violet. Occasional. Wet soil of alluvial floodplains, low rich woods. Widespread in TN. Extended range from n AL to the Great Lakes in most of the e U.S. May. The corms have been used for various medicinal purposes and have even produced a cement used to mend broken dishes. The genus name is from the Greek *a-* (without) and *plectron* (spur).

Jack Carman

The Orchid family is represented by 20 genera and 49 species in Tennessee.

Grass Pink
Calopogon tuberosus (L.) BSP.
Perennial from 12 to 28 in. tall that arises from a corm. The slender stem has 1 or 2 basal sheathing scales and a single, linear, grass-like leaf to 20 in. long and 1.6 in. wide that is attached near the base. A loose raceme of 3 to several flowers terminates the stem. Sepals and lateral petals are nearly alike, spreading, pink to rose-purple, from 0.6 to 1.0 in. long. The lip, from 0.6 to 0.8-in. long, has a narrow base and fan-shaped summit, and is rose-purple crested on the face with hairs tipped with yellow and magenta. Occasional. Moist meadows, open seepage slopes. Found in the eastern half of TN, also Lewis County. Extended range includes all of the e U.S., se CAN and the Maritime Provinces. Jun-Jul. *Calopogon pulchellus* (Salisbury) R.Brown. The genus name is from the Greek *calos* (beautiful) and *pogon* (beard).

Jack Carman

Spreading Pogonia, Rosebud Orchid
Cleistes divaricata (L.) Ames
Perennial from 8 to 24 in. tall that arises from fleshy-fibrous roots. The slender stem has a single, sessile, oblong-linear, sheathing leaf from 2 to 5 in. long and 0.3 to 0.8-in. wide that is attached above the middle of the stem. The erect floral bract is similar but much smaller. A single, stalked, somewhat nodding, tubular flower from 1.2 to 2 in. long terminates the stem. The flower tube is formed by the pink petals which overlap the greenish and purple-veined lip. Three purple-brown sepals from 1.2 to 2.4 in. long are spreading-ascending from the base of the tube. Occasional. Wet open woods, moist grassy fields. Widely distributed from Lincoln and Moore counties to the north and east in TN. Extended range from VA to south MS east. May-Jun. The genus name is from the Greek *cliestos* (closed), alluding somewhat to the shape of the flower.

Jack Carman

Genus *Corallorhiza*

Three species are found in Tennessee. The genus name is from the Greek *corallion* (coral) and *rhiza* (root).

Autumn Coralroot
Corallorhiza odontorhiza (Willdenow) Nuttall

Saprophytic perennial from 4 to 8 in. tall that arises from coral-like roots. The stem is erect and slender with a bulbous-thickened white base, otherwise purple to brown or greenish above. The inflorescence is a loose terminal raceme of 5 to 15 flowers. The 0.16-in. long flower extending out from the ovary is barely open. The petals and sepals are yellowish to purplish-green. The lip is declined and white spotted with purple. Occasional. Open moist woods. Found throughout TN and most of the e U.S. Aug-Oct.

Jack Carman

Spring Coralroot
Corallorhiza wisteriana Conrad

Saprophytic perennial from 4 to 16 in. tall that arises from coral-like roots. The stem is erect, slender, yellow-brown to purple with a loose terminal raceme of 5 to 25 flowers. Sepals and lateral petals arch forward over the lip, and are narrowly lance-shaped, from .2 to 0.3-in. long, green to yellow mottled with purple. The lip is white, spotted with purple, recurved, broadly ovate with a wavy margin and short claw. Occasional. Damp woods, rich ravines, stream banks. Widely scattered in TN, and found from s NJ to PA se NB south to FL and TX. Apr-May.

Spotted Coralroot (*Corallorhiza maculata* Rafinesque) Rafinesque) is similar, but taller (to 32 in.) and with more flowers (up to 40). The lip is 3-lobed, white spotted with purple. Rare. Rich woods. Found in Johnson, Washington and Carter counties in TN, and from Newfoundland to Labrador to British Columbia south to MD and IN, and south in the mountains to TN and NC. Jul-Sep.

Genus *Cypripedium*

Five species are found in Tennessee. The genus name is from the Latin *Cypris* (Venus) and *pedilon* (shoe or slipper). The lady's slippers are also called moccasin flowers.

Pink Lady's Slipper
Cypripedium acaule Aiton

Perennial with 2 opposite, narrowly-elliptic, basal leaves from 4 to 8 in. long that are deep green, thinly hairy, pale beneath, strongly ribbed. Juvenile or non-flowering plants may have only a single leaf. The 8 to 16 in. hairy scape arises between the leaves and has a solitary, somewhat nodding flower at the summit. The sepals are yellow-green to purple-brown, lanceolate, to 2 in. long. Petals are purple-brown, slender, twisted and spreading. The lip forms the large, pink, drooping pouch known as the lady's slipper. Occasional. Dry open acidic woods. Found from the Eastern Highland Rim east in TN, also in Hickman County. The U.S. range from n GA to n MN east. Apr-May.

Jack Carman

Jack Carman

Southern Lady's Slipper
Cypripedium kentuckiense Reed

Perennial from 24 to 32 in. tall. The stem leaves are mostly sheathing, veiny, oval to lance-ovate, from 6 to 8 in. long and half a wide. One or two flowers are borne at the top of the stem. Sepals and twisted petal are purple-brown, spreading, lance-shaped from 2 to 3.5 in. long. The lip forms the large, open, creamy to dull yellow pouch that is from 2 to 2.4 in. long and known as the lady's slipper. Rare. Moist low woods ravines. Known from only Franklin and Scott counties in TN, the U.S. range is from e K and e TN west to AR, OK and LA. May-Jun.

Small Yellow Lady's Slipper
Cypripedium parviflorum Salisbury
Slender, thinly-downy perennial that is 6 to
12 in. tall. The stem leaves are mostly
sheathing, veiny, oval to lance-ovate, from 2
to 6 in. long and half as wide. One or two
flowers are borne at the top of the stem.
Sepals and twisted petals are reddish-brown,
spreading, lance-shaped, from 0.8 to 2 in.
long. The lip forms the small, deep-yellow
pouch that is purple-spotted around the
opening, less than 1.0 in. long and known as
the lady's slipper. Infrequent. Moist upland
woods, swamps, wetlands, rocky slopes.
Found in Sullivan, Claiborne, Sevier, Blount,
Loudon, Polk, Cumberland and Van Buren
counties in TN. A northeastern U.S. species
extending south to GA in the mountains.
Apr-May. *Cypripedium calceolus* L. var.
parviflorum (Salisbury) Fernald.

Jack Carman

Large Yellow Lady's Slipper   *Cypripedium pubescens* Willdenow
Robust, densely downy perennial from 8 to 32 in. tall. The stem leaves are mostly sheathing,
veiny, oval to lance-ovate, from 2 to 8 in. long and half as wide. One or two flowers are
borne at the top of the stem. Sepals and twisted petals are greenish-yellow, spreading,
lance-shaped, from 1.0 to 3.5 in. long. The lip forms the large, bright-yellow pouch that is
purple-spotted within, more than 1.0 in. long and known as the lady's slipper. Occasional.
Open woods, rocky slopes. Thinly distributed throughout TN, and found in most of the e U.S.
except the southern Coastal Plain. Apr-May. *Cypripedium calceolus* L. var. *pubescens*
(Willdenow) Correll, *Cypripedium parviflorum* Salisbury var. *pubescens* (Willdenow) Knight.

George Hornal

Clay Thurston

Showy or Queen Lady's Slipper
Cypripedium reginae Walter

Robust, densely hairy perennial from 16 t
40 in. tall.   The stem leaves are clasping
strongly ribbed, elliptic-oval, from 4 to 10 ir
long and half as wide.   One to four flower
are borne at the top of the stem.   The sepal
are white, round-oval, from 1.2 to 1.8 ir
long.   The petals are white, spreading
narrowly oblong, from 1 to 1.9 in. long.   Th
lip forms the rose pouch that is streaked wit
white (or mostly white), from 1 to 2 in. lon
and known as the lady's slipper.   Rare
Mossy wooded slopes, wetlands.   Foun
throughout the northeastern and nort
central U.S. and adjacent CAN, extendin
southward to northeast TN and northwes
NC. May-Jun.

Jack Carman

Showy Orchis
Galearis spectabilis (L.) Rafinesque

Smooth perennial with 2 opposite, narrowly
obovate to broadly elliptic, basal leaves from
3 to 6 in. long that are dark green, fleshy.
The stout fluted scape, from 4 to 8 in. tall,
arises between the leaves and has a loose
terminal raceme of few to 15 flowers about
0.8-in. long.   The pink to red-purple sepals
and petals are overlapping and form a hood
over the white lip.   Occasional.   Rich open
woods, stream banks.   Found from the
Eastern Highland Rim east in TN, also in
Davidson, Cheatham, Montgomery and
Chester counties, and from n AL to the Great
Lakes in most of the e U.S.   Apr-May.
Orchis spectabilis L.

Jack Carman

Jack Carman

owny Rattlesnake Plantain *Goodyera pubescens* (Willdenow) R. Br.

ensely downy perennial with a rosette of basal leaves, from 1.2 to 2.4 in. long, that are vergreen, broadly lance-shaped, bluish-green with a prominent network of white veins. The owering stalk, from 8 to 16 in. tall, arises from the rosette and is terminated by a densely-owered, cylindrical spike of white flowers about 0.25-in. long that appear hooded. Frequent. ry woods. Found from the Western Highland Rim east in TN, also in Henry County. U.S. ange from n AL to the Great Lakes in most of the e U.S. Jul-Aug.

wo *Goodyera* species are found in TN. The genus name is in honor of John Goodyer, a 7th century English botanist.

reeping or Lesser Rattlesnake Plantain (*Goodyera repens* (L.) R. Brown) is similar, but only to 8 in. tall, and the raceme is usually one-sided. Infrequent. Cool, moist, mountain woods sually under or near conifers. Found in Sevier, Cocke, Unicoi, Washington, Carter and ohnson counties in TN. U.S. range from NY to MN to AK south in the Appalachians to TN nd NC. Jul-Aug.

John MacGregor

Crested Coralroot
Hexalectris spicata (Walter) Barnhart
Smooth, leafless, saprophytic perennial from 12 to 32 in. tall that arises from a stout, branching, jointed rhizome. The stem is erect, yellowish brown to deep purple with a loosely-flowered terminal raceme of 5 to 25 showy flowers. Sepals and petals, about 0.7-in. long, are yellowish-brown to buff with brown-purple lines, oblanceolate, spreading. The lip is shallowly 3-lobed, yellow to white with purple lines and 5 to 7 purple fleshy crests. The central column is prominent and white. Occasional. Dry open rich woods, shady stream banks. Found in East TN, also Grundy, Putnam, Rutherford and Davidson counties. The U.S. range is from MD to OH to MO south to FL and Mexico. Jul-Aug. The genus name is likely from the Greek *hex* (six) and *alectryon* (cock), alluding to the crests of the lip.

Genus *Isotria*

Two species are found in Tennessee. The genus name is from the Greek *isos* (equal) and *treis* (three), in reference to the 3 equal sepals.

Small Whorled Pogonia

Isotria medeoloides (Pursh) Rafinesque
Smooth glaucous perennial that arises from fleshy-fibrous roots. The stout, pale green stem, from 6 to 12 in. tall, has at the summit a whorl of 5 or 6 leaves that are elliptic, light green, from 1.2 to 2 in. long. A single (rarely 2) yellow-green flower extends above the leaves on a stalk from 0.4 to 0.6-in. long. The greenish sepals about 0.8-in. long are somewhat spreading and the greenish petals extend forward and cover most of the greenish-white lip. Rare. Open stands of second-growth woodlands. Known only from Hamilton and Washington counties in TN. Referred to as the rarest orchid east of the Mississippi River with isolated populations from TN and GA to ME. May.

Jack Carman

Jack Carman

Large Whorled Pogonia

Isotria verticillata (Muhl. *ex* Willd.) Raf.
Smooth perennial that arises from flesh fibrous roots. The stout purplish stem, fro 8 to 16 in. tall, has at the summit a whorl of or 6 leaves that are elliptic, green, from 1 to 2 in. long. A single (rarely 2) flow extends above the leaves on a stalk from 0 to 2.2 in. long. Sepals, from 1.4 to 2.6 i long, are purplish, very narrow, projectir forward or somewhat spreading. The pa yellow-green petals extend forward ar cover most of the 3-lobed lip that is whi with purple edges. Occasional. Open ac woods. Thinly scattered in TN and found most of the e U.S. Apr-May.

When not in flower, whorled pogonias m easily be confused with the Indian Cucumb Root (*Medeola virginiana*) because of simil leaves. However, the stem of the India Cucumber Root is slender and somewh woolly.

Jack Carman

Lily-Leaf Twayblade   *Liparis lilifolia* (L.) Richard *ex* Lindley
Smooth perennial arising from a solid bulb that has 2 opposite, glossy green, elliptic-ovate, sheathing, basal leaves from 2 to 6 in. long. A leafless scape from 4 to 10 in. tall rises between the leaves and is terminated by a loose raceme of 5 to 30 flowers. The sepals are pale green, spreading, to 0.4-in. long and 0.08-in. wide. The petals are filiform, purple, spreading, to 0.4-in. long. The lip is showy, somewhat translucent, brown-purple with purplish veining, obovate, recurved, to 0.4-in. long. Occasional. Rich moist woods and stream banks. Thinly scattered in TN. Extended range from n AL to the Great Lakes in most of the e U.S. May-Jun.

Jack Carman

Genus *Liparis*
Two species are found in Tennessee. The genus name is from the Greek *liparos* (fat or shining) in reference to the smooth and lustrous leaves.

Loesel's Twayblade
Liparis loeselii (L.) Richard
Smooth perennial arising from a solid bulb that has 2 opposite, glossy green, sheathing, elliptic-oblong, basal leaves from 2 to 6 in. long. A leafless scape from 4 to 10 in. tall rises between the leaves and is terminated by a loose raceme of 2 to 12 greenish flowers. The sepals are narrow, spreading, to 0.2-in. long. The petals are filiform, curved and spreading, to 0.2-in. long. The lip is recurved, obovate to oblong but tapered to the tip, to 0.2-in. long. Infrequent. Damp or wet woods, cool ravines, moist seepage slopes. Found in Carter, Coffee, DeKalb, Lewis, Roane, Stewart, Unicoi and Warren counties in TN, it is a mainly northern species that extends south to MO and AL. May-Jun.

Jack Carman

Genus *Listera*

Two species are found in Tennessee. The genus name is in honor of Martin Lister, a celebrated English naturalist in the late 17th and early 18th centuries.

Southern Twayblade
Listera australis Lindley

Erect delicate perennial from 3 to 12 in. tall arising from fibrous roots. Two opposite leaves are borne about halfway up the stem that are dark green, smooth, sessile, ovate, from 0.4 to 1.4 in. long. The purplish-green stem has a loose raceme of 5 to 25 small reddish-purple flowers at the top. Sepals and petals are less than 0.06-in. long. The lip, from 0.25 to 0.4-in. long, is linear but split halfway into 2 narrow lobes. Rare. Rich humus of low moist woods. Known from only Fayette and Coffee counties in TN, it is mainly a Coastal Plain species with disjunct populations inland. Mar-Apr. The first orchid to flower each year in TN.

Jack Carman

The Kidney-Leaf or Appalachian Twayblade (*Listera smallii* Wiegand) is similar, but the brownish-green lip is nearly as wide as long, and cleft at the tip into wide spreading lobes. Infrequent. Moist mountain woods, usually under hemlock or rhododendron. Found in Carter, Cocke, Greene, Johnson, Sevier and Unicoi counties in TN, and from n GA to PA in the Appalachians. Jun-Jul.

Green Adder's Mouth
Malaxis unifolia Michaux

Smooth green perennial from 4 to 12 in. tall that arises from a corm. A single leaf, borne about halfway up the stem, is bright green, shiny, sheathing, ovate, from 1.2 to 2.4 in. long. The stem has a terminal, loose, cylindric, densely-flowered raceme with as many as 50 green flowers. The sepals and petals are linear, less than 0.12-in. long. The lip, about 0.16-in. long and 0.12-in. wide, is mostly oblong but 2-lobed at the tip with a central tooth. Occasional. Rich moist to dry open woods. Found throughout TN and from FL to s CAN in all of the e U.S. May-Aug. The genus name is from *malacos* (weak or delicate), alluding to the frail character of another species of this genus.

Jack Carman

Rein or Fringed Orchids
Genus *Platanthera*
Twelve species are found in TN.

Yellow Fringed Orchid
Platanthera ciliaris (L.) Lindley
Erect perennial from 16 to 40 in. tall that arises from fleshy tuberous roots. From 2 to 4 leaves are borne on the stem that are glossy green, keeled, sheathing, lance-shaped, from 2 to 12 in. long, progressively reduced in size upward. The stem has a terminal, dense to loose, cylindric raceme of 30 to 60 bright orange flowers. The sepals are ovate, about 0.33-in. long, the upper concave and arching forward, the lateral spreading. Petals are linear, about 0.25-in. long. The lip, about 0.8-in. long, is narrow and deeply fringed on the margin, and the slender basal spur is from 1.0 to 1.4 in. long, directed downward. Occasional. Fields, meadows, open woods. Found in East and Middle TN, and most of the e U.S. Jul-Aug. *Habenaria ciliaris* (L.) R.Brown.

Jack Carman

Small Green Woodland Orchid
Platanthera clavellata (Michaux) Luer
Erect perennial from 4 to 16 in. tall that arises from fleshy spindle-shaped roots. Usually 1 leaf is borne low on the stem that is green, keeled, sheathing, oblanceolate, from 2 to 6 in. long. The green stem has a short terminal raceme of 3 to 15 yellow-green flowers. The sepals are ovate, about .16-in. long, arching forward. The petals are obovate, about 0.2-in. long, arching forward. The lip, about 0.25-in. long, is oblong, obscurely 3-lobed at the tip, recurved, and the slender basal spur is about 0.4-in. long, curved and directed downward, dilated at the tip. Frequent. Wet woods and along shady creek beds. Found throughout TN, and in all of the e U.S. except the Gulf coast. Jul-Aug. *Habenaria clavellata* (Michaux) Sprengel.

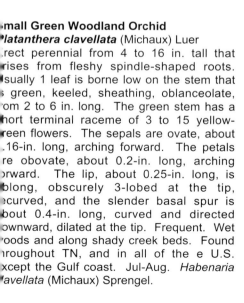

Crested Fringed Orchid
Platanthera cristata (Michaux) Lindley

Erect perennial from 12 to 32 in. tall that arises from fleshy tuberous roots. From 2 to 4 leaves are borne on the stem that are glossy green, keeled, sheathing, lance-shaped, from 2 to 8 in. long, progressively reduced in size upward. The stem has a terminal, dense to loose, cylindric raceme with as many as 80 bright orange flowers. The sepals are ovate to obovate, less than 0.2-in. long, the upper concave and arching forward, the lateral spreading. Petals are obovate with a hairy margin. The lip, less than 0.4-in. long, is ovate in outline, deeply fringed on the margin, and the slender basal spur is less than 0.4-in. long. Infrequent. Low moist meadows, open moist woods. Found in Fentress, Cumberland, Putnam, White, Coffee, Grundy, Franklin and Moore counties in TN. Mainly a se U.S. species, but extending north along the Atlantic coast. Jul-Aug. *Habenaria cristata* (Michaux) R.Brown.

Jack Carman

Jack Carman

Southern Rein Orchid, Tubercled Orchid
Platanthera flava (L.) Lindley

Erect perennial from 12 to 28 in. tall that arises from fleshy roots. From 1 to 4 leaves are borne on the stem that are dark green, keeled, sheathing, lanceolate, from 2 to 8 in. long, progressively reduced in size upward. The stem has a terminal loose spike with 10 to 40 yellow-green flowers. The dark green sepals are ovate, less than 0.2-in. long, the upper concave and arching forward, the lateral spreading. The yellow-green petals are ovate, about 0.15-in. long. The lip, less than 0.25-in. long, is ovate, recurved, and the slender basal spur is less than 0.25-in. long. Wet open woods and fields. Jul-Aug. Two varieties are found in TN:

var. *flava* (photo) has floral bracts that do not extend past the flowers. Occasional. Found in West and Middle TN, it is a mainly southern variety extending north into TN.

var. *herbiola* (Brown) Luer has floral bracts which extend well past the flowers. Rare. Found in a few mountain counties in East TN, it is a mainly northern variety extending south into TN and NC in the mountains.

Yellow Fringeless Orchid
Platanthera integra (Nuttall) Gray *ex* Beck
Erect perennial from 12 to 24 in. tall that arises from fleshy tuberous roots. From 1 to 2 leaves are borne on the stem that are green, keeled, sheathing, lanceolate, from 2 to 8 in. long, the upper much smaller. The stem has a terminal, dense, cylindric or conical raceme with 60 to 80 bright yellow flowers. The sepals are roundish to obovate, less than 0.2-in. long, the upper concave and arching forward, the lateral spreading. Petals are elliptic, about 0.16-in. long. The lip, about 0.25-in. long, is oblong, scalloped but not fringed on the margin, and the slender basal spur is about 0.25-in. long. Rare. Open acidic wet areas and moist meadows. Known from Coffee, Warren and Van Buren counties in TN, and found mainly in the Coastal Plain from NJ to TX with disjunct populations in Middle TN. Aug. *Habenaria integra* (Nuttall) Sprengel.

Jack Carman

George Hornal

Monkey-Face Orchid
Platanthera integrilabia (Correll) Luer
Erect perennial to 3 ft tall that arises from fleshy roots. From 2 to 3 leaves are borne on the stem that are green, keeled, sheathing, lance-shaped, to 8 in. long, progressively reduced in size upward. The stem has a terminal loose raceme of 6 to 15 white flowers. The sepals are roundish, less than 0.36-in. long, the upper concave and arching forward, the lateral reflexed. Petals are oblong, about 0.3-in. long. The lip, about 0.5-in. long, is narrowly spatulate and finely toothed toward the tip, and the slender basal spur is from 1.6 to 2.0 in. long, curved and directed downward. Occasional. Moist fields, open woodland stream banks. Found in Overton, Fentress, Cumberland, Van Buren, Bledsoe, Grundy, Franklin, Marion, Sequatchie, McMinn and Polk counties. U.S. range restricted to the sw Appalachian foothills and Cumberland Plateau. Aug. *Habenaria blephariglottis* (Willdenow) Hooker var. *integrilabia* Correll.

Jack Carman

Ragged Fringed Orchid
Platanthera lacera (Michaux) G. Don
Smooth erect perennial from 12 to 32 in. tall
that arises from fleshy roots. From 2 to 5
leaves are borne on the stem that are green
keeled, sheathing, elliptic to lanceolate, from
3 to 10 in. long, progressively reduced in
size upward. The stem has a terminal, loose
to dense raceme of 20 to 40 greenish
flowers. The sepals are ovate to oblong,
less than 0.33-in. long, the upper concave
and arching forward, the lateral spreading.
Petals are linear-oblong, less than 0.33-in
long. The lip, about 0.7-in. long, is 3-lobed
deeply cleft and divided into filiform
segments, and the slender basal spur is
about 1.0 in. long, curved and directed
downward. Occasional. Wet open woods,
moist meadows, moist roadside ditches.
Thinly scattered in Middle and East TN, also
found in Henderson County. Extended
range from central AL to the Great Lakes in
most of the e U.S. Jun-Jul. *Habenaria
lacera* (Michaux) R. Brown.

Jack Carman

Snowy Orchid
Platanthera nivea (Nuttall) Luer
Slender erect perennial from 12 to 24 in. tall
that arises from fleshy tuberous roots. From
2 to 3 leaves are borne on the stem that are
green, keeled, sheathing, lanceolate, from 2
to 10 in. long, progressively reduced upward.
The stem has a terminal, dense, cylindric or
conical raceme with 20 to 50 pure white
flowers. The sepals are ovate to oblong,
less than 0.25-in. long, the lower arching
forward, the lateral somewhat spreading.
Petals are oblong, about 0.2-in. long. The
lip, about 0.25-in. long, is uppermost, linear-
elliptic, bent backward, and the slender basal
spur is straight, about 0.6-in. long. Rare.
Open wet barrens. Known only from Coffee
County, it is found on the Coastal Plain from
NJ to TX with a disjunct population in TN.
Jul-Aug. *Habenaria nivea* (Nuttall) Sprengel.

John MacGregor

Large Round-Leaf Rein Orchid
Platanthera orbiculata (Pursh) Lindley

Smooth erect perennial arising from fleshy roots that has 2 opposite, shiny green, sheathing, almost round, prostrate basal leaves from 4 to 10 in. long. A leafless scape from 12 to 24 in. tall rises between the leaves and is terminated by a loose raceme of about 10 greenish-white or white flowers. The sepals are somewhat ovate, less than 0.5-in. long, the upper erect, the lateral reflexed. Petals are lance-shaped, from 0.2 to 0.45-in. long. The lip, from 0.35 to 0.7-in. long, is narrow and linear-oblong, drooping, and the slender basal spur, from 0.6 to 1 in. long, often curves upward. Infrequent. Moist open woods. Found in Claiborne, Carter, Sullivan, Johnson, Unicoi and Grundy counties in TN. Widespread in CAN, extending south into the ne U.S. and in the mountains to TN and NC. Jun-Aug. *Habenaria orbiculata* (Pursh) Torrey.

Jack Carman

urple Fringeless Orchid
latanthera peramoena (Gray) Gray

mooth erect perennial from 12 to 40 in. tall at arises from fleshy roots. From 2 to 5 aves are borne on the stem that are green, eeled, sheathing, elliptic to lanceolate, from to 8 in. long, progressively reduced in size oward. The stem has a terminal, dense to ose, cylindric raceme of 30 to 50 rose-urple flowers. The sepals are elliptic, to .36-in. long, the upper concave and arching orward, the lateral reflexed-spreading. etals are spatulate, finely toothed, from .16 to 0.32-in. long. The lip, from 0.4 to .6-in. long and 0.8-in. wide, is distinctly 3-bed, the middle lobe larger and notched, nd the slender basal spur is about 1.2 in. ng, directed downward. Occasional. Open et areas, often in acid soil. Widespread in N, but more prevalent in West TN and the estern Highland Rim. Found in the Ohio nd lower Mississippi River valleys, xtending east to c NC and MD. Jul-Aug. *abenaria peramoena* A.Gray.

Small Purple Fringed Orchid
Platanthera psycodes (L.) Lindley

Smooth erect perennial from 12 to 60 in. tall. The 2 to 5 stem leaves are dark green, keeled, sheathing, lance-shaped, 2 to 9 in. long, reduced in size upward. The stem has a terminal cylindric raceme of 30 to 50 pink-purple flowers. Sepals are elliptic, to 0.3-in. long, the upper concave and arching forward, the lateral spreading. Petals are obovate, to 0.3-in. long, finely toothed. The lip, to 0.5-in. long and 0.6-in. wide, is 3-lobed, shallowly fringed on the outer margin. The slender basal spur is from 0.5 to 0.7-in. long. Nectary entrance at the base of the lip shaped like a lateral dumbbell. Infrequent. Moist open areas at high elevation. Found in se CAN, the ne U.S. and south in the Blue Ridge to TN and GA. Jun-Jul. *Habenaria psycodes* (L.) Sprengel.

The Large Purple Fringed Orchid (*Platanthera grandiflora* (Bigelow) Lindley) is similar, but the lip is deeply fringed and the nectary opening is round. Rare. Moist open areas. A northern species found in Sullivan, Carter, Johnson and Greene counties in TN. Jun-Aug. *Habenaria grandiflora* (Big.) Torr.

Jack Carman

Jack Carman

Rose Pogonia
Pogonia ophioglossoides (L.) Jussieu

Slender erect perennial from 4 to 16 in. tall that arises from fibrous roots. A single leaf borne nearly halfway up the stem, is green, fleshy, elliptic to ovate, from 1.2 to 3.6 in. long. The stem usually has a single flower (rarely 2) at the top that is somewhat nodding. Sepals are pink, elliptic, from 0.7 to 0.9-in. long, somewhat spreading, and petals are pink, broadly elliptic, from 0.7 to 0.9-in. long, arching forward over the lip. The lip is about as long as the sepals, spatulate, pink with a dark-red fringed margin, yellow bristles along the center becoming fringed red crests at the tip. Infrequent. Open wet meadows and sphagnum marshes. Found in Coffee, Warren, Van Buren, White, Cumberland, Fentress, Blount and Johnson counties in TN, and in most of the eastern U.S. except the central Mississippi River valley. May-Jun. The genus name is from the Greek *pogonios* (bearded).

Shadow Witch
Ponthieva racemosa (Walter) Mohr
Erect perennial with a rosette of basal leaves from 2 to 4 in. long that are thin, prostrate, oblong-elliptic, glaucous beneath. The flowering stalk, from 5 to 24 in. tall, arises from the rosette and is terminated by a loosely-flowered raceme of greenish-white flowers. Sepals are white with green stripes, ovate to oblong, about 0.25-in. long. Petals are white with greenish-yellow veins, ovate, about 0.2-in. long. The lip is uppermost, white veined with green, rounded with a pointed tip. Rare. Shady limestone seeps, along woodland stream banks. Known only from Franklin and Warren counties in TN, and found mainly in the Atlantic Coastal Plain from se VA to FL with disjunct populations in TN. Sep-Oct.

Jack Carman

Ladies' Tresses   Genus ***Spiranthes***
Small delicate plants that are not always easy to identify without using a hand magnifier and paying close attention to detail. Eight species are found in TN. The genus name is from the Greek *speira* (a coil or spiral) and *anthos* (flower).

George Hornal

Nodding Ladies' Tresses
Spiranthes cernua (L.) Richard
Downy perennial with 3 to 6 basal leaves from 2 to 8 in. long that are green, linear-oblanceolate, relatively soft. The flowering stalk, from 4 to 16 in. tall, is terminated by a densely-flowered, cylindrical spike of up to 60 fragrant, somewhat nodding, tube-like, white flowers about 0.5-in. long that are usually in 3 or 4 spiraled or vertical columns. The lateral sepals are scarcely spreading, and the throat sometimes has a greenish-yellow tint. Frequent. Open, moist areas. Found throughout TN and most of the U.S. from central KS east. Sep-Oct.

Yellow Ladies' Tresses (*S. ochroleuca* (Rydb.) Rydb.) is similar, but slightly larger and leafier and flowers are pale yellowish. Rare. Well-drained areas. Found in Sevier, Dickson, Cumberland and Sumner counties in TN, but mainly found in the ne U.S. Oct.

Fragrant Ladies' Tresses (*S. odorata* (Nuttall) Lindley) is similar, but taller, leafier, colonial. Flowers strongly fragrant, white or cream with a yellow center. Rare. Wet areas. A se U.S. species found in Sumner, Robertson and Knox counties in TN. Oct.

Jack Carman

Green-Lipped Ladies' Tresses, or Slender Ladies' Tresses
Spiranthes lacera (Raf.) Rafinesque
   var. *gracilis* (Bigelow) Luer

Slender perennial with a rosette of 3 to 5 basal leaves from 0.8 to 2 in. long that are green, ovate, stalked, and usually wither before flowering. The flowering stalk, from 4 to 16 in. tall, is terminated by a densely-flowered, cylindrical spike of up to 40 somewhat nodding, tube-like, white flowers to 0.25-in. long that are usually in a single spiraled or vertical column. The lateral sepals are scarcely spreading and the throat is green. Frequent. Open woods, fields, barrens. Found from the Western Highland Rim east in TN, and in most of the eastern U.S. from the Great Lakes to the Gulf coast. Aug-Sep. *Spiranthes gracilis* (Bigelow) Beck.

Pearl Twist or Little Ladies' Tresses (*Spiranthes tuberosa* Rafinesque) is similar, but ranges from 6 to 12 in. tall and has pure white flowers. Occasional. Dry, open areas. Found throughout TN, and in most of the eastern U.S. from the Ohio River valley south. Jul-Sep.

Shining or Wide-Leaf Ladies' Tresses
Spiranthes lucida (Eaton) Ames

Perennial with 3 to 4 basal leaves from 1.2 to 5 in. long that are green, glossy, elliptic to lanceolate, clasping below. The flowering stalk, from 4 to 10 in. tall, is terminated by a densely-flowered, cylindrical spike of up to 20 somewhat nodding, tube-like, white flowers about 0.25-in. long that are usually in 3 spiraled columns. The lateral sepals are scarcely spreading and the throat is bright yellow. Infrequent. Open moist places, stream banks, lakeshores, marshes. Found in Claiborne, Carter, Franklin, Johnson, Pickett, Overton and Lewis counties in TN. A mainly ne U.S. species that extends south to AL. May-Jun.

Jack Carman

Jack Carman

Oval or Lesser Ladies' Tresses
Spiranthes ovalis Lindley
Downy perennial with 2 to 3 leaves from 1.2 to 6 in. long that are oblanceolate, narrow, green, relatively soft, basally disposed and sheathing the stem. The flowering stalk, from 6 to 12 in. tall, is terminated by a densely-flowered, cylindrical spike of up to 50 somewhat nodding, tube-like, white flowers about 0.2-in. long that are usually arranged in more or less 3 vertical columns. The lateral sepals are scarcely spreading and the throat is also white. The small spike tapers into older flowers below and buds toward the tip creating an "oval" appearance. Occasional. Moist woods, bottomlands. Found in scattered locations throughout TN, and in most of the se U.S. from northern KY south. Sep-Oct.

Spring Ladies' Tresses
Spiranthes vernalis Englemann & A. Gray
Downy perennial with 4 to 5 basal leaves from 2 to 10 in. long that are green, linear-lanceolate, narrow, keeled, sheathing below, mostly rigid. The flowering stalk, from 8 to 32 in. tall, is terminated by a densely-flowered, cylindrical spike of up to 50 somewhat nodding, tube-like, white flowers to 0.4-in. long that are usually spiraled, but sometimes arranged in a one-sided vertical column. The lateral sepals are scarcely spreading and the throat is usually yellowish. Occasional. Open places. Widespread in TN, its extended range is from central KS to TN to MA south. Jun-Sep.

Jack Carman

Jack Carman

Jack Carman

Cranefly Orchid   ***Tipularia discolor*** (Pursh) Nuttall
Perennial from an oval tuber that produces a solitary, stalked, ovate, prostrate, basal leaf in mid-autumn which is dark green and purple-spotted above, rich satiny purple beneath, from 2 to 4 in. long. The leaf lasts until May and then withers. In mid-summer, the 8 to 26 in. flower scape appears that is brownish-green suffused with bronze or purple, and has 20 to 40 greenish, lemon-yellow, rust-bronze or purplish flowers in a loosely-arranged raceme near the summit. Petals and sepals are 0.16 to 0.32-in. long. The lip is 3-lobed, from 0.24 to 0.32-in. long, and the slender basal spur is from 0.6 to 0.9-in. long. Frequent. Upland or rich, damp, acid woodlands. Found throughout TN, and the e U.S. from the Ohio River valley south. Jul-Aug. The flowers are said to resemble a cranefly. In fact, the genus name is from the fancied resemblance of the flowers to insects of the genus *Tipula*.

Jack Carman

Three-Birds Orchid
Triphora trianthophora (Swartz) Rydberg
Perennial that arises from short fleshy roots. The stem is delicate, erect, smooth, succulent, green tinged with purple, from 3 to 10 in. tall. Stem leaves are alternate, ovate, clasping, from 0.4 to 0.6-in. long. From 1 to 6, erect or nodding, stalked flowers arise singly from the upper leaf axils. Petals and sepals, to 0.6-in. long, are pinkish-white, and the lip is 3-lobed, white with 3 central, parallel, green crests. Individual flowers last only one day, but all mature buds in a colony may open at the same time on the same day. Frequently, a slight decrease in nighttime temperature is followed 2 days later by the mass flowering of a colony. Occasional. Rich damp woods. Thinly but widely distributed in TN, and found in the e U.S. from the Great Lakes south, except along the se Atlantic coast. Aug-Sep. The genus name is from the Greek *treis* (three) and *phoros* (bearing), alluding to the flowers frequently being borne in threes.

BIBLIOGRAPHY

Baskin, J.M., Quaterman, E., and Caudle, C. 1968. *Preliminary Check-List of the Herbaceous Vascular Plants of Cedar Glades.* J. Tenn. Acad. Sci. 43:65-71.

Batson, W.T. 1987. *Wildflowers in the Carolinas.* University Press of South Carolina, Columbia, SC.

Brown, Clair A. 1972. *Wildflowers of Louisiana and Adjoining States.* Louisiana State University Press, Baton Rouge, LA.

Brown, L. 1979. *Grasses, An Identification Guide.* Houghton Mifflin Co., Boston, MA.

Campbell, C.C., Hutson, R.W., Hutson, W.F., and Sharp, A.J. 1995. *Great Smoky Mountain Wildflowers, 5th ed.* Windy Pines Publishing, Northbrook, IL.

Chester, E.W. and Ellis, W.H. 1995. *Wildflowers of the Land Between the Lakes Region, Kentucky and Tennessee.* Austin Peay State University, Clarksville, TN.

Chester, E.W., Wofford, B.E., Kral, R., DeSelm, H.R., and Evans, A.M. 1993. *Atlas of Tennessee Vascular Plants, Vol. 1. Pteridophytes, Gymnosperms, Angiosperms: Monocots.* Austin Peay State University, Clarksville, TN.

Chester, E.W., Wofford, B.E., and Kral, R. 1997. *Atlas of Tennessee Vascular Plants, Vol. 2. Angiosperms: Dicots.* Austin Peay State University, Clarksville, TN.

Dean, B.E., Mason, A., and Thomas, J.L. 1973. *Wildflowers of Alabama and Adjoining States.* The University of Alabama Press, Tuscaloosa, AL.

DeSelm, H.R., Wofford, B.E., Kral, R., and Chester, E.W. 1994. *An Annonated List of Grasses (Poaceae, Gramineae) of Tennessee.* Castanea Vol. 59, No. 4:338-353.

Duncan, W.H. and Foote, L.E. 1975. *Wildflowers of the Southeastern United States.* University of Georgia Press, Athens, GA.

Fernald, M.L. 1950. *Gray's Manual of Botany, 8th ed.* American Book Co., NY.

Foster, S. and Duke, J.A. 1990. *A Field Guide to Medicinal Plants, Eastern and Central North America.* Houghton Mifflin Co., Boston, MA.

Gleason, H.A. 1963. *New Britton and Brown Illustrated Flora of the Northeastern United States and Adjacent Canada, Vols. 1, 2, and 3, 3rd ed.* The New York Botanical Garden, Bronx, NY.

Gleason, H.A. and Cronquist, A. 1991. *Manual of Vascular Plants of Northeastern United States and Adjacent Canada.* The New York Botanical Garden, Bronx, NY.

Gupton, O.W. and Swope, F.C. 1989. *Fall Wildflowers of the Blue Ridge and Great Smoky Mountains.* University Press of Virginia, Charlottesville, VA.

Gupton, O.W. and Swope, F.C. 1986. *Wild Orchids of the Middle Atlantic States.* The University of Tennessee Press, Knoxville, TN.

Hemmerly, T.E. 1990. *Wildflowers of the Central South.* Vanderbilt University Press, Nashville, TN.

BIBLIOGRAPHY

Hunter, C.G. 1988. *Wildflowers of Arkansas, 2nd ed.* Ozark Society Foundation, Little Rock, AR.

Hunter, C.G. 1989. *Trees, Shrubs, & Vines of Arkansas.* Ozark Society Foundation, Little Rock, AR.

Justice, W.S. and Bell, C.R. 1968. *Wildflowers of North Carolina.* The University of North Carolina Press, Chapel Hill, NC.

Ladd, D. 1995. *Tallgrass Prairie Wildflowers.* Falcon Press, Helena, MT.

Lewis, W. H. and Elvin-Lewis, M. P. F. 1977. *Medical Botany.* John Wiley and Sons, New York, NY.

Luer, C.A. 1975. *The Native Orchids of the United States and Canada excluding Florida.* The New York Botànical Garden, Bronx, NY.

Newcomb, L. 1977. *Newcomb's Wildflower Guide.* Little, Brown and Company, Boston, MA.

Peterson, Lee. 1978. *A Field Guide to Edible Wild Plants.* Houghton Mifflin Co., Boston, MA.

Peterson, R.T. and McKenny, M. 1968. *A Field Guide to Wildflowers of Northeastern and Northcentral North America.* Houghton Mifflin Co., Boston, MA.

Pohl, R.W. 1978. *How to Know the Grasses.* Wm. C. Brown Company Publishers, Dubuque, IA.

Radford, A.E., Ahles, H.E. and Bell, C.R. 1968. *Manual of the Vascular Flora of the Carolinas.* The University of North Carolina Press, Chapel Hill, NC.

Rickett, H.W. 1966. *Wildflowers of the United States, Volume Two: The Southeastern States, Parts One and Two.* The New York Botanical Garden, Bronx, NY.

Small, J.K. 1933. *Manual of the Southeastern Flora.* The University of North Carolina Press, Chapel Hill, NC.

Smith, A.I. 1979. *A Guide to Wildflowers of the Mid-South.* Memphis State University Press, Memphis, TN.

Smith, R.M. 1998. *Wildflowers of the Southern Mountains.* The University of Tennessee Press, Knoxville, TN.

Steyermark, J.A. 1963. *Flora of Missouri.* The Iowa State University Press, Ames, IA.

Timme, S.L. 1989. *Wildflowers of Mississippi.* University Press of Mississippi, Jackson, MS.

Wharton, M. E. and Barbour, R.W. 1971. *The Wildflowers and Ferns of Kentucky.* University Press of Kentucky, Lexington, KY.

Wofford, B.E. 1989. *Guide to the Vascular Plants of the Blue Ridge.* The University of Georgia Press, Athens, GA.

Wofford, B.E. and Kral, R. 1993. *Checklist of the Vascular Plants of Tennessee.* Botanical Research Institute of Texas, Fort Worth, TX.